Optimization Techniques

MATHEMATICS IN SCIENCE AND ENGINEERING

A Series of Monographs and Textbooks

Edited by

Richard Bellman

The RAND Corporation, Santa Monica, California

In preparation

Optimization Techniques

With Applications to Aerospace Systems

Edited by

GEORGE LEITMANN

Applied Mechanics Group, Mechanical Engineering Department
University of California, Berkeley, California

1962

New York   ACADEMIC PRESS   London

ACADEMIC PRESS INC.
111 FIFTH AVENUE
NEW YORK 3, N. Y.

United Kingdom Edition
Published by
ACADEMIC PRESS INC. (LONDON) LTD.
BERKELEY SQUARE HOUSE, LONDON, W.1

Library of Congress Catalog Card Number 62-13108

First Printing, 1962
Second Printing, 1963
Third Printing, 1965

PRINTED IN THE UNITED STATES OF AMERICA

Contributors

RICHARD BELLMAN, *The RAND Corporation, Santa Monica, California*

JOHN BREAKWELL, *Lockheed Missiles and Space Company, Sunnyvale, California*

R. W. BUSSARD,* *Los Alamos Scientific Laboratory of the University of California, Los Alamos, New Mexico*

THEODORE N. EDELBAUM, *Research Laboratories, United Aircraft Corporation, East Hartford, Connecticut*

FRANK D. FAULKNER, *U. S. Naval Postgraduate School, Monterey, California*

ROBERT KALABA, *The RAND Corporation, Santa Monica, California*

C. M. KASHMAR, *General Electric Company, Santa Barbara, California*

HENRY J. KELLEY, *Grumman Aircraft Engineering Corporation, Bethpage, New York*

RICHARD E. KOPP, *Grumman Aircraft Engineering Corporation, Bethpage, New York*

DEREK F. LAWDEN, *University of Canterbury, Christchurch, New Zealand*

G. LEITMANN, *University of California, Berkeley, California*

ANGELO MIELE, *Boeing Scientific Research Laboratories, Seattle, Washington*

E. L. PETERSON, *General Electric Company, Santa Barbara, California*

---

* *Present address*: Space Technology Laboratories, Redondo Beach, California

Foreword

Whatever man does he strives to do in the "best" possible manner. In attempting to reach a desired goal in an "optimum" fashion, he is faced immediately with two problems. The first of these is the decision of choosing the goal itself—the "payoff." For what is one man's optimum may well be another man's pessimum. Here he may decide to ignore the desires of the other interested parties and to choose a payoff solely on the basis of his own interests, whether or not these are in conflict with the interests of others. Thus, the scientist who wishes to carry out experiments using satellite-borne apparatus may desire an optimum ascent trajectory which results in maximum payload in orbit, even if such an "optimum" trajectory involves excessively large accelerations which are not tolerable from the point of view of the structural engineer whose job is the design of the carrier vehicle. On the other hand, he may temper his choice of payoff by considering the interests of others, that is, by imposing restrictions on the optimal policy so as not to violate the requirements of other interested parties. Consequently, the scientist may be forced to accept a somewhat smaller payload in orbit by placing bounds on the accelerations, resulting in loads which are tolerable and hence acceptable to the structural engineer. But even if a payoff and constraints agreeable to all parties involved can be decided upon, there still remains the choice of technique to be used for arriving at the optimum. It is primarily to this latter question that this book addresses itself.

During the past decade there has been a remarkable growth of interest in problems of systems optimization and of optimal control. And with this interest has come an increasing need for methods useful for rendering systems optimum. Rising to meet this challenge there have sprung up various "schools," often championing one method and regarding it superior to all others. Long experience has shown that life is not so simple, that the picture is not all white and black. In short, one may expect that a particular method is superior to others for the solution of some problems—rarely for all problems. Furthermore, since the basic mathematical formulation of optimization problems is often essentially the same in many approaches, it is not unreasonable to expect that there may be a great deal of similarity among various methods, a similarity—often, indeed, an identity—which is obscured by dissimilarities in language and notation. To help the uncommitted in his search for and choice of the optimum optimization technique is the fundamental aim of this volume.

To accomplish this aim there are assembled in one book ten chapters dealing with the various methods currently espoused for the solution of problems in systems optimization and optimal control. The choice of authors has been dictated solely by a consideration of an author's interest and expertness in a particular method. With the advantages of such an eclectic approach and the ensuing multiple authorship there comes some loss of smoothness of over-all presentation, for which the Editor must take the sole blame. On the one hand, correlation between the various chapters has been achieved by cross-referencing; on the other hand, each chapter can be read as a separate entity setting forth the technique championed by a particular "school."

While each of the ten chapters dealing with methods includes simple examples, primarily for didactic purposes, it has been thought useful to present four additional chapters dealing with applications alone. Of these, the first three, Chapters 11–13, cover specific optimization problems, and the final chapter contains a discussion of problems in the optimization of a complete system, in this case a nuclear propulsion system.

A word concerning coverage is in order. Whenever a method or peculiarities in its applications are not treated in standard works of reference, these points are covered in detail; such is the case especially in Chapters 1–7. When a technique is fully exposed in readily available sources or when applications to aerospace systems are as yet sparse, the method is presented in outline only, together with appropriate remarks concerning its application to the systems under discussion; this is largely so in Chapters 8–10. Niceties in notation for their own sake have been avoided in order to make the subject matter accessible to the widest possible audience which may include engineers, scientists, and applied mathematicians whose training in mathematics need not have progressed past the first graduate year of a standard engineering curriculum.

GEORGE LEITMANN

Berkeley, California

Contents

ix

4 The Calculus of Variations in Applied Aerodynamics and Flight Mechanics
ANGELO MIELE

5 Variational Problems with Bounded Control Variables
G. LEITMANN

6 Methods of Gradients
HENRY J. KELLEY

7   *Pontryagin Maximum Principle*
                        RICHARD E. KOPP

8 *On the Determination of Optimal Trajectories Via Dynamic Programming*
                        RICHARD BELLMAN

9 *Computational Considerations for Some Deterministic and Adaptive
                        Control Processes*
                        ROBERT KALABA

10   *General Imbedding Theory*
                 C. M. KASHMAR AND E. L. PETERSON

11   *Impulsive Transfer between Elliptical Orbits*
DEREK F. LAWDEN

12   *The Optimum Spacing of Corrective Thrusts in Interplanetary Navigation*
JOHN BREAKWELL

13   *Propulsive Efficiency of Rockets*
G. LEITMANN

14   *Some Topics in Nuclear Rocket Optimization*
R. W. BUSSARD

—1—

Theory of Maxima and Minima

THEODORE N. EDELBAUM

Research Laboratories, United Aircraft Corporation,
East Hartford, Connecticut

1

1.1 Necessary Conditions for Maxima or Minima

1.11 Introduction—Variational Terminology

The theory of ordinary maxima and minima is concerned with the problem of finding the values of each of n independent variables x_1, x_2, $\cdots$, x_n at which some function of the n variables $f(x_1, x_2, \cdots, x_n)$ reaches either a maximum or a minimum (an extremum). This problem may be interpreted geometrically as the problem of finding a point in an n-dimensional space at which the desired function has an extremum. This geometrical interpretation can be helpful in understanding this type of problem, particularly when there are only two independent variables. A representation of such a problem is shown as a contour map in Fig. 1.

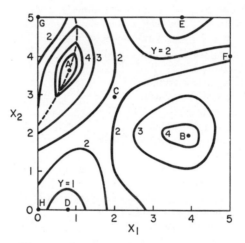

FIG. 1. Extrema and stationary points.

The independent variables are x_1 and x_2 while the dependent variable $y = f(x_1, x_2)$ is represented by the contour lines. The maximum of the function is located at point A at the top of a sharp ridge where the derivative of y with respect to both x_1 and x_2 is discontinuous. A second but lower maximum is located at point B which is "higher" than all points in its immediate vicinity. The highest of all the points in a suitably defined region, such as point A for the region shown, is called an absolute maximum while a point, such as B, that is higher than all the points in a suitably defined small neighborhood is called a local maximum.

The derivative of y with respect to x_1 and x_2 at point B is equal to zero. A point at which a function has all its partial derivatives with respect to the independent variables equal to zero is called a stationary point. The fact that a stationary point need not represent a local extremum is illustrated by point C. Point C represents the highest point in a "pass" between the "mountains" on either side. There are both lower points (along the pass) and higher points (towards the mountains) in the immediate neighborhood of C. A stationary point of this type is called a saddle point.

The minimum of the function y does not occur in the interior of the region illustrated but occurs on the boundary of this region defined by $x_1=0$, 5 and $x_2 = 0$, 5. Along the boundary $x_2 = 0$, a local minimum occurs at point D, while it occurs at point E along $x_2 = 5$ and at point F along $x_1 = 5$. The boundary $x_2 = 0$ has two local minima, one at each end of the interval in which the function is defined. It should be noted here that the "suitable neighborhood" for the definition of a local minimum does not include points outside of the region of definition of the function. The absolute minimum must be found by comparing the values of the local minima D, E, F, G, and H.

The basic problem of the theory of ordinary maxima and minima is to determine the location of local extrema and then to compare these so as to determine which is the absolute extremum. The example of Fig. 1 illustrates that a place to look for local extrema is along discontinuities in the first derivative and also along boundaries (another type of discontinuity). Where the function and its derivatives are continuous the local extema will always occur at stationary points although, as point C illustrates, stationary points are not always local extrema.

1.12 Necessary Conditions for Maxima or Minima

The existence of a solution to an ordinary minimum problem is guaranteed by the theorem of Weierstrass as long as the function is continuous. This theorem states[1]:

> Every function which is continuous in a closed domain possesses a largest and a smallest value either in the interior or on the boundary of the domain.

There is no corresponding general existence theorem for the solutions of problems in the calculus of variations, a circumstance which sometimes leads to difficulties. It should be noted that this theorem does not require the derivatives to be continuous so that the theorem applies to problems such as the example of Fig. 1.

The location of extrema in the interior of the region may be determined from the following theorem[2]:

> A continuous function $f(x_1, x_2, \cdots, x_n)$ of n independent variables $x_1, x_2, \cdots, x_n$ attains a maximum or a minimum in the interior of a

region R only at those values of the variables x_i for which the n partial derivatives $f_{x_1}, f_{x_2}, \cdots, f_{x_n}$ either vanish simultaneously (a stationary point), or at which one or more of these derivatives cease to exist (are discontinuous).

The location of the stationary points may be found by simultaneous solution of the n algebraic equations obtained by setting the n partial derivatives equal to zero. The question as to whether these stationary points constitute extrema will be considered in the next section.

The theorem of Weierstrass indicates that the extrema may occur on the boundary of the region. If the problem is an n-dimensional one, the search for an extremum on the boundary will generally lead to one or more ordinary minimum problems in $n-1$, $n-2$, $\cdots$, 1 dimensions. A good illustrative example of this is given by Cicala.[3] He considers a 3-dimensional problem where the function is defined in a cubic region. The complete solution of this problem requires the determination of the extrema on each of the 6 sides and on each of the 12 edges and comparison of the values of these extrema with the value of the function at the 8 vertices and at the extrema in the interior of the cube. A spherical region, on the other hand, requires only the determination of the extrema on the unbounded spherical surface and in the interior. The determination of the extrema on boundaries which are not coordinate surfaces may be considered as a problem with a subsidiary condition, to be considered in Section 1.3.

The existence of discontinuous first derivatives along lines, surfaces, etc., also requires the solution of extremal problems in 1, 2, etc., dimensions. The methods of Section 1.3 are not as satisfactory here because most of them require the existence of all partial derivatives. The substitution method of Section 1.31 is applicable in many cases.

1.2 Sufficient Conditions for Maxima or Minima

1.21 Introduction

The theorem of the preceding section states that an extremum in the interior of a region must occur at either a stationary point or at a point where one or more first partial derivatives are discontinuous. However, neither stationary points nor discontinuities have to be extrema. When the location of stationary points or points of discontinuity has been determined, the question as to whether or not they constitute extrema still has to be answered.

There are several methods of answering this question. Probably the most widely used method is the obvious one of direct comparison of the values of the function at stationary points, discontinuities, and at the boundaries. In spite of its simplicity, this method is the only rigorous method of determining absolute optima and is the only common method of treating discontinuities. The methods of the last section provide a means of determining all of the possible locations for both local extrema and the absolute extremum. A comparison of all these points is all that is needed for a rigorous determination of the absolute extremum even though it will not determine which of the other points is a local extremum.

In practice, the physical interpretation of the mathematical model will often result in an "obvious" determination of the extremal character of some stationary point. For many practical problems this intuitive result will be sufficient, although few of us are blessed with infallible intuition. The determination of the value of the function at a few neighboring points will often help to reinforce intuition. However, it should be realized that the investigation of many neighboring points cannot provide a rigorous proof of even a local extremum. Failure to realize this has led to serious errors in the past in calculus of variations problems and can lead to serious errors in ordinary minimum problems involving many independent variables.

If it is impractical to determine the values of the function at all possible stationary points, discontinuities, and boundaries, all that can be determined is whether or not a given point constitutes a local extremum. In many problems the determination of local extrema may be all that is desired. Sections 1.21 and 1.22 will consider the necessary conditions for a stationary point, having continuous second derivatives, to constitute a local extremum. Necessary conditions for points where the first derivatives are discontinuous are treated by Hancock.[4]

Excellent examples of the detailed proof that a solution is an absolute extremum may be found in Horner[5] and Munick *et al.*[6]

1.22 Two Independent Variables

The behavior of a function $f(x_1, x_2)$ in the vicinity of a point (a, b) may be determined by means of a Taylor series expansion:

$$f(x_1, x_2) = f(a, b) + f_{x_1}(a, b)(x_1 - a) + f_{x_2}(a, b)(x_2 - b)$$

$$+\frac{1}{2!}[f_{x_1x_1}(a,b)(x_1 - a)^2 + 2f_{x_1x_2}(a,b)(x_1 - a)(x_2 - b) + f_{x_2x_2}(a,b)(x_2 - b)^2]$$

$$+ \cdots \quad (1.1)$$

If the point a, b is a stationary point of $f(x_1, x_2)$ the two first order terms will be zero. It is necessary to examine the three second order terms in order to determine whether a, b is a maximum, a minimum, a saddle point, etc.

The sum of the three second order terms will always be positive, so that a, b will be a local minimum if

$$f_{x_1 x_1} > 0$$

$$f_{x_1 x_1} f_{x_2 x_2} - (f_{x_1 x_2})^2 > 0$$

$$(1.2)$$

the function will be a local maximum if

$$f_{x_1 x_1} < 0$$

$$f_{x_1 x_1} f_{x_2 x_2} - (f_{x_1 x_2})^2 > 0$$

$$(1.3)$$

In exceptional cases extrema may occur when the inequality in the second of Eqs. (1.2) and (1.3) becomes an equality. These cases are discussed by Hancock,[4] pages 20–69.

1.23 n Independent Variables

The corresponding sufficiency conditions for n variables may be expressed concisely by using a notation similar to that of Leitmann.[7] The necessary condition for a stationary point to be a local minimum is that

$$D_i > 0, \qquad i = 1, 2, \cdots, n \qquad (1.4)$$

The necessary condition for a stationary point to be a local maximum is that

$$D_i > 0, \qquad i = 2, 4, 6, \cdots$$

$$(1.5)$$

$$D_i < 0, \qquad i = 1, 3, 5, \cdots$$

where

$$D_i \equiv \begin{vmatrix} f_{x_1 x_1} & f_{x_1 x_2} & \cdots & f_{x_1 x_i} \\ f_{x_2 x_1} & f_{x_2 x_2} & \cdots & f_{x_2 x_i} \\ \cdot & \cdot & \cdot & \cdot \\ \cdot & \cdot & & \cdot \\ \cdot & \cdot & & \cdot \\ f_{x_i x_1} & f_{x_i x_2} & \cdots & f_{x_i x_i} \end{vmatrix}$$

A special case of this equation is the well-known sufficiency condition for a maximum or minimum of a function of one independent variable:

$$f_{x_1 x_1} \lessgtr 0$$

1.3 Subsidiary Conditions

1.31 Solution by Substitution

If the n variables x_1, x_2, $\cdots$, x_n are subject to m subsidiary conditions,

$$g_1(x_1, x_2, \cdots, x_n) = 0, \qquad g_2(x_1, x_2, \cdots, x_n) = 0, \cdots, g_m(x_1, x_2, \cdots, x_n) = 0$$

$$(1.6)$$

the number of independent variables is reduced to $n - m$. As long as n is greater than m there are one or more independent variables for which an extremum of $y = f(x_1, x_2, \cdots, x_n)$ may be sought subject to the m subsidiary equations (or constraints) $g_1 = 0$, $g_2 = 0$, $\cdots$, $g_m = 0$.

The most obvious method of solving this problem is to solve the m constraining equations simultaneously for m of the n variables. Substitution of these m equations into $y = f(x_1, x_2, \cdots, x_n)$ produces a new extremum problem $y = f(x_1, x_2, \cdots, x_{n-m})$ in $n - m$ variables.

This substitution method is often unsatisfactory because the m equations cannot be solved for m variables or because the solutions become unwieldy. In simple problems substitution can be the simplest method of solution as it is the only method that reduces the number of variables.

As a simple example of the use of substitution to solve problems with subsidiary conditions, the problem of determining an extremum in a cubic region (Section 1.12) will be considered. The cubic region will be assumed to be defined by the planes $x_1 = a, b$, $x_2 = a, b$, and $x_3 = a, b$. The extrema in the 6 sides of the cube are found by solving the 6 two-dimensional problems found by substituting, one at a time, a and b for x_1, x_2, and x_3 in $f(x_1, x_2, x_3)$. The extrema in the 12 edges of the cube are found by solution of the 12 one-dimensional problems formed by substituting a, a; a, b; b, a; b, b for x_1, x_2; x_1, x_3; x_2, x_3. Finally, the extrema in the interior, in the sides, and along the edges must be compared with the values of the function at the 8 vertices of the cube.

1.32 Solution by Constrained Variation

In the absence of the constraining equations g_1, g_2, $\cdots$, g_m, the location of stationary points is found by the solution of Eqs. (1.6):

$$f_{x_1} = 0, \qquad f_{x_2} = 0, \cdots, f_{x_n} = 0 \qquad (1.7)$$

The simultaneous vanishing of all the first partial derivatives implies that the total differential of the function will also be zero for any arbitrary differential displacements of the n variables:

$$df = \frac{\partial f}{\partial x_1} dx_1 + \frac{\partial f}{\partial x_2} dx_2 + \cdots + \frac{\partial f}{\partial x_n} dx_n = 0 \qquad (1.8)$$

When the m constraining equations are introduced, Eq. (1.8) will still remain true but the differential displacements of the n variables $x_1, x_2, \cdots, x_n$ will no longer be arbitrary. These n differential displacements will be subject to m constraints found by differentiating Eqs. (1.6):

$$dg_1 = \frac{\partial g_1}{\partial x_1} dx_1 + \frac{\partial g_1}{\partial x_2} dx_2 + \cdots + \frac{\partial g_1}{\partial x_n} dx_n = 0$$

$$\begin{matrix} \cdot & \cdot & \cdot \\ \cdot & \cdot & \cdot \\ \cdot & \cdot & \cdot \end{matrix} \qquad (1.9)$$

$$dg_m = \frac{\partial g_m}{\partial x_1} dx_1 + \frac{\partial g_m}{\partial x_2} dx_2 + \cdots + \frac{\partial g_m}{\partial x_n} dx_n = 0$$

Equations (1.8) and (1.9) together provide $m + 1$ linear and homogeneous equations in the n differential displacements dx_i for any given point in the n-dimensional space. A stationary point will be a point where Eqs. (1.8) and (1.9) will hold true for any arbitrary differential displacements of the $n - m$ independent variables. At such a point the following Jacobian determinants must vanish, there being one Jacobian for each $n - m$ independent variables:

$$J\left(\frac{f, g_1, g_2, \cdots, g_{m-1}, g_m}{x_1, x_2, x_3, \cdots, x_m, x_{m+1}}\right) = 0$$

$$J\left(\frac{f, g_1, g_2, \cdots, g_{m-1}, g_m}{x_1, x_2, x_3, \cdots, x_m, x_{m+2}}\right) = 0 \qquad (1.10)$$

$$\begin{matrix} \cdot & \cdot \\ \cdot & \cdot \\ \cdot & \cdot \end{matrix}$$

$$J\left(\frac{f, g_1, g_2, \cdots, g_{m-1}, g_m}{x_1, x_2, x_3, \cdots, x_m, x_n}\right) = 0$$

where

$$J \left(\frac{\lambda_1, \lambda_2, \cdots, \lambda_n}{t_1, t_2, \cdots, t_n} \right) \equiv \begin{vmatrix} \dfrac{\partial \lambda_1}{\partial t_1} & \dfrac{\partial \lambda_1}{\partial t_2} & \cdots & \dfrac{\partial \lambda_1}{\partial t_n} \\[2mm] \dfrac{\partial \lambda_2}{\partial t_1} & \cdots & \cdots & \\[2mm] \cdot & & & \cdot \\ \cdot & & & \cdot \\ \cdot & & & \cdot \\[2mm] \dfrac{\partial \lambda_n}{\partial t_1} & \cdots & \cdots & \dfrac{\partial \lambda_n}{\partial t_n} \end{vmatrix}$$

There is a simple geometric interpretation of Eqs. (1.10), at least in two or three dimensions. In Fig. 2 the maximum of the function $y = f(x_1, x_2)$

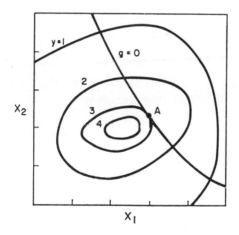

Fig. 2.   Extremum with a subsidiary condition.

consistent with the constraint $g(x_1, x_2) = 0$ occurs at point A. At this point the slope dx_2/dx_1 of a curve $f = $ constant is equal to the slope dx_2/dx_1 of $g(x_1, x_2) = 0$. For the curve $f(x_1, x_2) = $ constant

$$\frac{dx_2}{dx_1} = - \frac{\partial f/\partial x_1}{\partial f/\partial x_2} \tag{1.11}$$

while for the curve $g(x_1, x_2) = 0$

$$\frac{dx_2}{dx_1} = - \frac{\partial g/\partial x_1}{\partial g/\partial x_2} \tag{1.12}$$

Setting these two equations equal to each other,

$$\frac{\partial f/\partial x_1}{\partial f/\partial x_2} = \frac{\partial g/\partial x_1}{\partial g/\partial x_2}$$

(1.13)

$$\frac{\partial f}{\partial x_1}\frac{\partial g}{\partial x_2} - \frac{\partial f}{\partial x_2}\frac{\partial g}{\partial x_1} = 0$$

Equation (1.13) is precisely the relationship given by Eqs. (1.10) for this case.

The method of this section is not much used in practice, the Lagrange multiplier method of the next section generally being preferred. The two methods are closely related theoretically, but in practice the equations resulting from the Lagrange multiplier method are usually simpler to derive and to solve. The Jacobian determinants do provide a very compact notation, a fact which has been taken advantage of by Miele.[8]

1.33 Lagrange Multipliers

Figure 2 is a representation of the problem of finding an extremum of $f(x_1, x_2)$ subject to the subsidiary condition

$$g(x_1, x_2) = 0 \qquad (1.14)$$

In Section 1.32 the necessary condition for the existence of a stationary solution at point A was derived as Eq. (1.13):

$$\frac{\partial f}{\partial x_1}\frac{\partial g}{\partial x_2} - \frac{\partial f}{\partial x_2}\frac{\partial g}{\partial x_1} = 0 \qquad (1.13)$$

Equation (1.13) may be rewritten as follows:

$$\frac{\partial f/\partial x_1}{\partial g/\partial x_1} = \frac{\partial f/\partial x_2}{\partial g/\partial x_2} = -\lambda \qquad (1.15)$$

where λ is a constant which will be referred to as a Lagrange multiplier. Another form of Eqs. (1.15) is

$$\frac{\partial f}{\partial x_1} + \lambda \frac{\partial g}{\partial x_1} = 0$$

(1.16)

$$\frac{\partial f}{\partial x_2} + \lambda \frac{\partial g}{\partial x_2} = 0$$

Equations (1.16) may be recognized as the necessary conditions for the existence of a stationary point of the function $f + \lambda g$ without subsidiary conditions. The necessary conditions for a stationary point of $f(x_1, x_2)$ with a subsidiary condition $g(x_1, x_2) = 0$ is found by forming the augmented function $f + \lambda g$ and treating the problem as one without subsidiary conditions. The solution of the three equations (1.14) and (1.16) for the three variables x_1, x_2, and λ is equivalent to solving the two equations (1.14) and (1.13) for the two variables x_1 and x_2.

This result is readily extended to the general case. In fact, Eqs. (1.10) of the last section imply the existence of a set of constants (Lagrange multipliers) λ_1, λ_2, $\cdots$, λ_n such that each element of the first row of each Jacobian determinant can be expressed as the following linear combination of the elements of its column[3]:

$$\frac{\partial f}{\partial x_1} + \lambda_1 \frac{\partial g_1}{\partial x_1} + \lambda_2 \frac{\partial g_2}{\partial x_1} + \cdots + \lambda_m \frac{\partial g_m}{\partial x_1} = 0$$

$$\frac{\partial f}{\partial x_2} + \lambda_1 \frac{\partial g_1}{\partial x_2} + \lambda_2 \frac{\partial g_2}{\partial x_2} + \cdots + \lambda_m \frac{\partial g_m}{\partial x_2} = 0 \qquad (1.17)$$

$$\vdots \qquad \vdots \qquad \vdots \qquad \vdots$$

$$\frac{\partial f}{\partial x_n} + \lambda_1 \frac{\partial g_1}{\partial x_n} + \lambda_2 \frac{\partial g_2}{\partial x_n} + \cdots + \lambda_m \frac{\partial g_m}{\partial x_n} = 0$$

Equations (1.17) are the necessary conditions for the existence of a stationary solution of the augmented function $f + \lambda_1 g_1 + \lambda_2 g_2 + \cdots + \lambda_m g_m$. The use of the augmented function allows a problem with subsidiary conditions to be replaced by a problem without subsidiary conditions. This new problem is amenable to all of the techniques used for solving problems without subsidiary conditions, including the sufficiency conditions of Section 1.2. As with ordinary functions, discontinuities in the first derivative of the augmented function must be examined for the possible occurrence of extrema, particularly since the Lagrange multiplier method breaks down at such singularities.

This method of Lagrange multipliers has the disadvantage of introducing as additional variables the m Lagrange multipliers which must usually be evaluated with the aid of the m subsidiary conditions $g_1 = 0$, $g_2 = 0$, $\cdots$, $g_m = 0$. However, Eqs. (1.17) containing the Lagrange multipliers are usually so much simpler than the corresponding equations (1.10) of the last section (which do not contain Lagrange multipliers) that the determination of a solution is both simpler and faster. The Lagrange multiplier method is particularly advantageous in the common case where g depends upon a constant c as well as upon the n variables x_i. In this latter case the solutions for a series of values of c can be found by letting the corresponding Lagrange multiplier take on a series of values.

1.34 Penalty Functions

The use of penalty functions is a technique which has not seen much practical application as yet but in which interest is increasing. Kelley will discuss the application of this technique to gradient methods in Chapter 6. Examples of the use of penalty functions to prove theorems in the calculus of variations are given by Moser in an appendix to Courant.[9]

The basic idea of a penalty function is fairly simple. Assume that a minimum of $f(x_1, x_2)$ is sought subject to the subsidiary condition $g(x_1, x_2) = 0$. Form the new function

$$f_h(x_1, x_2) = f(x_1, x_2) + h[g(x_1, x_2)]^2 \qquad (1.18)$$

This function is now minimized as a problem without constraints for a succession of increasingly large values of h. In Courant[9] it is proven that as h goes to infinity the solution of this problem approaches the solution of the original problem which has a constraint.

There are several obvious modifications of this basic idea. One is to use the following form for the function f_h:

$$f_h = f + g^{2h} \qquad (1.19)$$

At present penalty functions appear to be most applicable to numerical solutions but further experience with them will be necessary to determine their true usefulness.

1.4 Application to Integrals

1.41 Relationship between the Theory of Ordinary Maxima and Minima and the Calculus of Variations

There are a number of practically important problems which can be solved by using the theory of ordinary maxima and minima to optimize integrals rather than functions. As the optimization of integrals is generally considered to fall within the province of the calculus of variations it is necessary to examine the relationships between the calculus of variations and the theory of ordinary maxima and minima.

The classic distinction between these two theories is clear and simple. The theory of ordinary maxima and minima is concerned with finding the values of each of n independent variables $x_1, x_2, \cdots, x_n$ for which a function of the n variables $f(x_1, x_2, \cdots, x_n)$ has an extremum. The calculus of variations is a generalization of this elementary theory and is concerned with finding an extremum for a quantity which depends upon n independent functions $x_1(t), x_2(t), \cdots, x_n(t)$. As this quantity depends upon the values of n complete functions rather than upon the values of n discrete variables, this quantity is a generalization of the concept of a function and is called a functional. A classic example of a functional is the following integral, where f is a specified function:

$$I = \int_{t_1}^{t_2} f(x, dx/dt, t) \, dt \tag{1.20}$$

The optimization of this integral requires the determination of a function $x(t)$ which will maximize (or minimize) the value of the integral. A more general problem requiring the determination of n functions $x_i(t)$ is

$$I = \int_{t_1}^{t_2} f\left(x_1, x_2, \cdots, x_n, \frac{dx_1}{dt}, \frac{dx_2}{dt}, \cdots, \frac{dx_n}{dt}, t\right) dt \tag{1.21}$$

The geometric interpretation of problems in the theory of ordinary maxima and minima is the determination of a point in an n-dimensional space, composed of the n independent variables $x_1, x_2, \cdots, x_n$, which maximizes a function of the n variables. The corresponding geometric interpretation of problems in the calculus of variations is the determination of a curve, specified by the n parametric equations $x_1(t) = x_1, x_2(t) = x_2, \cdots, x_n(t) = x_n$, which maximizes a functional of the n functions $x_1(t), x_2(t), \cdots, x_n(t)$. This curve may be considered to lie either in the n-dimensional space composed of $x_1, x_2, \cdots, x_n$ or in the $(n + 1)$-dimensional space composed of $t, x_1, x_2, \cdots, x_n$.

A typical problem of the theory of ordinary maxima and minima would be the determination of the values of thrust and propellant weight in each stage of a multistage space vehicle which will maximize the payload for some specific mission. A typical calculus of variation problem would be the determination of the optimum trajectory for minimum fuel consumption for some specified space vehicle and mission. The classic distinction between the two types of problems is whether the item to be optimized depends upon single values of the variables or upon functions of the variables.

One practically important special case of Eq. (1.21) is where no derivatives appear in the integral:

$$I = \int_{t_1}^{t_2} f(x_1, x_2, \cdots, x_n, t) \, dt \tag{1.22}$$

In this case the Euler equations of the calculus of variations (see Chapter 4) reduce to the following equations:

$$\frac{\partial f}{\partial x_1} = 0, \qquad \frac{\partial f}{\partial x_2} = 0, \cdots, \frac{\partial f}{\partial x_n} = 0 \qquad (1.23)$$

These equations are formally identical to the necessary conditions for a minimum of the integrand at each value of t. Because f does depend upon t, Eqs. (1.23) represent the solutions of a succession of ordinary minimum problems for every value of t from t_1 to t_2. In fact, the solutions of Eqs. (1.23) define a series of functions $x_1(t)$, $x_2(t)$, $\cdots$, $x_n(t)$ which provide the solution to the original calculus of variations problem, Eq. (1.22).

The fact that the solution of a calculus of variations problem can be regarded as the solution of a continuous series of ordinary minimum problems is a great simplification. The more general problem (1.21) requires the solution of n simultaneous ordinary differential equations which are usually nonlinear and highly resistant to analytic (or even numerical) solution. Equations (1.23), on the other hand, represent n simultaneous algebraic equations, which while often nonlinear, are far easier to solve than the differential equations.

It can be reasoned that the lack of derivatives in the integral (1.22) is responsible for the simple form of Eqs. (1.23). If there were any derivatives with respect to t in the integrand of (1.22) the value of f at any value of t would depend upon its value at neighboring values of t. As there are no derivatives the value of f at any t can be optimized without regard to the value of f at neighboring points. The integrand f may even be discontinuous. This complete independence upon the values of f at neighboring values of t allows the problem to be treated as a continuous succession of ordinary minimum problems and leads to Eqs. (1.23). This argument is admittedly not very rigorous because it does not involve limiting processes, but it seems to make Eqs. (1.23) more palatable.

This section indicates that if the derivatives in the integrand of a calculus of variations problem approach zero, the solution of the calculus of variations problem will usually approach the solution of an ordinary minimum problem. Miele has given a number of examples of this behavior.[10]

1.42 Relationship between the Theory of Ordinary Maxima and Minima and Linear Variational Problems

The preceding section discusses a special case of a more general calculus of variations problem where the necessary condition for a stationary solution becomes a set of algebraic equations instead of a set of differential equations. The question as to whether there are any other special cases where algebraic equations will be obtained is answered on page 30 of Courant[9] for the somewhat simpler problem represented by Eq. (1.20). All of the special cases where algebraic equations are obtained are represented by Eq. (1.24):

$$I = \int_{t_1}^{t_2} f\left(x, t, \frac{dx}{dt}\right) dt = \int_{t_1}^{t_2} \left[f_1(x, t) + f_2(x, t) \frac{dx}{dt}\right] dt \quad (1.24)$$

The case treated in Sections 1.41 and 1.43 is where f_2 vanishes. The case where f_2 does not vanish will be treated by Miele in Chapter 3. Miele treats this problem by means of a powerful technique which provides sufficiency conditions as well as necessary conditions and which can handle a variety of boundary conditions. Miele's technique can also be used for the simpler problems considered in Sections 1.41 and 1.43 and can provide sufficiency conditions for these problems.

1.43 Integral Problems with Subsidiary Conditions

A fairly general integral problem with subsidiary conditions which can be represented as a succession of ordinary minimum problems is to maximize the integral

$$I = \int_{t_1}^{t_2} f(x_1, x_2, \cdots, x_n, t) \, dt \quad (1.25)$$

subject to one or more subsidiary conditions of the form

$$J_i = \int_{t_1}^{t_2} g_i(x_1, x_2, \cdots, x_n, t) \, dt = \text{const} \quad (1.26)$$

The solution of this problem is to formulate the new integral

$$I + \sum \lambda_i J_i = \int_{t_1}^{t_2} \left[f + \lambda_1 g_1 + \lambda_2 g_2 + \cdots + \lambda_m g_m\right] dt \quad (1.27)$$

where the λ_i are constant Lagrange multipliers. The optimization of the integral (1.27) as a succession of ordinary minimum problems for each value of t from t_1 to t_2 solves the problem, the necessary conditions for a stationary solution being

$$\frac{\partial[f + \lambda_1 g_1 + \lambda_2 g_2 + \cdots + \lambda_m g_m]}{\partial x_i} = 0 \quad (1.28)$$

for each x_i and all values of t from t_1 to t_2.

The n variables x_i must be independent of each other for this approach to be valid. If there are any subsidiary conditions of the form

$$G\left(x_1, x_2, \cdots, x_n, \frac{dx_1}{dt}, \frac{dx_2}{dt}, \cdots, \frac{dx_n}{dt}, t\right) = 0 \tag{1.29}$$

the problem must be treated by the general methods of the calculus of variations. If the subsidiary condition takes the form

$$x_1 = \int_{t_1}^{t_2} f(x_2, x_3, \cdots, x_n, t)\ dt \tag{1.30}$$

so that one of the x_i is a functional of the others the methods of Chapter 3 will generally have to be used. Section 1.63 contains an example where a problem of this form can be transformed into one with a subsidiary condition of the form (1.26).

1.5 Remarks on Practical Application

1.51 Direct Methods vs. Indirect Methods

The methods described in this chapter constitute the classic indirect method of solving problems of ordinary maxima and minima. An indirect method is considered to be a method where the minimum is sought by means of a necessary condition for a minimum. A direct method, on the other hand, is a method that depends upon direct comparison of the values of the function at two or more points. A number of systematic numerical procedures have been developed for the solution of ordinary minimum problems (and calculus of variations problems) by direct methods. The Fibonaccian search[11] is an interesting example of such methods because it represents an optimum method of solving an optimization problem with one independent variable. When there are many independent variables, the method of gradients (Chapter 6), also known as the method of steepest descent, provides a rapid and efficient method of obtaining a numerical solution.

When an analytic solution is sought, the indirect methods that have been discussed in this chapter are generally used. When a numerical solution is sought, direct methods are often preferable. A simple example will illustrate this. Consider the problem of finding a minimum for a problem with one independent variable:

$$y = f(x) = \text{minimum} \tag{1.31}$$

The direct problem is to find the value of x that makes y a minimum. The indirect problem is to find the value of x that causes the derivative of y with respect to x to vanish:

$$dy/dx = f'(x) = 0 \tag{1.32}$$

The numerical solution of the direct problem Eq. (1.31) is essentially no more difficult than the numerical solution of the indirect problem Eq. (1.32) and has two advantages. The first advantage is that the direct solution can easily handle discontinuities, end points, and points of inflection. The indirect solution has to consider discontinuities and end points separately and cannot distinguish between maxima, minima, and inflection points (i.e., $y = x^3$ at $x = 0$) as solutions of (1.32). The second advantage of the direct method is that the behavior of the function in the neighborhood of the minimum can be found from the points calculated in seeking the minimum. If an indirect method is used, this behavior must be found by additional calculations.

The indirect method has one inherent advantage, even when numerical methods are used. If an accurate value for the value of x at which y is a minimum is sought, it can generally be obtained more accurately from Eq. (1.32) than from Eq. (1.31). This will be true as long as the minimum is stationary because, by definition, the changes in x corresponding to a discernible change in y will be orders of magnitude greater than the change in y. An example of the use of an indirect method to obtain a precise value for an independent variable for a special case of a problem that was solved by direct methods is given by Carstens and Edelbaum.[12] If, as is true in many engineering problems, only the value of the minimum is sought and not a precise value for the independent variable, then there is generally no advantage to using indirect numerical methods.

If there is more than one independent variable, the advantages of the direct method for numerical solution are increased. In this case the direct solution requires the consideration of one n-dimensional equation

$$y = f(x_1, x_2, \cdots, x_n) = \text{minimum} \qquad (1.33)$$

while the indirect method requires the simultaneous solution of n, n-dimensional equations:

$$\frac{dy}{dx_1} = f_{x_1}(x_1, x_2, \cdots, x_n) = 0$$

$$\frac{dy}{dx_2} = f_{x_2}(x_1, x_2, \cdots, x_n) = 0$$

$$\cdots \qquad \cdots \qquad (1.34)$$

$$\frac{dy}{dx_n} = f_{x_n}(x_1, x_2, \cdots, x_n) = 0$$

The initial mass of the vehicle is assumed to consist of the electrical propulsion engine, propellant, and payload:

$$M_0 = M_W + M_P + M_L \tag{1.35}$$

The engine mass is assumed to be proportional to the power developed, the power being equal to one-half the product of thrust and exhaust velocity:

$$M_W = \alpha W = \alpha T V_x / 2 \tag{1.36}$$

The rate of propellant consumption is proportional to the thrust and inversely proportional to the exhaust velocity:

$$dM_P / dt = T / V_x \tag{1.37}$$

It will be assumed that the thrust can be varied at constant power so that the rate of propellant consumption will be proportional to the square of the thrust:

$$\frac{dM_P}{dt} = -\frac{dM}{dt} = \frac{\alpha}{2} \frac{T^2}{M_W} = \frac{\alpha}{2M_W} \left(\frac{T}{M}\right)^2 M^2 \tag{1.38}$$

The final mass of the vehicle may be determined by integrating Eq. (1.38)[19]:

$$-\frac{dM}{M^2} = \frac{\alpha}{2M_W} \left(\frac{T}{M}\right)^2 dt$$

$$\frac{1}{M_1} = \frac{1}{M_0} + \frac{\alpha}{2M_W} \int_0^{t_1} \left(\frac{T}{M}\right)^2 dt \tag{1.39}$$

$$\frac{M_0}{M_1} = 1 + \frac{M_0}{M_W} \frac{\alpha}{2} \int_0^{t_1} \left(\frac{T}{M}\right)^2 dt$$

The payload will be maximized by minimizing the propellant consumption for any given power supply size and flight time and then determining what power supply size is optimum for each flight time. The propellant consumption will be minimized by optimizing both the direction and magnitude of the thrust vector as a function of time.

1.62 Trajectory Optimization for Small Changes in the Orbital Elements

Electric propulsion devices normally produce very small vehicle accelerations, typical values being on the order of one ten-thousandth of the standard acceleration of gravity. These very small accelerations allow for substantial simplifications in the analysis. The changes in the orbital elements during any one revolution may be established by a perturbation technique and then the changes over many revolutions may be established by summing these small changes. The trajectory optimization can thus be broken into two parts, the first of which will be treated in this section.

In order to establish the 24-hour orbit it is necessary to change both the radius and the inclination of the initially circular orbit. It is assumed that the intermediate orbit should remain quasi-circular and not become elliptic. Recent analysis has shown that this assumption is correct for the 24-hour mission but that very large changes in inclination should involve elliptic intermediate orbits. The equations for small changes in these elements are given by Eqs. (1.40) where the symbols are defined in the nomenclature:

$$\frac{dR}{R} = \frac{2}{V}\frac{T}{M}\cos\beta\cos\gamma\,dt$$

$$(1.40)$$

$$di = \frac{1}{V}\frac{T}{M}\sin\beta\cos\theta\,dt$$

In order to evaluate the changes in a single revolution the polar coordinate angle θ will be used as the independent variable. As the radius of the orbit will not change much during any revolution this angle may be considered proportional to time:

$$\frac{\Delta R}{R} = \frac{4R}{V^2}\int_0^\pi \frac{T}{M}\cos\beta\cos\gamma\,d\theta$$

$$(1.41)$$

$$\Delta i = \frac{2R}{V^2}\int_0^\pi \frac{T}{M}\sin\beta\cos\theta\,d\theta$$

Equation (1.39) may also be written with θ as the independent variable.

$$\frac{M_0}{M_1} = 1 + \frac{M_0}{M_w}\frac{\alpha R}{V}\int_0^\pi \left(\frac{T}{M}\right)^2 d\theta \qquad (1.42)$$

As no derivatives with respect to the independent variable θ appear in the integral and as none of the variables in the integrands depend upon the values of any of the integrals, this is a degenerate problem which can be treated by the theory of ordinary maxima and minima (Section 1.43). If large changes in R were allowed both radius and velocity would vary and the method of analysis would have to change.

The problem is now formulated by combining Eqs. (1.41) and (1.42) with the aid of Lagrange multipliers:

$$1 + \int_0^\pi \left[\frac{M_0}{M_w} \frac{\alpha R}{V} \left(\frac{T}{M} \right)^2 - \lambda_1 \frac{4R}{V^2} \frac{T}{M} \cos \beta \cos \gamma - \lambda_2 \frac{2R}{V^2} \frac{T}{M} \sin \beta \cos \theta \right] d\theta$$

(1.43)

The optimum values of β, γ, and T/M are found by differentiating the integrand of Eq. (1.43) with respect to these three variables and setting them equal to zero:

$$\lambda_1 \frac{4R}{V^2} \frac{T}{M} \cos \beta \sin \gamma = 0$$

$$\lambda_1 \frac{4R}{V^2} \frac{T}{M} \sin \beta \cos \gamma - \lambda_2 \frac{2R}{V^2} \frac{T}{M} \cos \beta \cos \theta = 0 \qquad (1.44)$$

$$\frac{M_0}{M_w} \frac{2\alpha R}{V} \frac{T}{M} - \lambda_1 \frac{4R}{V^2} \cos \beta \cos \gamma - \lambda_2 \frac{2R}{V^2} \sin \beta \cos \theta = 0$$

Simultaneous solution of these three equations yields the following optimum values for the variables:

$$\sin \gamma = 0$$

$$\tan \beta = \frac{\lambda_2}{2\lambda_1} \cos \theta \qquad (1.45)$$

$$\frac{T}{M} = \frac{2\lambda_1}{V} \frac{M_w}{\alpha M_0} \sqrt{1 + \left(\frac{\lambda_2}{2\lambda_1} \right)^2 \cos^2 \theta}$$

Substitution of these optimum values back into Eqs. (1.41) and (1.42) and integration yields the changes in the parameters during a single revolution:

$$\frac{\Delta R}{R} = \frac{8\pi\lambda_1 R}{V^3} \frac{M_w}{\alpha M_0}$$

$$\Delta i = \frac{\pi\lambda_2 R}{V^3} \frac{M_w}{\alpha M_0} \qquad (1.46)$$

$$\frac{M_0}{M_1} = 1 + \frac{R}{V^3} \frac{M_w}{\alpha M_0} \left(4\pi\lambda_1^2 + \frac{\pi}{2} \lambda_3^2 \right)$$

The variables in Eqs. (1.46) can be replaced by others having more physical significance. This may be done by calculating the value of M_0/M_1 if T/M were held constant during a revolution and considering this value of T/M as an average value $\bar{T}/M$. The Lagrange multipliers may be evaluated by setting the last of Eqs. (1.46) equal to the equation obtained with a constant T/M:

$$1 + \pi \frac{M_0}{M_W} \frac{\alpha R}{V} \left(\frac{\bar{T}}{M}\right)^2 = 1 + \pi \frac{R}{V^3} \frac{M_W}{\alpha M_0} \left(4\lambda_1{}^2 + \frac{\lambda_2{}^2}{2}\right)$$

$$(1.47)$$

$$4\lambda_1{}^2 + \frac{\lambda_2{}^2}{2} = \left(V \frac{\alpha M_0}{M_W} \frac{\bar{T}}{M}\right)^2$$

Another variable k will now be defined by Eqs. (1.48):

$$\cos k = \frac{2\lambda_1}{\sqrt{4\lambda_1{}^2 + (\lambda_2{}^2/2)}} \qquad \sin k = \frac{\lambda_2/\sqrt{2}}{\sqrt{4\lambda_1{}^2 + (\lambda_2{}^2/2)}} \qquad (1.48)$$

Substituting Eqs. (1.47) and (1.48) into Eqs. (1.46) yields the final Eqs. (1.49):

$$\frac{\Delta R}{R} = \frac{4\pi R}{V^2} \frac{\bar{T}}{M} \cos k$$

$$\Delta i = \frac{\sqrt{2}\pi R}{V^2} \frac{\bar{T}}{M} \sin k \qquad (1.49)$$

$$\frac{M_0}{M_1} = 1 + \pi \frac{\alpha M_0}{M_W} \frac{R}{V} \left(\frac{\bar{T}}{M}\right)^2$$

One interesting characteristic of Eqs. (1.49) is that they are simpler than the corresponding equations for the case where T/M is maintained constant and not programmed.[20] In this latter case the trade between changes in radius and inclination is given by elliptic integrals rather than by trigonometric functions.

1.63 Trajectory Optimization for Large Changes in the Orbital Elements

The trajectory optimization for large changes in inclination and radius will be carried out by summing a large number of the changes of the preceding section. Equations (1.49) will be assumed to hold for each revolution but will be written in differential form with time as the independent variable:

$$\frac{dR}{R} = \frac{2}{V} \frac{\bar{T}}{M} \cos k \, dt$$

$$di = \frac{\sqrt{2}}{2V} \frac{\bar{T}}{M} \sin k \, dt \qquad (1.50)$$

$$M_0 \frac{dM}{M^2} = -\frac{\alpha}{2} \frac{M_0}{M_w} \left(\frac{\bar{T}}{M}\right)^2 dt$$

As velocity appears in the first and second of Eqs. (1.50), the first equation will be rewritten in terms of velocity. The unique relation between radius and velocity for circular orbits allows this change of variable:

$$dV = -\frac{V}{2} \frac{dR}{R} = -\frac{\bar{T}}{M} \cos k \, dt \qquad (1.51)$$

If the problem was now formulated with time as the independent variable, it would be necessary to account for the fact that the velocity V in the second of Eqs. (1.50) is dependent on Eq. (1.51). This would result in a problem of the calculus of variations, although it would be the degenerate problem of linear type treated by Miele in Chapter 3. This problem can be brought within the domain of the theory of ordinary maxima and minima by interchanging the independent variable t for the dependent variable V. In terms of this new independent variable, the problem is formulated by Eq. (1.52):

$$1 + \int_{V_0}^{V_1} \left[\frac{M_0}{M_w} \frac{\alpha}{2} \frac{\bar{T}}{M} \sec k + \lambda_3 \frac{\sec k}{\bar{T}/M} - \lambda_4 \frac{\sqrt{2} \tan k}{2V} \right] dV \qquad (1.52)$$

This new problem, which may be interpreted as the problem of maximizing the final weight for a given change in velocity in a specified time with a specified change in inclination, is completely equivalent to the original problem with time as the independent variable. This is an example of the reciprocity property of isoperimetric problems (Courant and Hilbert,[1] p. 258).

As there are no derivatives in Eq. (1.52) and as no variables but the control variables $\bar{T}/M$ and k and the independent variable V appear in the integrals, this is a problem that may be treated by the theory of ordinary maxima and minima with constant Lagrange multipliers. The optimum values of $\bar{T}/M$ and k are found by setting the derivatives of the integrands equal to zero, as in the last section:

$$\frac{M_0}{M_{\mathrm{W}}}\frac{\alpha}{2}\sec k - \frac{\lambda_3 \sec k}{(\bar{T}/M)^2} = 0$$

$$\frac{M_0}{M_{\mathrm{W}}}\frac{\alpha}{2}\frac{\bar{T}}{M}\tan k \sec k + \frac{\lambda_3 \tan k \sec k}{\bar{T}/M} - \frac{\lambda_4\sqrt{2}\sec^2 k}{2V} = 0$$

(1.53)

Solving these equations for the optimum value of $\bar{T}/M$ and k results in Eqs. (1.54):

$$\frac{\bar{T}}{M} = \sqrt{\frac{2M_{\mathrm{W}}}{\alpha M_0}}\,\lambda_3 = \mathrm{const}$$

(1.54)

$$\sin k - \frac{\sqrt{2}\lambda_4}{2(M_0/M_{\mathrm{W}})(\bar{T}/M)\alpha}\frac{1}{V} = \frac{V_0 \sin k_0}{V}$$

The final solution of the problem is found by integrating the equations with these optimum values of the control variables. Some care must be taken with these integrations because the independent variable V may be double valued. The intuitive knowledge that large changes in inclination may require the velocity to first decrease and then increase allows the derivation of Eqs. (1.55):

$$\frac{M_0}{M_1} = 1 + \frac{M_0}{M_{\mathrm{W}}}\frac{\alpha t}{2}\left(\frac{\bar{T}}{M}\right)^2$$

$$t = \frac{V_0 \cos k_0 \mp \sqrt{V^2 - V_0^2 \sin^2 k_0}}{\bar{T}/M} \qquad \left(\frac{(\bar{T}/M)t}{V_0} \gtrless \cos k_0\right)$$

$$i = \frac{\sqrt{2}}{2}\sin^{-1}\frac{V_0 \sin k_0}{V} - \frac{\sqrt{2}}{2}k_0 \qquad \left(\frac{(\bar{T}/M)t}{V_0} \le \cos k_0\right)$$

$$= 127.28° - \frac{\sqrt{2}}{2}\sin^{-1}\frac{V_0 \sin k_0}{V} - \frac{\sqrt{2}}{2}k_0 \qquad \left(\frac{(\bar{T}/M)t}{V_0} \ge \cos k_0\right)$$

(1.55)

These second equations may be rewritten in a nondimensionalized form with time as the independent variable:

$$\frac{V}{V_0} = \sqrt{1 - 2\frac{(\bar{T}/M)t}{V_0}\cos k_0 + \left(\frac{(\bar{T}/M)t}{V_0}\right)^2}$$

$$i = \frac{\sqrt{2}}{2}\sin^{-1}\frac{\sin k_0}{\sqrt{1 - 2\dfrac{(\bar{T}/M)t}{V_0}\cos k_0 + \left(\dfrac{(\bar{T}/M)t}{V_0}\right)^2}} - \frac{\sqrt{2}}{2}k_0$$

$$\left(\frac{(\bar{T}/M)t}{V_0} \le \cos k_0\right) \quad (1.56)$$

$$= 127.28° - \frac{\sqrt{2}}{2}\sin^{-1}\frac{\sin k_0}{\sqrt{1 - 2\dfrac{(\bar{T}/M)t}{V_0}\cos k_0 + \left(\dfrac{(\bar{T}/M)t}{V_0}\right)^2}} - \frac{\sqrt{2}}{2}k_0$$

$$\left(\frac{(\bar{T}/M)t}{V_0} \ge \cos k_0\right)$$

Equations (1.56) are plotted in Fig. 3 with i as the ordinate and V/V_0 as the abscissa. The required values of $(\bar{T}/M)t/V_0$ for transfer from a circular orbit to any other circular orbit may be read from the graph. The lines of constant values of $(\bar{T}/M)t/V_0$ represent the loci of orbits that have the same time and fuel requirements. The value of k_0 determines the particular point on each locus that will be reached by a given trajectory. The lines of constant k_0 represent the optimum trajectories (in the velocity, inclination plane) to reach any desired combination of velocity and inclination. It should be noted that where only changes in i are desired, the optimum trajectory always involves expending some fuel to first decrease and then increase the velocity. The decreased fuel requirements for changing i at smaller velocities more than makes up for this fuel expenditure.

By eliminating k_0 in Eqs. (1.55) it is possible to write an equation for the total time requirement in terms of the final inclination and velocity:

$$\frac{(\bar{T}/M)t}{V_0} = \sqrt{1 - 2\frac{V}{V_0}\cos\sqrt{2}i + \frac{V^2}{V_0^2}}$$

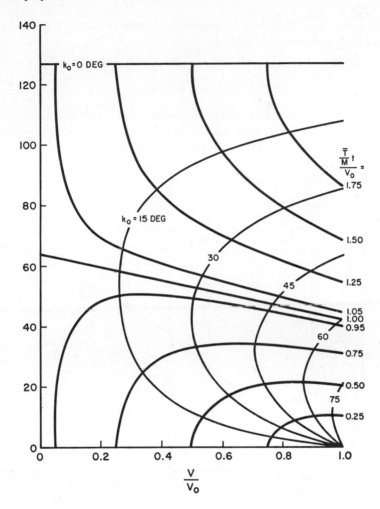

Fig. 3. Minimum propulsion requirements for transfer between inclined circular orbits of different radii.

1.64 Propulsion System Optimization

The preceding two sections have derived the thrust magnitude and direction programs that minimize propellant consumption for transfer between any two circular orbits in a given time. Time considerations are important because electrical propulsion systems typically involve times measured in tens, or even hundreds, of days. The propellant required for transfer between any two circular orbits may be decreased by increasing the transfer time. This may be shown by means of Eqs. (1.55). The propellant mass may be expressed as

$$\frac{M_P}{M_0} = \frac{M_0 - M_1}{M_0} = 1 - \left(1 + \frac{M_0}{M_W}\frac{\alpha}{2}\frac{[(\bar{T}/M)t]^2}{t}\right)^{-1} \qquad (1.57)$$

The value of $(T/M)t$ is a unique function of the velocities and relative inclination of the initial and final circular orbits and is independent of t itself. As t increases, M_P/M_0 decreases monotonically.

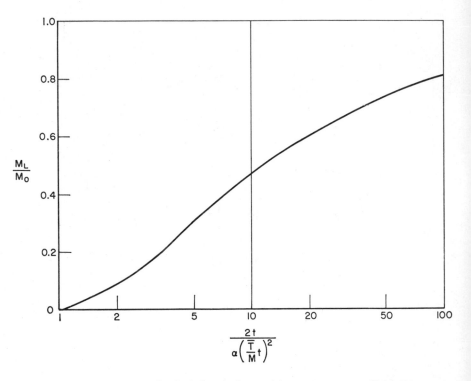

FIG. 4.   Maximum payload of electrical propulsion system versus flight time.

   If the mission time is allowed to increase, the power plant mass, instead of the propellant mass, may be decreased. The maximization of payload requires an optimum proportioning of mass between propellant and power supply.[17-19] This problem is simple enough to be solved by substitution:

$$\frac{M_L}{M_0} = 1 - \frac{M_W}{M_0} - \frac{M_P}{M_0} = \left(1 + \frac{M_0}{M_W}\frac{\alpha}{2}\frac{[(\bar{T}/M)t]^2}{t}\right)^{-1} - \frac{M_W}{M_0} \qquad (1.58)$$

Differentiating with respect to M_W/M_0,

$$\frac{d(M_L/M_0)}{d(M_W/M_0)} = 0 = \frac{\left(\dfrac{M_0}{M_W}\right)^2 \dfrac{\alpha}{2} \dfrac{[(T/M)t]^2}{t}}{\left[1 + \dfrac{M_0}{M_W} \dfrac{\alpha}{2} \dfrac{[(\bar{T}/M)t]^2}{t}\right]^2} - 1 \qquad (1.59)$$

The solution of Eq. (1.59) is

$$\frac{M_W}{M_{0_{opt}}} = \sqrt{\frac{\alpha}{2} \frac{[(T/M)t]^2}{t}} - \frac{\alpha}{2} \frac{[(T/M)t]^2}{t} \qquad (1.60)$$

The corresponding values of payload and propellant mass are

$$\frac{M_L}{M_0} = \left[1 - \sqrt{\frac{\alpha}{2} \frac{[(T/M)t]^2}{t}}\right]^2 \qquad (1.61)$$

$$\frac{M_P}{M_0} = \sqrt{\frac{\alpha}{2} \frac{[(T/M)t]^2}{t}} \qquad (1.62)$$

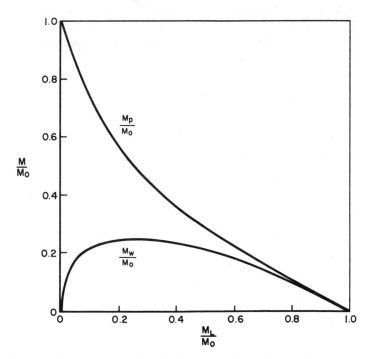

FIG. 5.   Optimum mass distribution of an electrical propulsion system.

Equation (1.61) is plotted in Fig. 4 and shows the possible increases of payload with increases in flight time. By eliminating time between Eqs. (1.60) and (1.61) it is possible to derive an expression for the optimum power plant mass as a function of payload mass:

$$\frac{M_W}{M_0} = \sqrt{\frac{M_L}{M_0}} - \frac{M_L}{M_0}$$

$$\tag{1.63}$$

$$\frac{M_P}{M_0} = 1 - \sqrt{\frac{M_L}{M_0}}$$

Equations (1.63) are plotted in Fig. 5. For large payloads, the propellant mass should be approximately equal to the power plant mass. The fact that the optimum power plant mass levels off for smaller payloads has the important practical consequence that a fixed size power supply can yield near optimum performance for a fixed initial mass and a fairly large range of payload sizes.

Nomenclature for Section 1.6

i Dihedral angle between orbit plane and original orbit plane

k Variable defined by Eqs. (1.48)

M Mass

M_L Payload mass

M_P Propellant mass

M_W Power plant mass

R Radius of orbit

t Time

T Thrust

$\bar{T}/M$ Average thrust to mass ratio, see Eq. (1.47) and text

V Velocity in circular orbit

V_x Exhaust velocity of propellant

W Power in exhaust jet

α Power plant specific mass, mass per unit power

β Angle between thrust vector and plane of orbit

γ Angle between the velocity vector and the component of the thrust vector in the plane of the orbit

θ Central polar coordinate angle, true anomaly measured from line of nodes

λ Constant Lagrange multiplier

ACKNOWLEDGMENT

The author is indebted to Dr. Henry Kelley for suggestions and references that greatly assisted the preparation of this chapter. He would also like to thank George Leitmann, Angelo Miele, Frank Deutsch, and William Fimple for their helpful comments.

REFERENCES

1. R. Courant and D. Hilbert, "Methods of Mathematical Physics," p. 164. Interscience, New York, 1953.
2. I. S. Sokolnikoff and R. M. Redheffer, "Mathematics of Physics and Modern Engineering," p. 247. McGraw-Hill, New York, 1958.
3. P. Cicala, "An Engineering Approach to the Calculus of Variations." Libreria Editrice Universitaria Levrotto and Bella, Torino, 1957.
4. H. Hancock, "Theory of Maxima and Minima." Dover, New York, 1960, also Ginn, Boston, 1917.
5. J. M. Horner, "Optimum Orbital Transfers." American Rocket Society Undergraduate Competition, 1960.
6. H. Munick, R. McGill, and G. E. Taylor, Analytic Solutions to Several Optimum Orbit Transfer Problems. *J. Astronaut. Sci.* **7**, 73 (1960).
7. G. Leitmann, The Optimization of Rocket Trajectories—A Survey, Appendix A, *in* "Progress in the Astronautical Sciences" (S. F. Singer, ed.). North-Holland, Amsterdam, 1962.
8. A. Miele, Lagrange Multipliers and Quasi-Steady Flight Mechanics, *J. Aero/Space Sci.* **26**, 592–598 (1959).
9. R. Courant, "Calculus of Variations." Lecture notes, New York University 1956–1957.
10. A. Miele, Interrelationship of Calculus of Variations and Ordinary Theory of Maxima and Minima for Flight Mechanics Applications. *ARS Journal* **29**, 75 (1959).
11. S. M. Johnson, Best exploration for maxima is fibonaccian, The RAND Corporation, Santa Monica, California, Rept. No. P–856 (1959).
12. J. P. Carstens and T. N. Edelbaum, Optimum Maneuvers for Launching Satellites into Circular Orbits of Arbitrary Radius and Inclination, *ARS Journal* **31**, 943–949 (1961).
13. S. E. Dreyfus and T. F. Cartaino, Application of Dynamic Programming to the Airplane Minimum Time-to-Climb Problem, *Aeronaut. Eng. Rev.* **16**, 74 (1957).
14. R. Bellman and S. E. Dreyfus, An Application of Dynamic Programming to the Determination of Optimal Satellite Trajectories. *J. Brit. Interplanet. Soc.* **17**, 78 (1959).
15. T. N. Edelbaum, Unpublished analyses.
16. M. L. Williams, Calculation of Fuel Distribution in Step Rockets, *J. Brit. Interplanet. Soc.* **16**, 211 (1957).
17. H. Preston-Thomas, Interorbital Transport Techniques *in* "Realities of Space Travel" (L. J. Carter, ed.). McGraw-Hill, New York, 1957.

18. E. Stuhlinger, Electrical Propulsion System for Space Ships with Nuclear Power Source, *J. Astronaut. Sci.* **2,** 149–152 (1955); **3,** 11–14 (1956).
19. J. H. Irving, Low Thrust Flight: Variable Exhaust Velocity in Gravitational Fields, *in* "Space Technology" (H. S. Seifert, ed.). Wiley, New York, 1959.
20. T. N. Edelbaum, Propulsion Requirements for Controllable Satellites, *ARS Journal* **31,** 1079–1089.

—2—

Direct Methods

FRANK D. FAULKNER

U.S. Naval Postgraduate School, Monterey, California

2.0 Introduction and Summary

Direct methods are applied in this chapter to some of the simpler problems of determining an optimum thrust program for a rocket. The emphasis is on elementary procedures for finding the trajectories and on some elementary sufficiency proofs.

There are several unusual features in the treatment given here. There is a general use of integral relations, equivalent to Green's formula, par-

33

ticularly in establishing sufficiency conditions. The adjoint system of differential equations, as defined by G. A. Bliss, is used systematically in deriving formulas and in proofs. Differential formulas similar to those which Bliss introduced for calculating differentials in ballistics are used for determining trajectories. A maximum principle is used to define or characterize the optimum trajectories. Canonical variables are introduced to simplify the differential equations.

The chapter is elementary. Though these are problems in the calculus of variations, few of the methods and conditions usually associated with that branch of mathematics will be needed or used here, except for information and for correlating with other work. The method of approach is more along the lines of the optimum control methods which are being developed in this country and in Russia. The essential principle which characterizes an optimum trajectory is that the acceleration vector must be chosen so as to maximize the integral of its scalar product with a vector defined by the adjoint system. Part of the problem is to find the particular solution to the adjoint system which corresponds to the solution. There are conditions on the adjoint system at the end of the trajectory, and the problem is a two-point boundary value problem. A problem peculiar to trajectory studies is that there may be a limited amount of energy (fuel) available and part of the problem is that of choosing the rate at which this is to be expended, the throttling problem.

The chapter is divided into three sections. The first treats a method of solution for problems such as the interception of a ballistic missile with minimum fuel consumption, above the sensible atmosphere, or rendezvous in minimum time. To simplify the problem, it is assumed that gravity can be approximated by at most a linear function of the coordinates. A routine is set up for obtaining the trajectory on a digital computer; if it converges, it yields the desired trajectory. A sufficiency proof and a Mayer-reciprocal relation are also given.

The second section gives a simple graphic solution to problems of the above type for cases wherein the gravity can be considered constant, or at most, approximated by a function of time, and the velocity is not involved at one end. In this case, there are two principles of optimum performance: (i) thrust must be fixed in direction and (ii) it must be as large as possible for a suitably chosen initial period and zero thereafter, the impulse representing an upper bound to performance. In this case a single graph can be drawn which gives the displacement of the rocket due to thrust versus time, with the time of thrust as a parameter. The solutions are obtained by plotting on this graph a second curve which corresponds to the particular problem. All of the numbers associated with the solution can be obtained directly from the relations between the graphs. It is obvious from the solution in many cases that the conditions are also sufficient, and if the problem as posed should not have a solution, this also is often obvious.

The third section treats the problem of programming the thrust magnitude of a rocket so as to move in an optimum way along an arbitrary given path in space when the thrust is tangential to the path and when time does not enter explicitly in either the differential equation or in the constraint. The problem of Goddard is the typical example. A flow chart is given for determining on a digital computer the thrust schedule for maximum range. The differential equation is reduced to canonical form to simplify the theory.

Direct methods allow the only complete sufficiency proofs known to the author, with the exception of those problems which can be treated by Green's theorem.

The use of the acceleration rather than the mass of the rocket as a variable has the advantage of simplifying the differential equations. On the other hand, the bounds on the acceleration are not so simple. They are expressed as functions of time in the examples given here, but in general do not have this simple form. The impulse solution, corresponding to unbounded thrust, can be handled by similar techniques, sometimes being simpler since there is no problem of determining bounds on the acceleration.

It is assumed throughout that the thrust may be selected arbitrarily between zero and some constant maximum value as long as fuel remains. It is assumed also that the speed of the emitted gases is constant so that the thrust force is proportional to the fuel consumption rate. It is usually assumed that the initial conditions are all given, since this is the case of particular interest.

2.1 A Routine for Determining Some Optimum Trajectories

2.10 Introduction and Summary

In this section a numerical routine is given for determining some optimum trajectories on a digital computer. The two problems taken as typical examples are, first, that of intercepting a ballistic target with minimum fuel consumption, and, second, that of effecting rendezvous in minimum time. It is assumed that the two bodies are near enough together that the difference in gravitational acceleration may be approximated by at most a linear function of position.

When the differential equations of motion are linear, some simple integral formulas can be derived which have the nice property of making it apparent what should be done, and also allow a simple, absolute, suffi-

ciency proof. There appear to be two general principles of optimization for
thrust programming above the atmosphere. The adjoint system of differential equations generates a vector. The first principle is that the direction
of the thrust is such that the resulting acceleration has a maximum projection onto the adjoint vector. The second principle is that the acceleration
is to be as large as possible when the magnitude of this adjoint vector is
above a certain value and as small as possible when it is smaller than that
value; part of the problem may be to determine this value.

It is shown that a trajectory whereon these principles are observed
furnishes an optimum relation among the various initial and terminal
values of the variables, and it defines a class of so-called Mayer-reciprocal
optimum relations. The principal problem treated here is that of finding a
trajectory which satisfies the specified constraints and the maximum
principles.

This is done by successive approximations, equivalent to Newton's
method. A trajectory of the above type is guessed. This involves choosing
some parameters, initial values, or constants of integration for the adjoint
system. The resulting trajectory will generally not satisfy the constraints
on the terminal values of the variables. The differentials of the terminal
values are expressed in terms of the differentials of the parameters. The
differentials are chosen so as to reduce the errors in the terminal values
to zero; the system of equations is inverted to obtain the corresponding
changes in the parameters, and a new trajectory is obtained. This is repeated until the errors in the terminal values are below some predetermined
value.

If the solution to the adjoint system can be found in closed form, the
differentials are relatively simple to calculate. For other cases, the method
which G. A. Bliss introduced in calculating differentials in ballistics is used.
If the differential equations are not linear, the adjoint system is adjoint
to the linear system of equations for the variations of the original variables.

2.11 Basic Equations

The equation of motion of a rocket in a gravitational field, subject to no
outside forces, may be written as

$$\ddot{\mathbf{r}} = \mathbf{g} + \mathbf{a} \tag{2.1}$$

where $\mathbf{r}$ is the position vector, $\mathbf{g}$ is the acceleration due to gravity, $\mathbf{a}$ is the
acceleration due to thrust, and a dot ($\cdot$) over a variable indicates its time

derivative. We may write

$$\mathbf{a} = \frac{c'\dot{m}\mathbf{e}}{1 - m} \qquad (2.2)$$

where m is the ratio of the mass of fuel which has been consumed to the initial gross mass of the rocket, c' is the constant speed of the emitted gases, and $\mathbf{e}$ is a unit vector in the direction of the thrust.

A useful kinematic relation is the following:

$$\int_0^t a \, dt = c' \int_0^t \frac{\dot{m} \, dt}{1 - m} = -c' \log (1 - m) \qquad (2.3)$$

where $a = |\mathbf{a}|$. Since the fuel consumed is proportional to m and $\log (1 - m)$ is a monotonic function of m, conditions involving the final value of the mass may be rephrased in terms of the integral of the acceleration, subject to the constraints on the size of $\dot{m}$. The use of a as a variable in place of m simplifies the equations of motion since a enters linearly.

For the case where gravity may be considered constant, the equations of motion may be written

$$\ddot{x} = a \cos p$$

$$\qquad (2.4)$$

$$\ddot{y} = a \sin p - g$$

for two-dimensional motion, with the y-axis vertical. If the gravitational field of a heavy central body is approximated as a linear function of the displacement, these are replaced by

$$\ddot{x} = -b^2 x + a \cos p$$

$$\qquad (2.5)$$

$$\ddot{y} = B^2 y - g + a \sin p$$

where g is the gravitational acceleration at the origin of coordinates, $b^2 = g/r_E$, with r_E the distance from the origin of coordinates to the center of the body, and $B^2 = 2b^2$.

2.12 Adjoint Equations, Green's Formula

The integral formulas needed in the remainder of this section are derived here. This is done by introducing new variables and integrating by parts, yielding formulas of a type which go by the general name of Green's formula (see Coddington and Levinson,[1] p. 86).

Let us take Eqs. (2.5) as the equations of motion for the moment. Two new variables, u, v, one for each equation of motion are introduced; they are called multipliers, or Lagrange multipliers, and they are unspecified except that they have continuous second derivatives in the interval of interest. Let us multiply Eqs. (2.5) through by u, v, respectively, add, and integrate. The result may be written

$$\int_0^T [u(\ddot{x} + b^2 x - a \cos p) + v(\ddot{y} - B^2 y + g - a \sin p)]dt = 0 \quad (2.6)$$

whenever x, y are any solutions to Eqs. (2.5). If Eq. (2.6) is integrated by parts to eliminate derivatives of x, y from the integrand, it becomes

$$\int_0^T [x(\ddot{u} + b^2 u) + y(\ddot{v} - B^2 v) - a(u \cos p + v \sin p) + gv]dt$$

$$+[\dot{x}u - x\dot{u} + \dot{y}v - y\dot{v}]_0^T = 0 \quad (2.7)$$

Equation (2.7) is one of several forms which may be called Green's formula.

Now, to simplify Eq. (2.7), let us choose the multipliers u, v so that the dependent variables x, y drop from the integrand; set

$$\ddot{u} + b^2 u = 0$$

$$\ddot{v} - B^2 v = 0 \quad (2.8)$$

This is the adjoint system of differential equations for Eqs. (2.5). It is the operations of integrating by parts to eliminate the derivatives and setting the coefficients of the dependent variables to zero in the integrand which defines the adjoint system. Equations (2.5) are each called self-adjoint, since Eqs. (2.8) and (2.5) involve the same differential operators. Comment: one may introduce four multipliers, one each for x, y, $\dot{x}$, $\dot{y}$. In this case the system corresponding to Eqs. (2.5) is not formally self-adjoint (see Coddington and Levinson,[1] p. 84), but the resulting equations and formulas are equivalent. If Eqs. (2.4) were used in place of Eqs. (2.5), the adjoint system would be

$$\ddot{u} = 0$$

$$\ddot{v} = 0 \quad (2.9)$$

In either case, if u, v are solutions to the adjoint system, Eq. (2.7) reduces to

$$[\dot{x}u - x\dot{u} + \dot{y}v - y\dot{v}]_0^T = \int_0^T [a(u \cos p + v \sin p) - gv] \, dt \quad (2.10)$$

This is the basic formula for this section, it being understood that u, v are solutions to the corresponding adjoint system.

Particular formulas. If we are interested in a particular variable, say x at time T, we may obtain a formula for it by choosing the particular solution u_1, v_1 to the adjoint system such that $u_1(T) = v_1(T) = \dot{v}_1(T) = 0$, $\dot{u}_1(T) = -1$. For Eqs. (2.8), $u_1 = (1/b) \sin b(T - t)$, $v_1 = 0$; for Eqs. (2.9), $u_1 = T - t$, $v_1 = 0$. In the same way, to obtain a formula for y choose u_2, v_2 such that $u_2(T) = v_2(T) = \dot{u}_2(T) = 0$, $\dot{v}_2(T) = -1$. When these are substituted into Eq. (2.10) the formulas for x, y are obtained:

$$x = x_0 + \dot{x}_0 T + \int_0^T (T - t)a \cos p \, dt$$

$$y = y_0 + \dot{y}_0 T - \frac{g T^2}{2} + \int_0^T (T - t)a \sin p \, dt$$

$$(2.11)$$

or

$$x = x_0 \cos bT + \frac{\dot{x}_0}{b} \sin bT + \frac{1}{b} \int_0^T a \cos p \sin b(T - t) \, dt$$

$$(2.12)$$

$$y = \left(y_0 - \frac{g}{B^2}\right) \cosh BT + \left(\frac{\dot{y}_0}{B}\right) \sinh BT + \frac{g}{B^2}$$

$$+ \frac{1}{B} \int_0^T a \sin p \sinh B(T - t) \, dt$$

accordingly as Eqs. (2.4) or (2.5) are used.

If an equation for $\dot{x}(T)$ is desired, it may be obtained by differentiating Eqs. (2.11) or (2.12), or it may be obtained by choosing the solution u_3, v_3 such that $u_3(T) = 1$, $v_3(T) = \dot{u}_3(T) = \dot{v}_3(T) = 0$. In a similar way, u_4, v_4 may be defined to yield $\dot{y}(T)$ from Eq. (2.10).

2.13 Maximum Principles

In this subsection it will be shown that if a trajectory satisfies two maximum principles, to be specified, then it is an optimum trajectory for a certain problem. In the next subsection it will be shown that it is an optimum trajectory for a related class of problems.

Let us consider now the problem of maximizing the integral in Eq. (2.10). First, we note that the first terms in the integral could be written as a scalar product $\mathbf{a} \cdot \mathbf{w}$, where $\mathbf{a} = a(\mathbf{i} \cos p + \mathbf{j} \sin p)$ and $\mathbf{w} = u\mathbf{i} + v\mathbf{j}$.

Suppose that u, v have already been determined in some way and are solutions to the adjoint system of differential equations. Let us consider what properties **a** should have which would maximize the integral. To begin, we would only allow acceleration functions a which are bounded:

$$0 \leqq a \leqq A_m \tag{2.13}$$

where A_m is a known function of t determined by the rocket mechanism. Further, the amount of fuel may be limited, so that it is also required, by Eq. (2.3), that

$$\int_0^T a \, dt \leqq -c' \log (1 - m_{\max}) \tag{2.14}$$

where $m_{\max}$ is the largest value of the burned fuel ratio, corresponding to using all of the fuel.

Now one principle is that whenever $a \neq 0$, the direction of **a** should be such as to give a maximum projection onto **w**; that is,

$$\tan p = \frac{v}{u} \tag{2.15}$$

p being chosen in Eq. (2.15) to give the maximum rather than the minimum. This determines the direction of **a** and is called the steering equation.

If the total quantity of fuel is limited, so that

$$\int_0^T A_m \, dt > -c' \log (1 - m_{\max})$$

then there also is the problem of determining the time to apply **a**. The second principle is this: It should be chosen so that

$$a = \begin{cases} A_m & \text{whenever} \quad |\mathbf{w}| = w > L \\ 0 & \text{whenever} \quad w < L \end{cases} \tag{2.16}$$

and L is a constant such that all fuel is burned, so that

$$\int_0^T a \, dt = -c' \log (1 - m_{\max})$$

In the proof of the theorem which follows it will be shown that such conditions on **a** maximize the integral, and in following subsections methods for obtaining some optimum trajectories will be given.

For the theorem which follows, let us consider a specific problem; the solution to other problems differs in the way that the initial and final values of the variables enter, but not in the nature of the extremals. Let us consider the problem of maximizing $x(T)$. Assume that all initial values are given, and some of the terminal values $y(T)$, $\dot{x}(T)$, $\dot{y}(T)$; some of these last three may not be involved in the constraints. Assume that the amount of fuel is specified as not to exceed a certain amount so that there are constraints like Eqs. (2.13) and (2.14) on a.

Now suppose a trajectory C^* has been found, and a set of multipliers u, v which satisfy the following relations together.

H.1. The trajectory is admissible. This means that the prescribed end values are all assumed and the constraints on a are satisfied.

H.2. u, v are solutions to the adjoint system of differential equations. Also, $-\dot{u}(T)$, the coefficient of $x(T)$ in Eq. (2.10), is positive, and if any of the set $y(T)$, $\dot{x}(T)$, $\dot{y}(T)$ is not specified, its coefficient, $-\dot{v}(T)$, $u(T)$, or $v(T)$ in Eq. (2.10) vanishes.

H.3. For each value of t, p is such as to maximize the integrand $\mathbf{a \cdot w}$; that is, $\mathbf{a}$ and $\mathbf{w}$ are parallel and of the same sense.

H.4. There is a value L and

$$ a = \begin{cases} A_m & \text{when} \quad w > L \\ 0 & \text{when} \quad w < L \end{cases} $$

and $w = L$ only at isolated points. Also, all fuel is used, so that

$$ \int_0^T a \, dt = -c' \log (1 - m_{\max}) $$

Theorem. *The trajectory C^* which satisfies conditions H.1, H.2, H.3, and H.4 furnishes a maximum value to $x(T)$ and is unique.*

Proof. Assume there is a second admissible path. Denote quantities associated with C^* by an asterisk ($*$) and corresponding quantities on the other path by capital letters.

Let T_1 denote the points of the interval $(0, T)$ where $w > L$ and T_2 the points where $w < L$. Let

$$ B = \int_{T_1} (a^* - A) \, dt \geq 0 \tag{2.17} $$

Then, by Eq. (2.3),

$$ \int_{T_2} A \, dt \leq B \tag{2.18} $$

since the second path requires no more fuel than C^*.

The quantities associated with each path must satisfy Eq. (2.10), with u, v as specified as above. If we substitute the set of values for each path into Eq. (2.10) and subtract the resulting equations, we get

$$-\dot{u}(T)[x^*(T) - X(T)] = \int_0^T (\mathbf{a}^* - \mathbf{A}) \cdot \mathbf{w} \, dt \qquad (2.19)$$

The integral on the right-hand side may be rewritten

$$\int_{T_1} (a^* - A)w \, dt + \int_{T_1} Aw[1 - \cos(p^* - P)] \, dt$$

$$- \int_{T_2} Aw \cos (p^* - P) \, dt \qquad (2.20)$$

We see that

$$\int_{T_1} (a^* - A)w \, dt \geq L \int_{T_1} (a^* - A) \, dt = LB$$

and

$$\int_{T_2} A \cos (p^* - P)w \, dt \leq \int_{T_2} Aw \, dt \leq L \int_{T_2} A \, dt$$

$$\leq LB$$

Hence the sum of the first and third terms in Eq. (2.20) is not negative. Clearly, the second term is not negative. Hence the sum (2.20) is positive or zero. Further inspection reveals that it is positive unless $\mathbf{A} = \mathbf{a}^*$, except possibly on a set of measure zero. Since $-\dot{u}(T)$ is positive, this establishes the theorem; $x^*(T) > X(T)$ unless $\mathbf{A} = \mathbf{a}^*$. Thus, the maximum principles laid down are sufficient to ensure a maximum value for the integral and hence for $x(T)$.

The paths whereon H.2–H.4 are satisfied will be called extremals. If $a(t)$ is a given function, H.4 will be omitted.

Comments. If the terminal velocity is not involved in the given conditions, then by H.2 choose $u(T) = v(T) = 0$, so that $w(T) = 0$. It follows that w is a decreasing function of t, at least in a neighborhood of T. In some cases of interest, this is enough to ensure that $w(t)$ is decreasing for $0 < t < T$. In particular, this is true if gravity is considered constant, since $w = (\text{const}) \, (T - t)$. It is also true for the linearized approximation, at least if $T < \pi/(2b)$, since both $\sin b(T - t)$ and $\sinh B(T - t)$ are decreasing in magnitude for $0 < t < T$.

For constant gravity, we see also that if $u(T) = 0 = v(T)$, then $u = c_1(T - t)$, $v = c_2(T - t)$, and if p is to maximize the integral, $\tan p = v/u = $ constant, by Eq. (2.15).

2.14 A Mayer-Reciprocal Relation

It will be shown here that an extremal such as C^* does not furnish just a maximum value to one variable, such as $x(T)$, but rather an optimum relation among all of the set $x(0)$, $y(0)$, $\dot{x}(0)$, $\dot{y}(0)$, $x(T)$, $y(T)$, $\dot{x}(T)$, $\dot{y}(T)$ whose coefficients in Eq. (2.10) do not vanish for the particular solution u, v, and the fuel consumption $m(T)$. From the proof just given, it is clear that if $x(0)$, $\cdots$, $\dot{y}(T)$ have the values they assume on C^*, then $m(T)$ is a minimum for functions a which satisfy Eq. (2.13).

Consider any other one of the set whose coefficient in Eq. (2.10) does not vanish. Suppose, for example, that $u(0)$ does not vanish, but is positive. Then $\dot{x}(0)$ is a minimum if $x(0)$, $y(0)$, $\dot{y}(0)$, $\cdots$, $\dot{y}(T)$, $m(T)$ all assume the values on C^*. The proof is as before except that the left-hand side of Eq. (2.19) is replaced by $-u(0)[\dot{x}^*(0) - \dot{X}(0)]$.

A similar result holds if neither $\dot{u}(T)$ nor $\dot{v}(T)$ vanishes; in this case the linear combination $-\dot{u}(T)x(T) - \dot{v}(T)y(T)$ is a maximum compared with its value on other curves which assume the other end values associated with C^*.

This argument breaks down if the coefficient of the corresponding quantity in Eq. (2.10) vanishes. If, for example, $u(T) = 0$, then $\dot{x}(T)$ is not a maximum or a minimum on C^*; $\dot{x}^*(T)$ is the only possible value that $\dot{x}(T)$ can assume on a curve whereon the remaining quantities $x(0)$, $\cdots$, $\dot{y}(T)$, $m(T)$ assume the values they have on C^*, and also C^* is the only admissible curve on which it can assume that value.

Thus we see that an extremal does not just furnish a maximum value to one quantity but rather furnishes an optimum relation among the end values of the variables. The relations of the above type, wherein the role of various end values are interchanged, go by the generic name of Mayer-reciprocal relations.[2]

2.15 Numerical Routine for a Simple Optimum Trajectory

The problem of determining the trajectory for attaining a prescribed point X, Y in a prescribed time T with minimum fuel consumption is taken up here.

Since the terminal velocity is irrelevant, set $u(T) = v(T) = 0$. Also, following the observations at the end of Section 2.13, consider only an initial period of thrust, $(0, t_1)$, where t_1 is to be found.

Then $\tan p = v/u$ has the form $\tan p = c$ if gravity is constant or $\tan p = (c/B) \sinh B(T - t)/[(1/b) \sin b(T - t)]$, where $c = (\tan p)_{T-0}$. If these are used, together with

$$\cos p = u/w$$

$$(2.21)$$

$$\sin p = v/w$$

Eqs. (2.11) may be rewritten

$$x = x_0 + \dot{x}_0 T + \cos p \int_0^{t_1} (T - t) a \, dt$$

$$(2.22)$$

$$y = y_0 + \dot{y}_0 T - \frac{g T^2}{2} + \sin p \int_0^{t_1} (T - t) a \, dt$$

with p constant, and Eqs. (2.12) may be rewritten

$$x = x_0 \cos bT + \frac{\dot{x}_0}{b} \sin bT + \frac{1}{b^2} \int_0^{t_1} \frac{a}{w} \sin^2 b(T - t) \, dt$$

$$(2.23)$$

$$y = \left(y_0 - \frac{g}{B^2} \right) \cosh BT + \frac{\dot{y}_0}{B} \sinh BT + \frac{g}{B^2}$$

$$+ \frac{c}{B^2} \int_0^{t_1} \frac{a}{w} \sinh^2 B(T - t) \, dt$$

where $w^2 = (1/b)^2 \sin^2 b(T - t) + (c/B)^2 \sinh^2 B(T - t)$ in the latter equations.

Throughout the remainder of this section let us deal with Eqs. (2.23). We will determine the trajectory and then show that it furnishes the desired minimum for the fuel consumption. If the thrust of the rocket is constant, then the acceleration has a bound A_m as a function of t,

$$a \leqq \begin{cases} c' \dot{m}_{max}/(1 - \dot{m}_{max} t) & \text{when} \quad t < m_{max}/\dot{m}_{max} \\ c' \dot{m}_{max}/(1 - m_{max}) & \text{when} \quad t > m_{max}/\dot{m}_{max} \end{cases}$$

$$(2.24)$$

where m_{max}, $\dot{m}_{max}$ are the maximum values of m, $\dot{m}$, respectively.

Consider now any trajectory, defined by a choice of t_1, c in Eq. (2.23), and a neighboring trajectory, defined by $t_1 + \delta t_1,\, c + \delta c$. The first variations (differentials) of $x(T),\, y(T)$ are

$$\delta x(T) = \left[\frac{a \sin^2 b\,(T-t)}{b^2 w} \right]_{t_1} \delta t_1 - \frac{1}{c} \int_0^{t_1} aw \sin^2 p \cos^2 p \; dt \; \delta c$$

$$\tag{2.25}$$

$$\delta y(T) = \left[\frac{ac \sinh^2 B\,(T-t)}{B^2 w} \right]_{t_1} \delta t_1 + \frac{1}{c^2} \int_0^{t_1} aw \sin^2 p \cos^2 p \; dt \; \delta c$$

where $\tan p = bc \sinh B(T-t)/[B \sin b(T-t)]$.

Computational routine. Guess values for t_1, c, and calculate the corresponding trajectory. The values $x(T),\, y(T)$ will be in error. Set

$$\delta x(T) = X - x(T)$$

$$\tag{2.26}$$

$$\delta y(T) = Y - y(T)$$

where δx, δy are given by Eq. (2.25). Solve Eq. (2.26) for δt_1, δc to get a new estimate of t_1, c. Compute the corresponding trajectory. Repeat until some convergence criterion is satisfied, say $[X - x(T)]^2 + [Y - y(T)]^2$ is less than some preassigned number.

Proof of minimum fuel consumption. To see that the path found above furnishes the desired minimum, multiply the second of Eqs. (2.23) by c and add the two. All of the hypotheses of the theorem which involve the resulting integrand are satisfied: $u = u_1(t)$, $v = cv_2(t)$ are solutions to the adjoint system, chosen to vanish at $t = T$ because the velocity was not involved there; $\tan p = v/u$; and

$$a = \begin{cases} A_m(t) & \text{when} \quad w > L = w(t_1) \\ 0 & \text{when} \quad w < L = w(t_1) \end{cases}$$

Hence the integral is a maximum and no other allowed acceleration function leads to the same value. The terms on the left are all determined by the given conditions and the value of c found above.

A similar result holds if Eqs. (2.22) are used.

2.16 Interception with Minimum Fuel Consumption

The problem of intercepting a target following a known course above the atmosphere is discussed here. For simplicity the discussion is confined to the case of a ballistic target in a uniform gravitational field.

In this case, the equations for interception may be written

$$X_0 + \dot{X}_0 T - \cos p \int_0^{t_1} (T - t)a \, dt = 0$$

$$(2.27)$$

$$Y_0 + \dot{Y}_0 T - \sin p \int_0^{t_1} (T - t)a \, dt = 0$$

where X_0, Y_0 is the relative position of the target with respect to the rocket initially and $\dot{X}_0$, $\dot{Y}_0$ is the corresponding velocity.

If we differentiate these, we obtain the equations for the variation of an interception trajectory:

$$\left(\dot{X}_0 - \cos p \int_0^{t_1} a \, dt \right) \delta T - \cos p (T - t_1)a(t_1) \, \delta t_1$$

$$+ \sin p \int_0^{t_1} (T - t)a \, dt \, \delta p = 0$$

$$(2.28)$$

$$\left(\dot{Y}_0 - \sin p \int_0^{t_1} a \, dt \right) \delta T - \sin p (T - t_1)a(t_1) \, \delta t_1$$

$$- \cos p \int_0^{t_1} (T - t)a \, dt \, \delta p = 0$$

If δp is eliminated between these, the following equation is obtained:

$$\left[\left(\dot{X}_0 - \cos p \int_0^{t_1} a \, dt \right) \cos p + \left(\dot{Y}_0 - \sin p \int_0^{t_1} a \, dt \right) \sin p \right] \delta T$$

$$= (T - t_1)a(t_1) \, \delta t_1 \quad (2.29)$$

The condition for a stationary value of t_1, and hence $m(T)$, then, is that

$$\left(\dot{X}_0 - \cos p \int_0^{t_1} a \, dt \right) \cos p + \left(\dot{Y}_0 - \sin p \int_0^{t_1} a \, dt \right) \sin p = 0 \quad (2.30)$$

This may be interpreted as the condition that the direction of thrust be perpendicular to the relative velocity for $t > t_1$, as observed by Faulkner[3] (Chapter VII). More generally, whenever the terminal velocity does not enter, this has the form $(\mathbf{v}_{rel} \cdot \dot{\mathbf{w}})_T = 0$, where $\mathbf{v}_{rel}$ is the relative velocity.

Computational routine. The trajectory is obtained as follows. Values are guessed for the variables t_1, T, p, a trajectory is run, and the errors for that trajectory

$$E = X_0 + \dot{X}_0 T - \cos p \int_0^{t_1} (T - t)a \, dt$$

(2.31)

$$F = Y_0 + \dot{Y}_0 T - \sin p \int_0^{t_1} (T - t)a \, dt$$

are calculated. If t_1, T, p are changed by small amounts,

$$\delta E = \left(\dot{X}_0 - \cos p \int_0^{t_1} a \, dt \right) \delta T - (T - t_1)a(t_1) \cos p \, \delta t_1$$

$$+ \sin p \int_0^{t_1} (T - t)a \, dt \, \delta p$$

(2.32)

$$\delta F = \left(\dot{Y}_0 - \sin p \int_0^{t_1} a \, dt \right) \delta T - (T - t_1)a(t_1) \sin p \, \delta t_1$$

$$- \cos p \int_0^{t_1} (T - t)a \, dt \, \delta p$$

The new estimate of p is made from Eq. (2.30), and hence δp is obtained. Set

$$\delta E = -E$$

(2.33)

$$\delta F = -F$$

using the values from Eqs. (2.31) and (2.32). Since δp is already determined, this defines two equations for δt_1, δT. Hence new estimates for t_1, T, p are obtained.

The iteration is continued until $E^2 + F^2$ is less than some preassigned value. No convergence problems have been encountered.

The above routine yields a stationary value of t_1; it can be checked by varying T whether this is a maximum or a minimum. In the above problem it is always a minimum.

2.17 Rendezvous in Minimum Time

The problem of effecting rendezvous or transfer from one orbit to another in a uniform gravitational field in minimum time is discussed here.

The optimum thrust schedule is parallel to the plane defined by the initial relative position and velocity. Let us choose the axes so that the initial position of the target relative to the rocket is X_0, Y_0, with $Y_0 > 0$ and the relative velocity has components $\dot{X}_0$, 0, with $\dot{X}_0 > 0$. Let us define the errors

$$E' = X_0 + \dot{X}_0 T - \int_0^T (T - t) a \cos p \, dt$$

(2.34)

$$F' = Y_0 - \int_0^T (T - t) a \sin p \, dt$$

$$G = \dot{X}_0 - \int_0^T a \cos p \, dt$$

(2.35)

$$H = - \int_0^T a \sin p \, dt$$

For rendezvous it is necessary and sufficient to determine a, p as functions of time so that at some time T, $E' = F' = G = H = 0$. Since G, H must be zero, we may replace E', F' by new error functions E, F and write the system as

$$E = X_0 + \int_0^T t a \cos p \, dt$$

$$F = Y_0 + \int_0^T t a \sin p \, dt$$

(2.36)

$$G = \dot{X}_0 - \int_0^T a \cos p \, dt$$

$$H = - \int_0^T a \sin p \, dt$$

It is necessary and sufficient for rendezvous that all of these vanish.

We may consider this as a minor variation of the problem of the theorem in Section 2.13. Multiply Eqs. (2.36) through by constants c_3, c_2, -1, $-c_1$, respectively, and add. For any solution, we have

$$\dot{X}_0 - c_3 X_0 - c_2 Y_0 = \int_0^T a[(1 + c_3 t) \cos p + (c_1 + c_2 t) \sin p] \, dt \quad (2.37)$$

This is a particular case of Eq. (2.10) with the gravitational term eliminated. The terms $u = 1 + c_3 t$, and $v = c_1 + c_2 t$ are solutions to the adjoint system (2.9), so that hypothesis H.2 of the theorem is satisfied.

Now suppose we have found a solution which satisfies two maximum principles, corresponding to H.3 and H.4. First, let $a = a_{max}$, $0 < t < T$, and let p be chosen to maximize the integrand,

$$\tan p = \frac{v}{u} = \frac{c_1 + c_2 t}{1 + c_3 t} \quad (2.38)$$

The trajectory then satisfies all the hypotheses of the theorem, that is, it is admissible, u, v are solutions to the adjoint system, and a, p are such as to maximize the integral in Eq. (2.37). There is then no other trajectory which can effect rendezvous at time T. Now suppose that there is a trajectory which effects rendezvous at time T', with $0 < T' < T$. If the thrust schedule for this latter trajectory is followed until T'', at which time rendezvous is effected, and then thrust is zero, the resulting trajectory would lead to rendezvous at time T as well, since once rendezvous is effected, the two remain together in the absence of thrust. But the theorem establishes that there is no other trajectory which can effect rendezvous at time T, and hence there cannot be one which effects rendezvous at an earlier time.

Hence the trajectory described above yields the minimum time T, if we can find it.

Numerical routine. The trajectory is determined as follows. First, let us obtain formulas for the variations of the errors:

$$\delta E = (ta \cos p)_T \, \delta T - \int_0^T ta \sin p \, \delta p \, dt$$

$$\delta F = (ta \sin p)_T \, \delta T + \int_0^T ta \cos p \, \delta p \, dt$$

$$(2.39)$$

$$\delta G = -(a \cos p)_T \, \delta T + \int_0^T a \sin p \, \delta p \, dt$$

$$\delta H = -(a \sin p)_T \, \delta T - \int_0^T a \cos p \, \delta p \, dt$$

wherein, from Eq. (2.38),

$$\delta p = \frac{(1 + c_3 t)(\delta c_1 + t \delta c_2) - (c_1 + c_2 t) t \delta c_3}{(1 + c_3 t)^2 + (c_1 + c_2 t)^2} \tag{2.40}$$

Now guess a set of values for c_1, c_2, c_3, T and calculate the values of E, F, G, H and the various integrals associated with Eqs. (2.39). Then set

$$\delta E = -E$$
$$\cdots \tag{2.41}$$
$$\delta H = -H$$

There are four equations for the four quantities δc_1, δc_2, δc_3, T, and hence new estimates for c_1, c_2, c_3, T. If the routine converges, it yields the desired trajectory.

2.18 Discussion

This chapter has been restricted to elementary techniques for simplicity. Complete foundations for the method were given in papers by Bliss.[4-6]

For those interested in classic calculus of variations the hypotheses H.2 and H.3 define the Euler equations for the steering problem. All of the problems discussed here are problems of Mayer (see Bliss,[7] Section 69) with separated end conditions. In the problem of Mayer, the form of the Euler equations is independent of the particular quantity to be maximized and the constraints, except as these determine the constants in the solutions u, v to the adjoint system. It is interesting that the Euler equations are inferred here from a maximum principle and yield a sufficient condition for an extremal, rather than a necessary condition. For the steering problem, the maximum principle implies also the Weierstrass and Legendre conditions (see Bliss,[7] p. 223); the Weierstrass condition has the form $1 - \cos (p^* - P) < 0$ and is always satisfied.

The significance of conditions H.2 and H.3 has been stressed recently in various papers. Emerson[8] gives necessary and sufficient conditions and an existence proof for an isoperimetric problem involving two integrals. Breakwell[9] gives a fairly general theoretical discussion for optimum trajectories, bringing out these relations. Okhotsimskii and Eneev[10] give a discussion of a launching problem similar to the problems treated in this section. Leitmann[11] gives a general treatment of the theory of two-dimensional problems for a constant gravitational field. Incidentally, there are no problems in a constant gravitational field for which three-dimensional thrust is required; there is always a plane such that the thrust is parallel to it for the optimum.

The vector **w** may be considered as the impulse-response vector, familiar in one-dimensional problems to electrical engineers. Lawden[12] defines it in more general problems; the steering equation (2.15) was apparently first published by him.

The condition that the energy input be at the time when w is large, H.4, may also be expressed as a Weierstrass condition (see Leitmann[11]).

The differential equations are simplified by the introduction of a, which is a canonical variable of the differential equations, in place of the mass M, which enters nonlinearly. This allows some very simple proofs of the type given in this section. However the bounds on a are more complicated, since they generally involve integrals of a. The variable V introduced by Okhotsimskii and Eneev is an equivalent variable.

Corners. If a *corner* is defined as a point where **a** is discontinuous, there are essentially two kinds of corners. A point where a is discontinuous seems characterized as a *throttling* corner, and a corner where the direction of **a** is discontinuous as a *steering* corner. As Leitmann observed in his paper, steering corners occur when $w = 0$. Throttling corners apparently occur whenever w reaches a certain finite value, denoted by L in the theorem.

In normal problems (for a discussion of normality, see Bliss,[7] Section 77) steering corners only occur in the extreme case where a has its maximum value for all t, and in the indeterminate case for which $w = $ constant. Okhotsimskii and Eneev say that there is a case where an impulse should be given at an interior point of the time interval. For the problem they are discussing this is misleading. In that problem and in the problem discussed by Leitmann, the curve for $w(t)$ is a hyperbola, or degenerates into a straight line, and w never has a maximum in the interior of an interval. In these problems, the lower bound to fuel consumption occurs for at most two impulses, at the beginning and the end, when w assumes its maximum values.

The theory of this section is similar to the theory of optimum control as investigated by LaSalle[13] and Pontryagin.[14] The functional of Pontryagin (first formula, p. 16) is the integral of Eqs. (2.19) and (2.37). It has a simple form here because the differential equations are linear in the coordinate variables and they do not appear in the functional. The determination of the functional for a problem in this section is that of solving the adjoint system, subject to the constraints. The domain of **a** is spherical in the rocket thrust programming problem and rectangular in some optimum control problems, where $|a_i| \leqq c_i$.

The method of gradients of Kelley[15] (also Chapter 6, this book) and dynamic programming as suggested by Bellman and Dreyfus[16] are apparently the only other methods available for determining optimum trajectories (see also Chapter 8, this book.)

The procedure for computing differentials is also directly applicable to control and prediction problems (see Drenick[17] and Tsien[18]). Tyndall[19] also has had the idea of unifying the control and the optimization problem through the use of the adjoint system of differential equations.

Computations. The problems discussed in Sections 2.16 and 2.17 have been programmed and run. The integrals were set up as differential equations and a Runge-Kutta routine used, which allowed varying time steps (Faulkner and Ward,[20] Section 8), necessary in the vicinity of t_1 and T. Each iteration takes somewhat less than a second computing time on the CDC 1604 in these problems, and the error tends to diminish by a factor of about 7 each iteration, if the routine converges. The total computing time in the examples was from 3 to 10 seconds. No convergence problem was found in the interception problem, but in the rendezvous routine there seems to be a problem of obtaining initial estimates in the proper ranges.

ACKNOWLEDGMENT

The author is indebted to E. N. Ward, Mathematician, U.S. Naval Postgraduate School, for all of the programming and computation done on problems in this section.

2.2 Elementary Graphic Solution

2.20 Introduction and Summary

A graphic method is given in this section for reducing the solution of some simple optimization problems to elementary algebra. Most of the section treats the problem of intercepting a ballistic missile as being a typical problem. The solution of some other problems, such that of effecting maximum range, is outlined. The method can be applied generally to optimum trajectory problems where aerodynamic forces are negligible, where gravity may be considered constant, and where the final velocity does not enter in the conditions.

There are several nice features of the solution. It is completely elementary. The graph reveals at once whether or not a solution exists. The solutions corresponding to minimum time of interception, maximum time of interception, and to minimum fuel consumption are all obtained from the graph. The corresponding impulse solutions are also obtained directly, and if desired, the solutions corresponding to a constant thrust of properly chosen magnitude applied during the entire time of flight, all from the same graph. In many problems the interpretation is so straight-forward that it is obvious that the conditions given are necessary and sufficient for the desired extremum. If dimensionless quantities are used, a single grid serves for all rockets.

It is well known that under the assumptions given above, thrust must be fixed in direction during the period of application, and the thrust must be maximal during an initial period and then zero. The method of solution given in this chapter make it more or less obvious, and an elementary proof was given by Faulkner.[21]

2.21 Construction of the Graph

The equation of motion for a rocket subject to no external forces may be written

$$a = \frac{c'\dot{m}}{1 - m} \tag{2.42}$$

when the thrust if fixed in direction; the various quantities were defined in Section 2.1. This may be integrated to obtain the velocity

$$v = -c' \log (1 - m) \tag{2.43}$$

if the initial velocity is zero.

If the rate of burning fuel is constant, $\dot{m} = \dot{m}_0$ during the period of thrust, this may be integrated again to give the displacement,

$$r = c't[1 + (1/m - 1) \log (1 - m)] \tag{2.44}$$

if $r(0) = 0$. In the following section, $\dot{m}$ is assumed to be constant during the period of thrust. If thrust is applied for a time t_1, and the rocket then coasts, the displacement is given by

$$r(t, t_1) = -c't \log (1 - m_1) + c't_1[1 + (1/m_1) \log (1 - m_1)] \tag{2.45}$$

for $t \geq t_1$; this includes Eq. (2.44) if we set $t = t_1$ during the period of thrust.

Dimensionless terms. If dimensionless terms are used, one graph will suffice to describe the motion of all rockets whose thrust is constant; let

$$t^* = \dot{m}t$$

$$v^* = v/c' \tag{2.46}$$

$$r^* = r/(c'/\dot{m})$$

The equations describing the motion become

$$v^* = -\log (1 - t^*) \tag{2.47}$$

or

$$v_1^* = -\log (1 - t_1^*)$$
$$r^*(t^*) = t^* + (1 - t^*) \log (1 - t^*) \tag{2.48}$$

and

$$r^*(t^*, t_1^*) = -t^* \log (1 - t_1^*) + t_1^* + \log (1 - t_1^*) \tag{2.49}$$

These equations describe the motion due to thrust of any rocket whose thrust is constant, except for the parameters c' and $\dot{m}$ of the rocket.

Figure 1 is a graph of $r^*(t^*, t_1^*)$ versus t^* with t_1^* as a parameter. An

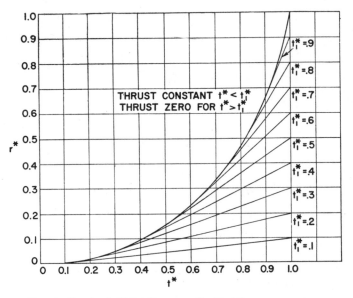

FIG. 1. Graph of $r^*(t^*, t_1^*)$ versus t^* with t_1^* as a parameter.

interesting property of the curve which will be used is the following. It can be verified by substitution into Eq. (2.49) that

$$r^*(1, t_1^*) = t_1^* \tag{2.50}$$

This is used as follows. It is necessary to determine the point t_1^* of tangency for lines tangent to the curve for $r^*(t^*, t_1^*)$. Since the contact of these curves is of the first degree, it is not easy to do this accurately by direct means. The point of intersection of the tangent line with the line $t^* = 1$ can be determined much more accurately, since these lines cross at a finite angle, yielding t_1^*.

2.22 Solution of an Interception Problem

Let us consider the problem of intercepting a ballistic target with a rocket whose thrust is as just described. The position of the target with respect to the rocket may be written

$$\varrho = \mathbf{R} - r\mathbf{e}_r \qquad (2.51)$$

where

$$\mathbf{R} = \mathbf{R}_0 + \dot{\mathbf{R}}_0 t \qquad (2.52)$$

$\mathbf{R}_0$ is the initial relative position vector, $\dot{\mathbf{R}}_0$ is the initial relative velocity, r is given by Eq. (2.45), and $\mathbf{e}_r$ is a unit vector in the direction of the thrust vector.

The form of ϱ is important. The vector $\mathbf{R}$ is determined as a function of t independent of the thrust. The vector $\mathbf{r} = r\mathbf{e}_r$ is determined entirely by the thrust and has a form which is invariant under rotation of coordinates.

For interception it is necessary that $\varrho = 0$, and hence that

$$r = R = |\mathbf{R}| \qquad (2.53)$$

Now R is a known function of t from the initial conditions. Convert it into a dimensionless form

$$R^* = \frac{R}{c'/\dot{m}} \qquad (2.54)$$

and sumperimpose the graph of R^* versus t^* on the grid of Fig. 1 (see Fig. 2).

The rocket will have available a certain amount of fuel, described by the maximum value of t_1^*, say t_{1m}^*. The graph for

$$r^* = \begin{cases} r^*(t^*), & \text{for} \quad 0 < t^* < t_{1m}^* \\ r^*(t^*, t_{1m}^*), & \text{for} \quad t_{1m}^* < t^* \end{cases} \qquad (2.55)$$

indicated by the heavy curve of Fig. 2, represents a curve of maximum performance in that it represents the maximum possible value of r as a function of t for that rocket. It will be indicated as $r_m^*(t^*)$ or r_m^* when it is desired to emphasize this property.

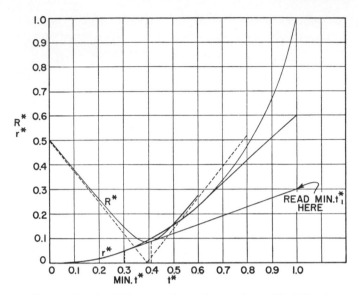

FIG. 2. Graph of R^* versus t^* superimposed on grid of Fig. 1.

Interception is possible for all times $t_2{}^*$ when the curve for R^* lies on or below this curve for $r_m{}^*$ and is not possible at any other time. This completely describes the times when interception can be effected.

The maximum and minimum values of the interception time may be read directly.

Interception with minimum fuel consumption corresponds to minimum $t_1{}^* = m_1$. This is determined by the common tangent to the curve for $r^*(t^*)$ and R^* with $t_1{}^* < t_1{}^*$: for any smaller value of $t_1{}^*$, the curve for $r^*(t^*, t_1{}^*)$ lies entirely below the convex curve for R^*.

A path of minimum fuel consumption is possible only for a target which is essentially incoming; the range rate must be negative at $t = 0$. If the target is outgoing initially, or if it is incoming too rapidly so that it overshoots before interception can occur, then there is no common tangent. In the former case, when there is a minimum, it is found that $-\log(1 - t_1{}^*) < |\dot{R}_0{}^*|$; in the latter case, when no minimum exists, $-\log(1 - t_1{}^*) > |\dot{R}_0{}^*|$.

Example. As an example consider a rocket with an initial gross weight of 3000 lb of which 1800 is fuel, thrust of 30,000 lb, and $c' = 8000$ ft/sec. Then $\dot{m} = 0.04$ and $c'/\dot{m} = 200,000$. Let the initial position of the rocket be (100,000; 0; 300,000), and the target (166,667; 66,667; 333,333), so that $R_0 = 100,000$. Let the velocity of the rocket have initial components (1157; 2157; 3919), and the target $(-5000; -4000; -1000)$ so that the initial relative speed is 10,000 ft/sec.

The value for R is given by $R^2 = (66{,}667 - 6157t)^2 + (66{,}667 - 6157t)^2 + (33{,}333 - 4919t)^2$. This is converted into dimensionless form and plotted in Fig. 2. It may be seen that the initial range becomes $R_0{}^* = 100{,}000/200{,}000 = \frac{1}{2}$, and the magnitude of the initial relative velocity becomes $V^* = 10{,}000/8000 = 1.25$, and $t^* = t/25$. From the graph it is seen that interception is possible for $0.39 \leq t_2{}^* \leq 0.49$, and a period of thrust corresponding to $0.3 \leq t_1{}^* \leq 0.49$. For minimum fuel consumption, $t_1{}^* = 0.3$, $t_2{}^* = 0.41$, and $t_2 = 10.25$ sec. The corresponding direction of thrust is that of the vector

$$\mathbf{R}(t_2) = [66{,}667 - 6157(10.25)]\mathbf{i} + [66{,}667 - 6157(10.25)]\mathbf{j}$$
$$+ [33{,}333 - 1919(10.25)]\mathbf{k}$$

The other desired values may be obtained easily.

2.23 Solution of Some Other Problems

Some other problems which can be solved in a related manner are described here. Still others are given in the report and paper by Faulkner,[22,23] but these indicate the general type which can be solved, and the procedure.

Attaining a fixed point. Suppose we wish to attain a certain point in space, x_2, y_2, z_2, starting from rest, with minimum fuel consumption. The relative displacement of the point is given by

$$\varrho = x_2\mathbf{i} + y_2\mathbf{j} + \left(z_2 + \frac{gt^2}{2}\right)\mathbf{k} - r\mathbf{e}_r \tag{2.56}$$

the z-axis is positive upward. In this case, set $R^2 = x_2{}^2 + y_2{}^2 + (z_2 + gt^2/2)^2$, convert to a dimensionless form, and plot R^* on the same graph with $r^*(t^*, t_1{}^*)$. The values associated with minimum fuel consumption are again obtained from the common tangent to the curves for $r^*(t^*)$ and $R^*(t^*)$. The earliest and latest times when the rocket can reach the point correspond to the two times where the curve for R^* crosses the curve for $r_m{}^*$, assuming of course that the performance is adequate.

If the time of arrival t_2 is specified, then there is a single point $R^*(t_2{}^*)$. The corresponding line tangent to the curve for $r^*(t^*)$ defines the minimum value for fuel consumption to attain the specified point at the specified time. If the initial velocity and displacement are not zero, they are included in R. The direction of the thrust is the direction of $x_2\mathbf{i} + y_2\mathbf{j} + (z_2 + gt^2/2)\mathbf{k}$.

Impulsive thrust. The lower bound to fuel consumption is given by the limit as $\dot{m}$ becomes infinite, with m_1 remaining finite. The corresponding solutions to various problems may be read directly off the same graph. If, for example, the curve for R^* is given as in Fig. 3 and t_2 is selected, the lower bound to fuel consumption is determined for interception at that time as follows.

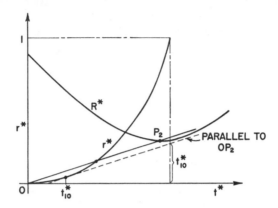

FIG. 3. Solutions for thrust applied as an impulse.

Let P_2 denote the point which corresponds to the desired interception point. Draw OP_2 and the line parallel to it but tangent to the curve for $r^*(t^*)$. The point of tangency t_{10}^* yields the lower bound to fuel consumption for that interception time. The lower bound, for t_2 free, is clearly obtained if the line OP_2 is tangent to the curve for R^* at P_2. It is easily verified that for the ballistic missile interception problem, the corresponding direction for the impulse is perpendicular to the initial line of sight (see Faulkner,[3] Chapter VI).

Maximum range at specified altitude. The problem of attaining maximum range is somewhat simpler; indeed the graph is not needed, principally because t_1 is known. Let us consider the problem of attaining maximum range x_2 at a specified altitude y_2, with specified fuel consumption.

In this case we may write

$$r^2 = x^2 + \left(y + \frac{gt^2}{2} \right)^2$$

where r is obtained from Eq. (2.45). If this is rewritten

$$x^2 = r^2 - \left(y_2 + \frac{gt^2}{2} \right)^2$$

the right-hand side is a known function of t. One way to determine the maximum value of x is to differentiate and solve the resulting cubic for t_2.

Though this problem is Mayer reciprocal to the first one discussed in this subsection, it is easier to solve, since t_1 is known.

2.24 Comments

A detailed discussion of the simple ballistic missile interception problem is given in a report by Faulkner.[3] The method of solution of this section was given in an accompanying report[22] and in a recent paper.[23] The latter also contain applications to some problems of determining the performance required of a rocket, for preliminary design studies.

If the final mass, rather than the initial mass, is specified, a similar method of solution can be carried out. In this case two curves on the same grid are required. One is for $r(t_1)$; the other is the envelope of the family of straight lines $r(t, t_1)$ for coasting flight.

2.3 Optimum Thrust Programming along a Given Curve

2.30 Introduction and Summary

A complete and elementary solution is given for some problems in programming the thrust along a given curve in space. The problem of Goddard is a typical example. The problem is set up for computing and a sufficiency proof is given.

An important feature in the theory is the reduction of the differential equation to a canonical form.

Suppose a path in space has been selected, and that the equation of motion along the path can be written in the form

$$Pdv + QdM + Rds = 0 \qquad (2.57)$$

where P, Q, R are functions of v, M, s, which are, respectively, the speed along the curve, the mass of the rocket, and the distance along the curve. An optimum is sought for some function of the end values of v, M, s; enough end conditions are assumed to be given that the problem is properly specified.

A change in variable is made which reduces the above differential equation to the canonical form

$$u - u_0 = \int_0^s K(u, v, s) \, ds$$

Inspection of the integrand suggests that the integral represents a loss of velocity and hence it is desirable to minimize it. Further investigation then reveals that all optima follow from this principle. For each value of M, s, or u, s there is a best speed v^*, obtained from setting $\partial K/\partial v = 0$. Generally, if $v < v^*$, maximum thrust must be applied, and if $v > v^*$, the rocket should coast. This, with modifications at the two ends to attain the prescribed values, characterizes the trajectories. For example, in simple problems, such as that of Goddard, it is necessary and sufficient for the desired optimum that the trajectory satisfies the prescribed end values and consists of at most three subarcs as follows. On the first subarc, either $v < v^*$ and the rocket exerts full thrust or $v > v^*$ and the rocket coasts, depending on the initial values. On the second subarc, thrust is applied to maintain $v = v^*$. On the third subarc, the fuel is used up and the rocket coasts, with $v < v^*$.

The entire procedure is elementary and the section is somewhat expository.

2.31 Reduction to Canonical Form, Condition for a Minimum

To be definite, let us consider the specific equation of motion

$$Mdv + cdM + [Mg \sin \theta + D(s, v)] \, ds/v = 0 \qquad (2.58)$$

where c is the speed of the emitted gases, g is the acceleration of gravity, considered constant, θ is the angle between the trajectory and the horizontal direction, and D is the aerodynamic drag force.

To simplify this equation, let us introduce a new variable, determined by the method used in solving an integrable total differential equation.[24] Let us treat one variable, s, in this case, as a constant and integrate the resulting differential equation

$$Mdv + cdM = 0 \qquad (2.59)$$

This has an integral (a solution) $U(v, M) = -v - c \log M$. If the new variable $u = U(v, M)$ is introduced and one of the variables, say M, is eliminated, Eq. (2.58) becones

$$du = \left[g \sin \theta + D \exp \left(\frac{u + v}{c} \right) \right] ds/v \qquad (2.60)$$

which has the form

$$du = K(u, v, s) \, ds \qquad (2.61)$$

This is a canonical form for the differential equation[25] (2.58). The alternate integrated form is more revealing:

$$u - u_0 = \int_0^s \left[\frac{g \sin \theta}{v} + \frac{D}{v} \exp \left(\frac{u + v}{c} \right) \right] ds \qquad (2.62)$$

The first term in the integrand represents a loss in velocity because of gravity; the second term represents a loss in velocity due to drag. It seems apparent that it is desirable to minimize this integral, to maximize $-u = v + c \log M$.

This characterizes the optima; all optima are attained as a consequence of minimizing u, subject to the constraints.

We note that the differential equation puts no constraint on v and the problem is to choose v as a function of s to effect the optimization.

If v is to minimize the integral, then v must satisfy the equation

$$\frac{\partial K}{\partial v} = 0 \tag{2.63}$$

Assume that this equation has a solution, defining $v = v^*(u, s)$ which minimizes K; that is,

$$K(u, v^*[u, s], s) < K(u, v, s), \quad \text{for} \quad v \neq v^*(u, s) \tag{2.64}$$

Note also that

$$\frac{\partial K}{\partial u} \geq 0 \tag{2.65}$$

Finally, assume that

$$\text{sgn} \frac{\partial K(u, v, s)}{\partial v} = \text{sgn}\ (v - v^*[u, s]) \tag{2.66}$$

when $v \neq v^*(u, s)$; sgn denotes the arithmetic sign.

2.32 Maximum Range

The essential results and method of proof are illustrated in this section by considering a particular problem. Let us consider the problem of sending a rocket the greatest distance along a specified path in space with a given amount of fuel, with all initial conditions given. To be specific, assume that the initial value $v_0 < v^*(u_0, 0)$.

In the next section a numerical routine will be given for determining the thrust program. Suppose now that we have already found it and it consists of at most three subprograms, as follows.

1. On the initial part $(0, s_1)$ $v < v^*(u, s)$ and maximum thrust is applied, at least so long as any fuel remains.

2. On the second part (s_1, s_2) the thrust is just sufficient to maintain $v = v^*(u, s)$. This part continues until $M = M_f$, its specified final value. This part may be missing if the rocket never attains the optimum speed $v^*(u, s)$.

3. On the final part (s_2, s_f), $v < v^*(u, s)$. This continues until v drops to the stalling speed, or for vertical flight, $v = 0$.

Theorem. *The path C^* described above maximizes the range along the given curve and is unique.*

Proof. Let U^*, V^*, M^* denote the functions associated with C^* and U, V, M denote the same quantities associated with any other thrust program. The essential feature of the proof is to establish that $U^* \leqq U$ for every value of s, and hence $V^* \geqq V$ on the last segment.

The proof is by contradiction. We assume that there is a first value S where $U^* > U$ and then show that S cannot be on any of the three segments given above.

Suppose that S is on the first segment $(0, s_1)$, and consider

$$U(S) - U^*(S) = \int_0^S [K(U, V, s) - K(U^*, V^*, s)] \, ds \qquad (2.67)$$

obtained from Eq. (2.62), since the initial values of U and U^* are equal. The integrand may be rewritten

$$K(U, V, s) - K(U^*, V, s) + K(U^*, V, s) - K(U^*, V^*, s) \qquad (2.68)$$

Now $K(U, V, s) \geqq K(U^*, V, s)$ on $(0, S)$, by Eq. (2.65), since $U \geqq U^*$. Also $K(U^*, V, s) \geqq K(U^*, V^*, s)$ by Eq. (2.66) since $V \leqq V^*$ (thrust is maximum on C^*) and $V^*(s) < v^*(U^*, s)$.

Hence the integrand is either positive or zero at all points of $(0, S)$; the value S cannot be in $(0, s_1)$.

Now suppose that S is in the second segment (s_1, s_2). We may write

$$U(S) - U^*(S) = U(s_1) - U^*(s_1)$$

$$+ \int_{s_1}^S [K(U, V, s) - K(U^*, V^*, s)] \, ds \qquad (2.69)$$

Now $U(s_1) \geqq U^*(s_1)$, as we have just seen. Let us rewrite the integrand of Eq. (2.69) as in Eq. (2.68). Then $K(U, V, s) \geqq K(U^*, V, s)$ by Eq. (2.65), since $U \geqq U^*$ on (s_1, S). Also, the last two terms in Eq. (2.68) are positive or zero, by Eq. (2.64). Hence the right-hand side of Eq. (2.69) cannot be positive and S cannot be in the segment (s_1, s_2).

Finally, suppose that S is in (s_2, s_f). We may write

$$U(S) - U^*(S) = U(s_2) - U^*(s_2)$$

$$+ \int_{s_2}^S [K(U, V, s) - K(U^*, V^*, s)] \, ds \qquad (2.70)$$

Now $U(s_2) \geq U^*(s_2)$ as we have just seen. Further, the integrand cannot be negative at any point. For $K(U, V, s) \geq K(U^*, V, s)$, by Eq. (2.65), since $U \geq U^*$ on (s_2, S), so that the first two terms of Eq. (2.68) are positive. Also $V^* + c \log M^* = V^* + c \log M_f \geq V + c \log M$, by the definition of $u = -v - c \log M$; since $M_f \leq M$, $V^* \geq V$. Hence $K(U^*, V, s) \geq K(U^*, V^*, s)$, by Eq. (2.66), since $V < V^* < v^*(U^*, s)$. Hence the right-hand side of Eq. (2.71) is positive or zero, and S is not in (s_2, s_f).

Further inspection reveals that if V differs from V^* over any finite interval, then $U^* < U$ for larger values of s and hence $V^* > V$ on the third interval. At the point where stalling speed is reached for the comparison curve $V^* > V$ and hence stalling speed is not yet reached on C^*. This completes the proof.

2.33 Flow Chart for Computation

A flow chart is given for the problem just discussed, for determining the thrust program on a digital computer (Fig. 4).

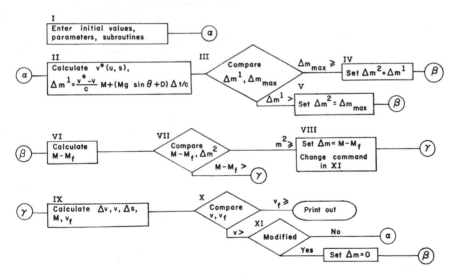

Fig. 4. Flow chart for optimum thrust programming along a given path with initial values given.

Though time was eliminated in the mathematical discussion, it is generally better to reintroduce it if there is any possibility that v may go to zero. The reason is that the differential equation (2.58) has a singularity when $v = 0$ which is eliminated if time is the independent variable. In this case we will use the equation of motion

$$M \frac{dv}{dt} + c \frac{dM}{dt} + Mg \sin \theta + D(v, s) = 0 \qquad (2.71)$$

Flow chart. In box I the parameters are entered, together with the subroutines for calculating the various functions. For example, there must be a routine for calculating v_f, the stalling speed, as a function of M, s. At some point the speed v will be compared with this, and if $v \leqq v_f$, the computation is terminated.

In box II, the ideal velocity v^* is calculated, and the fuel consumption necessary to raise the speed to this value by an impulse is determined from the equation

$$\Delta m = M(v^* - v)/c + (Mg \sin \theta + D) \Delta t/c$$

In this equation m is the mass of fuel consumed, so that $m + M = M_0$. This gives the first estimate Δm^1 of the amount of fuel to be used in this time step. In box III this is compared with the maximum amount of fuel Δm_{max} which the rocket motor can burn in that period. The smaller of these is Δm^2, the next estimate of Δm. In box VI the amount of fuel remaining is determined and this is compared with Δm^2 in the next box. The smaller of these becomes Δm, the amount of fuel used in that interval. Also, if the last of the fuel will be used up in that round, Δm will be zero for all subsequent iterations. When this occurs the switch in box XI is changed to eliminate the routine for determining Δm.

In box IX the various quantities Δv, v, Δs, M, v_f are calculated. In box X the speed v is compared with v_f, and if $v \leqq v_f$, the computation is terminated.

As long as fuel remains, the switch in box XI is set so that the program returns to the subroutine for determining Δm. After the fuel is all consumed, this switch command is changed so that Δm is set to zero. The routine for determining Δm is then bypassed and the routine goes directly to box IX.

If there is a possibility that $v > v^*$, as may occur on a downward section of the trajectory, then a further comparison must be made.

2.34 Discussion

The problems discussed here are among the simplest in calculus of variations, since they involve a single differential equation. In this case the Euler equation (2.63) is finite; that is, it is not a differential equation. It is the same for all problems provided no integral conditions are adjoined, since the Euler equation is implicit in the given differential equation. Equation (2.64) is the Weierstrass condition.

The problem of Goddard is the problem of attaining a prescribed altitude with a minimum amount of fuel, the final mass being prescribed. Hamel[26] gave a brief, abstract existence proof for the problem. Tsien and Evans[27] gave a more complete classic treatment, including some computations. Their treatment involved two differential equations, since they did not eliminate time. A related problem was treated by Leitmann.[28]

The paper by Faulkner[29] outlines a complete elementary solution, including the sufficiency proof and a procedure for calculating the trajectory, by the method given here. The problem is Mayer reciprocal to the one discussed in this section. Since the terminal values are given, the trajectory is computed backwards, from the top down. It consists of three segments, like the one discussed here, provided the rocket has enough performance to attain the speed v^*; otherwise only the first and third segments occur. The paper also contains a list of problems where the solutions are reduced to quadrature.

The canonical variable u seems characterized as the "velocity dissipation" from the integral in Eq. (2.62). Apparently all optima, even for very involved trajectories are obtained by minimizing it, subject to the constraints.

An equivalent canonical variable was discovered by Ross.[30] The variable which he found, ϕ, differs from the one given here in that it is the exponential, $\phi = \exp(-u/c)$. Two such canonical variables, say u, ϕ, are functionally related by an equation of the form $F(u, \phi, s) = 0$, since both are obtained from the same differential equation (2.59).

The paper by Miele[31] treats the case where the curve is a straight line. He derives some necessary conditions in terms of aerodynamic quantities and gives an equivalent proof for sufficiency for the case of level flight using Green's theorem.

Some of the problems which can be treated by direct methods can also be treated by Green's theorem in establishing sufficiency (see Chapter 3, this book). This is the case if the differential equation can be written in a form which does not involve one variable explicitly, as in the above-mentioned case of level flight, where s does not appear explicitly.

References

1. E. A. Coddington and N. Levinson, "Theory of Ordinary Differential Equations." McGraw-Hill, New York, 1955.
2. O. Bolza, "Vorlesungen Über Variationsrechnung," p. 574. Teubner, Leipzig, 1909.
3. F. D. Faulkner, Homing in a vacuum with minimum fuel consumption, UMM No. 18, Aeronautical Research Center, University of Michigan, Ann Arbor, Michigan (ASTIA No. ATI 50732) February 1, 1949.

4. G. A. Bliss, The use of adjoint systems in the problem of differential corrections for trajectories, *J. U.S. Artillery* **51**, 296–311 (1919).
5. G. A. Bliss, Differential equations containing arbitrary functions, *Trans. Am. Math. Soc.* **21**, 79–92 (1920).
6. G. A Bliss, Functions of lines in ballistics, *Trans. Am. Math. Soc.* **21**, 93–106 (1920).
7. G. A. Bliss, "Lectures on the Calculus of Variations." Univ. Chicago Press, Chicago, 1946.
8. R. C. Emerson, On maximizing an integral with a side condition, *Proc. Am. Math. Soc.* **5**, 291–295 (1954).
9. J. V. Breakwell, The optimization of trajectories, *J. Soc. Ind. Appl. Math.* **7**, 215–247 (1959).
10. D. E. Okhotsimskii and T. M. Eneev (English translation), Certain variational problems associated with the launching of an artificial earth satellite, *in* "The Russian Literature of Satellites," Part 1. International Physical Index, New York, 1958.
11. G. Leitmann, On a class of variational problems in rocket flight, *J. Aero/Space Sci.* **26**, 586–591 (1959).
12. D. F. Lawden, Interplanetary rocket trajectories, *Advances in Space Sci.* **1**, 8–14 (1959).
13. J. P. LaSalle, Time optimal control systems, *Proc. Natl. Acad. Sci. U.S.* **45**, 573–577 (1959).
14. L. S. Pontryagin, Optimal control processes, *Automation Express* **1**, 15–18, 26–30 (1959).
15. H. J. Kelley, Gradient theory of optimal flight paths, *ARS Journal* **30**, 947–954 (1960).
16. R. Bellman and S. E. Dreyfus, An application of dynamic programming to the determination of optimal satellite trajectories, *J. Brit. Interplanet. Soc.* **17**, 78–83 (1959).
17. R. Drenick, A perturbation calculus in missile ballistics, *J. Franklin Inst.* **25**, 423–436 (1951).
18. H. S. Tsien, "Engineering Cybernetics," Chapter 13. McGraw-Hill, New York, 1954.
19. J. W. Tyndall, University of Colorado Extension Course Aero Engineering, Lecture Notes. The Martin Company, Denver, Colorado, 1960.
20. F. D. Faulkner and E. N. Ward, Optimum interception of a ballistic missile at moderate range, Proc. 5th Navy Sci. Symposium, pp. 27–44, Annapolis, Maryland, April 1960.
21. F. D. Faulkner, Some results from direct methods applied to optimum rocket trajectories, *Proc. 9th Intern. Astronaut. Congr. Amsterdam, 1958* p. 694 ff (1959).
22. F. D. Faulkner, Solution of the problem of homing in a vacuum with a point mass, UMM No. 19, Aeronautical Research Center, University of Michigan, Ann Arbor, Michigan (ASTIA No. ATI 50731) February 1, 1949.
23. F. D. Faulkner, Complete elementary solution to some optimum trajectory problems, *ARS Journal* **31**, 33–39 (1961).
24. A. Cohen, "Differential Equations," p. 211. Heath, New York, 1933.
25. E. Goursat, "Lecons sur le probleme de Pfaff," Chapter 1. Hermann & Cie, Paris, 1922.
26. G. Hamel, "Über eine mit dem Problem der Rakete zusammenhangende Aufgabe der Variationsrechnung," *ZAMM* **7**, 51–2 (1927).
27. H. S. Tsien and R. C. Evans, Optimum thrust programming for a sounding rocket, *Jet Propulsion* **21**, 99 (1951).

28. G. Leitmann, A calculus of variations solution of Goddard's problem, *Astronaut. Acta* **2**, 55 (1956).
29. F. D. Faulkner, The problem of Goddard and optimum thrust programming, *Proc. 3rd Ann. Meeting Am. Astronaut. Soc.* New York, December 1956, pp. 43–51 (1957).
30. S. E. Ross, Minimality for problems in vertical and horizontal rocket flight, *Jet Propulsion* **28**, 55 (1958).
31. A. Miele, Minimality for arbitrarily inclined rocket trajectories, *Jet Propulsion* **28**, 481–3 (1958).

—3—

Extremization of Linear Integrals by Green's Theorem

ANGELO MIELE

Boeing Scientific Research Laboratories, Seattle, Washington

3.1 Introduction

Several new problems of applied mathematics have arisen in the study of trajectories of high-speed aircraft and missiles which cannot be handled by the conventional methods of performance analysis. These problems, which are concerned with the determination of optimum flight programs, fall within the domain of the calculus of variations and are treated from a general point of view in Chapter 4 which deals with the indirect methods.

69

In this chapter, a particular class of variational problems is considered: this is the class of *linear problems* whose distinctive characteristic is that the functional form to be extremized and the possible isoperimetric constraint are linear in the derivative of the unknown function. This apparently simplifying circumstance is actually the cause of important analytical difficulties, since the Legendre-Clebsch condition of the calculus of variations becomes ineffectual along some portion of the extremal arc. An analogous situation arises when applying the more stringent Weierstrass condition.

Because of these reasons and because of the rather frequent occurrence of linear problems in the dynamics of flight of turbojet, turbofan, ramjet, and rocket-powered vehicles, this author has devoted considerable effort to their solution and, in a succession of research papers[1-7], has developed a new procedure based on Green's theorem relative to the transformation of line integrals into surface integrals. This procedure, which applies to linear problems of both the simple type and the isoperimetric type, is illustrated in the following sections, where the general theory and several engineering applications are presented.

3.2 Linear Problem

In this section, a linear integral having the form

$$H = \int_{i}^{f} \left[\varphi(x, y) + \psi(x, y)y' \right] dx \tag{3.1}$$

is considered, where φ and ψ are known functions of the variables x and y, where y' denotes the derivative dy/dx, and where the subscripts i and f refer to the initial and final points, respectively. It is assumed that (a) the class of arcs being investigated is contained within the region bounded by the closed curve (see Fig. 1)

$$\epsilon(x, y) = 0 \tag{3.2}$$

and (b) the prescribed initial and final points belong to the boundary of this region and, therefore, satisfy the relationships

$$\epsilon(x_i, y_i) = \epsilon(x_f, y_f) = 0 \tag{3.3}$$

Furthermore, after an admissible arc is defined as any path consistent with conditions (a) and (b), the extremal problem is formulated as follows: *In the class of admissible arcs $y(x)$, find that particular arc which maximizes or minimizes the integral* (3.1). This special arc is called the *extremal arc*.

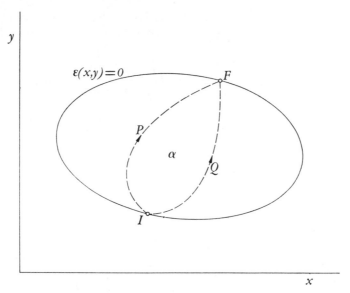

FIG. 1. Class of admissible arcs.

Incidentally, in the case where a discontinuity in the derivative of the unknown function occurs at some point of the extremal arc, the terminology is as follows: The point where the discontinuity occurs is called the *corner point*; the portions of the extremal arc preceding and following the corner point are called *subarcs*.

3.21 Fundamental Function

The first step in the analysis is to consider two admissible paths IPF and IQF as in Fig. 1 and determine the relative advantages or disadvantages of one path with respect to another. In order to do so, it is necessary to consider the difference between their respective line integrals, that is,

$$\Delta H = \int_{IQF} (\varphi \, dx + \psi \, dy) - \int_{IPF} (\varphi \, dx + \psi \, dy) \qquad (3.4)$$

which is equivalent to the cyclic integral

$$\Delta H = \oint_{IQFPI} (\varphi \, dx + \psi \, dy) \qquad (3.5)$$

If the two functions φ and ψ and their first partial derivatives are continuous everywhere in the area α bounded by the two admissible paths under consideration, Green's theorem relative to the transformation of line integrals into surface integrals is applicable. Consequently, the following result is obtained*:

$$\oint_{IQFPI} (\varphi\, dx + \psi\, dy) = \iint_\alpha \left(\frac{\partial\psi}{\partial x} - \frac{\partial\varphi}{\partial y} \right) dx\, dy \qquad (3.6)$$

and can be rewritten in the form

$$\Delta H = \iint_\alpha \omega(x, y)\, dx\, dy \qquad (3.7)$$

where ω denotes the *fundamental function*

$$\omega(x, y) = \frac{\partial\psi}{\partial x} - \frac{\partial\varphi}{\partial y} \qquad (3.8)$$

In conclusion, important information concerning the relative advantages or disadvantages of one integration path with respect to another can be obtained by studying the properties of the fundamental function ω within the admissible domain. In this connection, two types of extremal problems are now considered: problems where the function ω has a constant sign everywhere and problems where the function ω changes sign within the admissible domain.

3.22 Case Where the Sign of the Fundamental Function Is Constant

If the function ω has the same sign everywhere within the admissible domain, three possibilities exist: ω is positive, negative, or zero. If the function ω is positive, Eq. (3.7) leads to

$$\Delta H > 0 \qquad (3.9)$$

which implies that

$$H_{IQF} > H_{IPF} \qquad (3.10)$$

By the same reasoning, any path to the right of IQF yields a further increase in the value of the integral, while any path to the left of IPF yields a further decrease in the value of the integral. Thus, by a limiting process, the following conclusions are reached (Fig. 2):

(a) The integral (3.1) is *maximized* by the path IBF which is located on the boundary of the admissible domain and is traveled in such a way that this domain is always on the left.

---

* The transformation of integrals is accompanied by a positive sign when proceeding counterclockwise along the integration path and by a negative sign when proceeding clockwise.

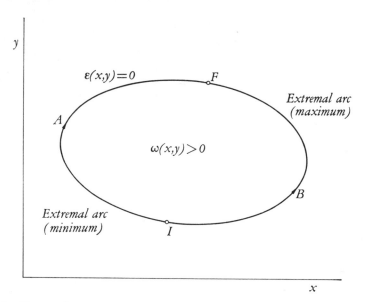

y

$\varepsilon(x,y)=0$ F

Extremal arc
(maximum)

A

$\omega(x,y)>0$

B

Extremal arc
(minimum) I

x

FIG. 2.   Extremal arcs for problems where the sign of the fundamental function is constant.

(b) The integral (3.1) is *minimized* by the path IAF which is located on the boundary of the admissible domain and is traveled in such a way that this domain is always on the right.

The results relative to the case where $\omega < 0$ are identical to those relative to the case where $\omega > 0$, except that maximum paths are transformed into minimum paths and vice versa. Finally, the case where $\omega = 0$ everywhere is *degenerate* in that the integral (3.1) becomes independent of the integration path.

3.23 Case Where the Sign of the Fundamental Function Is Not Constant

The more general case where the function ω changes sign within the admissible domain is now considered; for simplicity, it is assumed that the geometrical locus of the points where $\omega = 0$ has only two intersections M and N with the boundary curve $\varepsilon = 0$ (Fig. 3). Several subcases are possible, depending on the relative position of the end points with respect to the curve $\omega = 0$ and the sign taken by the fundamental function on both sides of this curve. Since the systematic treatment of all these subcases is rather tedious, the use of Green's theorem is demonstrated for only the following set of conditions: (a) the fundamental function is positive to the left of the curve $\omega = 0$ and negative to the right; and (b) the initial point

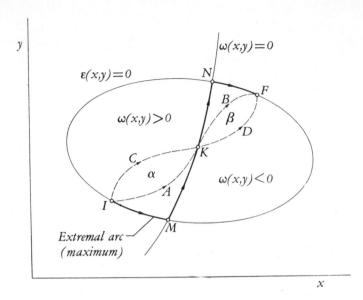

Fig. 3.   Extremal arc for problems where the sign of the fundamental function is not constant.

is located in the region where $\omega > 0$, while the final point is located in the region where $\omega < 0$.

Under these hypotheses, consider two admissible paths $IAKBF$ and $ICKDF$ which intersect the curve $\omega = 0$ at an arbitrarily specified point K as in Fig. 3. The difference between the line integrals for these paths is given by

$$\Delta H = \int_{IAKBF} (\varphi \, dx + \psi \, dy) - \int_{ICKDF} (\varphi \, dx + \psi \, dy) \qquad (3.11)$$

and can be rewritten as

$$\Delta H = \oint_{IAKCI} (\varphi \, dx + \psi \, dy) + \oint_{KBFDK} (\varphi \, dx + \psi \, dy) \qquad (3.12)$$

Notice that the circuit $IAKCI$ is traveled in the counterclockwise sense and the circuit $KBFDK$ in the clockwise sense; consequently, the application of Green's theorem yields the following result:

$$\Delta H = \iint_\alpha \omega \, dx \, dy - \iint_\beta \omega \, dx \, dy \qquad (3.13)$$

where α and β denote the areas enclosed by the above circuits. Since the fundamental function is positive in the region α and negative in the region β, the difference ΔH is positive and implies that

$$H_{IAKBF} > H_{ICKDF} \tag{3.14}$$

By proceeding in much the same way, any path which is closer to the curve $\omega = 0$ than the path $IAKBF$ can be shown to increase the value of the linear integral. Consequently, by a limiting process, the path $IMNF$ can be shown to yield the highest value of the integral in the class of arcs which pass through the prescribed end points and intersect the curve $\omega = 0$ at one arbitrarily specified point K.

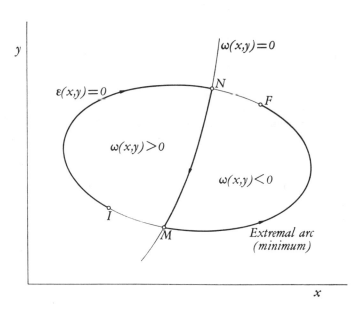

Fig. 4.   Extremal arc for problems where the sign of the fundamental function is not constant.

The final step is to compare the path $IMNF$ with another crossing the line $\omega = 0$ at an arbitrary number of points. In this connection, by further application of Green's theorem, the path $IMNF$ can be shown to maximize the linear integral with respect to every possible admissible path. An analogous technique can be employed to show that the path $INMF$ of Fig. 4 yields the minimum value for the linear integral.

3.24 Conclusions

When dealing with the extremization of linear integrals, it is important to study the behavior of the fundamental function ω within the admissible domain. If the function ω has a constant sign, the equation of the extremal arc is

$$\epsilon(x, y) = 0 \tag{3.15}$$

The sense in which this extremal arc is to be traveled depends on the sign of the function ω and whether a maximum or a minimum value is desired for the integral. On the other hand, if the function ω changes sign within the admissible domain, the extremal arc is discontinuous and is composed of subarcs along which

$$\epsilon(x, y) = 0 \tag{3.16}$$

and subarcs along which

$$\omega(x, y) = 0 \tag{3.17}$$

The way in which these subarcs must be combined and the sense in which they must be traveled depend on the distribution of signs of the function ω, the boundary conditions of the problem, and whether a maximum or a minimum value is desired for the integral.

3.3 Linear Isoperimetric Problem

An interesting modification of the previous problem occurs when the integral (3.1) to be extremized must satisfy not only conditions (a) and (b) but also the linear isoperimetric constraint

$$\int_i^f \left[\varphi_1(x, y) + \psi_1(x, y)y' \right] dx = C \tag{3.18}$$

where φ_1 and ψ_1 are known functions of the variables x and y, and where C is a prescribed constant.

For any two admissible paths IPF and IQF, the difference between the line integrals is expressed by

$$\Delta H = \oint_{IQFPI} (\varphi \, dx + \psi \, dy) \tag{3.19}$$

However, owing to the isoperimetric constraint, these paths cannot be arbitrary but must satisfy the relationship

$$0 = \oint_{IQFPI} (\varphi_1 \, dx + \psi_1 \, dy) \tag{3.20}$$

Consequently, after introducing an undetermined, constant Lagrange multiplier λ and combining Eqs. (3.19) and (3.20) linearly, one obtains the following result:

$$\Delta H = \oint_{IQFPI} (\varphi_* \, dx + \psi_* \, dy) \tag{3.21}$$

where

$$\varphi_* = \varphi + \lambda \varphi_1, \qquad \psi_* = \psi + \lambda \psi_1 \tag{3.22}$$

This means that, if Green's theorem is employed, the difference between the line integrals becomes

$$\Delta H = \iint_{\alpha} \omega_* (x, y, \lambda) \, dx \, dy \tag{3.23}$$

where ω_* denotes the *augmented fundamental function*

$$\omega_* (x, y, \lambda) = \frac{\partial \psi_*}{\partial x} - \frac{\partial \varphi_*}{\partial y} \tag{3.24}$$

Comparison of Eqs. (3.7) and (3.23) stresses the basic analogy between the simple problem and the isoperimetric problem. Consequently, the results of Section 3.24 are applicable to the present problem, provided that the following precepts are kept in mind:

(a) The function ω must be replaced by the augmented function ω_*.

(b) While the equation $\omega = 0$ of the simple problem represents a curve of the xy-plane, the equation $\omega_* = 0$ of the isoperimetric problem represents a family of curves, more specifically, one curve for each value of the Lagrange multiplier (Fig. 5). The particular value of λ associated with the problem under consideration is to be determined from the prescribed boundary conditions and the given isoperimetric constraint.

3.4 Linear Problems in Flight Mechanics

As far as the calculus of variations is concerned, the mathematical technique previously developed has a rather limited importance, since it refers to linear problems only. However, it is quite useful in flight mechanics, in view of the rather frequent occurrence of linear problems in the dynamics of flight of turbojet, turbofan, ramjet, and rocket vehicles.

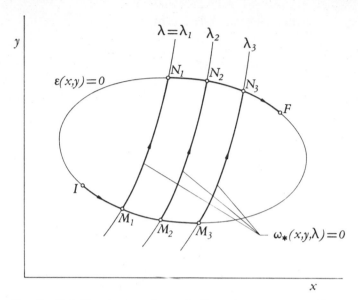

FIG. 5. Totality of extremal arcs for linear isoperimetric problems.

The following are examples of linear problems of the simple type which can be solved by Green's theorem: (a) the burning program which extremizes the altitude increase of a rocket in vertical flight in either a vacuum or a homogeneous atmosphere; (b) the burning program which extremizes the range of a rocket-powered aircraft in level flight; (c) the burning program which extremizes the range of a nonlifting, air-to-air missile; (d) the climbing technique which extremizes the time, the fuel consumed, or the horizontal distance traveled by a turbojet, turbofan, or ramjet aircraft; and (e) the drag modulation technique which minimizes the heat convected from the boundary layer to the skin of a variable-geometry ballistic missile during re-entry.

Analogously, the following are examples of linear problems of the isoperimetric type: (a) the burning program which extremizes the altitude increase of a rocket in vertical flight in a homogeneous atmosphere for a given time; (b) the burning program which extremizes the range of a rocket-powered aircraft in level flight for a given time; (c) the burning program which extremizes the range of a nonlifting, air-to-air missile for a given time; (d) the climbing technique which extremizes the horizontal distance traveled by a turbojet, turbofan, or ramjet aircraft for a given amount of fuel; and (e) the drag modulation technique which minimizes the heat convected from the boundary layer to the skin of a variable-geometry ballistic missile during re-entry assuming that the flight time is given.

Among these problems, those associated with the flight trajectory of a short-range, air-to-air missile and with the re-entry of a variable-geometry ballistic missile are now treated in detail.

3.5 Optimum Burning Program for a Short-Range, Nonlifting Missile

As a first application of the previous theory, this section considers the flight trajectory of a rocket-powered, air-to-air missile under the following hypotheses: (a) the lift is zero; (b) the drag is a quadratic function of the velocity and is given by

$$D = KV^2 \tag{3.25}$$

where K is a constant (this situation arises when the drag coefficient is regarded to be constant and the variations in the flight altitude are so small that the atmosphere can be thought of as being homogeneous); (c) the thrust is tangent to the flight path and is given by

$$T = c\beta \tag{3.26}$$

where β is the propellant mass flow and c the equivalent exit velocity of the rocket engine, assumed constant; (d) the inclination of the flight path with respect to the horizon γ is so small that its square is negligible with respect to one; and (e) the weight component on the tangent to the flight path is negligible with respect to the thrust and/or the drag.

In the light of these hypotheses, the motion of an air-to-air missile is governed by the following differential equations*:

$$\dot{X} - V = 0$$

$$\dot{h} - V\gamma = 0$$

$$\dot{V} + \frac{KV^2 - c\beta}{m} = 0 \tag{3.27}$$

$$\dot{\gamma} + \frac{g}{V} = 0$$

$$\dot{m} + \beta = 0$$

---

* The first two equations are the kinematical relationships in the horizontal and vertical directions, the third and the fourth are the dynamical equations on the tangent and the normal to the flight path, and the fifth is the definition of the mass flow of propellant.

where X denotes the horizontal distance, h the altitude, m the mass, g the acceleration of gravity, and the dot a derivative with respect to time. Furthermore, after the mass is selected as the new independent variable, these equations are rewritten in the form

$$\frac{dX}{dm} = -\frac{V}{\beta}$$

$$\frac{dh}{dm} = -\frac{V\gamma}{\beta}$$

$$\frac{dV}{dm} = \frac{KV^2}{m\beta} - \frac{c}{m} \qquad (3.28)$$

$$\frac{d\gamma}{dm} = \frac{g}{V\beta}$$

$$\frac{dt}{dm} = -\frac{1}{\beta}$$

and involve one independent variable (m), six dependent variables $(X, h, V, \gamma, t, \beta)$ and, hence, one degree of freedom.* Consequently, for a given set of initial conditions, infinite trajectories exist which are physically and mathematically possible, more specifically, one trajectory for each arbitrarily prescribed burning program $\beta(m)$. However, there exist limitations to the choice of this program, since the rocket can only develop instantaneous mass flows bounded by a lower limit and an upper limit. Thus, if the lower limit is assumed to be zero, the following inequality must be satisfied at all points of the flight path:

$$0 \leq \beta \leq \beta_{\max} \qquad (3.29)$$

This important inequality has considerable influence on the solution of the extremal problems of air-to-air missiles in that it defines both the class of admissible displacements and the region of admissible paths for the vehicle.

3.51 Class of Admissible Displacements

Consider a rocket which, at a given time instant, has the velocity V and the mass m, and let P be its associated point in the velocity-mass plane

---

* By definition, the number of degrees of freedom of a differential system is the difference between the number of dependent variables and the number of equations.

(Fig. 6). After an infinitesimal time interval, the new velocity of the rocket is $V' = V + dV$, the new mass is $m' = m + dm$, and the new position in the velocity-mass plane is represented by point P'. Consequently, the vector $\overline{PP'}$ is the infinitesimal displacement of the rocket in the Vm-plane.

As the third of Eqs. (3.28) indicates, there exists one infinitesimal displacement for each mass flow β. However, owing to Ineq. (3.29), not every displacement is physically possible. More specifically, the *class of admissible displacements* is bounded by two limiting conditions: a displacement $\overline{PR}$ corresponding to zero burning rate and a displacement $\overline{PT}$ corresponding to the maximum burning rate of the engine.

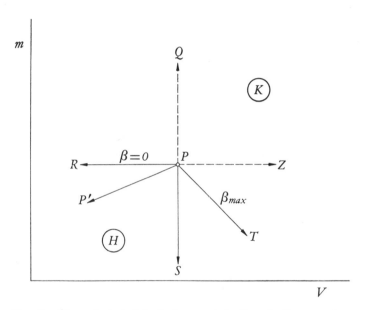

Fig. 6.   Class of admissible displacements in the velocity-mass plane.

As an example, if the rocket is coasting, the infinitesimal velocity variation is negative, and the infinitesimal variation in the mass is zero; thus, while the displacement $\overline{PR}$ is physically possible, the displacement $\overline{PZ}$ is not possible. As another example, if the instantaneous thrust is equal to the drag, the infinitesimal velocity variation is zero, and the infinitesimal variation in the mass is negative; hence, while the displacement $\overline{PS}$ is physically possible, the displacement $\overline{PQ}$ is not possible. In conclusion, the two limiting displacements $\overline{PR}$ and $\overline{PT}$ divide the velocity-mass plane into two regions: a region H whose points are accessible to the rocket and a region K which is forbidden by the physics of the motion.

3.52 Region of Admissible Paths

Consider a rocket which must be transferred from the initial state V_i, m_i to the final state V_f, m_f. Observe that, if the burning program $\beta(m)$ is specified, the third of Eqs. (3.28) can be integrated by separation of variables. In particular, if the mass flow is constant, the following solution is obtained:

$$m \left| \frac{1 + V\sqrt{K/\beta c}}{1 - V\sqrt{K/\beta c}} \right|^{\sqrt{(\beta/4Kc)}} = \text{const} \tag{3.30}$$

and, for the two limiting cases where $\beta = 0$ (zero burning rate) and $\beta = \infty$ (pulse-burning), simplifies to

$$m = \text{const}$$

$$m \exp\left(\frac{V}{c}\right) = \text{const} \tag{3.31}$$

respectively.

By calculating the integration constants in terms of the known initial conditions, one can trace the two limiting lines $\beta = 0$ and $\beta = \beta_{max}$ which began at point F; on the other hand, by calculating the constants in terms of the known final conditions, one can trace the other two limiting lines

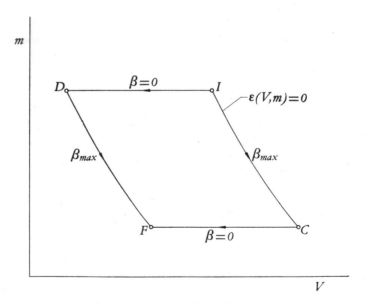

Fig. 7.   Region of admissible arcs.

$\beta = 0$ and $\beta = \beta_{\max}$ which arrive at point F. These four limiting lines determine the curve $IDFCI$ which encloses the *region of admissible paths* (Fig. 7), that is, the region of the Vm-plane containing all the trajectories which are consistent with the prescribed end values of the velocity and the mass. No trajectory connecting the end points I and F may cross the boundary of this region without violating the inequality constraint (3.29). Conversely, every trajectory internal to the region under consideration is physically possible provided that the mass flow constraint (3.29) is satisfied at each point.

3.53 Extremization of the Range

After the propellant mass flow is eliminated from the first and third of Eqs. (3.28), the following differential relationship is obtained:

$$dX = \varphi \, dV + \psi \, dm \tag{3.32}$$

where

$$\varphi = -\frac{m}{KV}, \qquad \psi = -\frac{c}{KV} \tag{3.33}$$

Consequently, after it is assumed that $X_i = 0$ and $X_f = X$, the total range is given by the linear integral

$$X = \int_i^f (\varphi \, dV + \psi \, dm) \tag{3.34}$$

which depends on the integration path $m(V)$. In this connection, the problem of the optimum burning program is formulated as follows: *In the class of functions m (V) which satisfy the prescribed end values of the velocity and the mass and which are consistent with Ineq. (3.29), determine that particular function which extremizes the integral (3.34).*

Because of the mass flow constraints (3.29), the class of admissible arcs is contained in the region bounded by the closed contour $IDFCI$ of Fig. 7, whose equation can be symbolically written as

$$\epsilon(V, m) = 0 \tag{3.35}$$

Furthermore, the initial and final points belong to the contour in question and, hence, satisfy the conditions

$$\epsilon(V_i, m_i) = \epsilon(V_f, m_f) = 0 \tag{3.36}$$

Since the problem represented by Eqs. (3.34)–(3.36) is mathematically identical with the linear problem represented by Eqs. (3.1)–(3.3), the results of Section 3.2 are applicable to the present problem.

Thus, the first step in the analysis is to investigate the sign of the fundamental function which is defined as

$$\omega(V, m) = \frac{\partial \psi}{\partial V} - \frac{\partial \varphi}{\partial m} \qquad (3.37)$$

and, after simple manipulations, becomes

$$\omega = \frac{V + c}{KV^2} > 0 \qquad (3.38)$$

Since the fundamental function is positive everywhere, the extremal arc

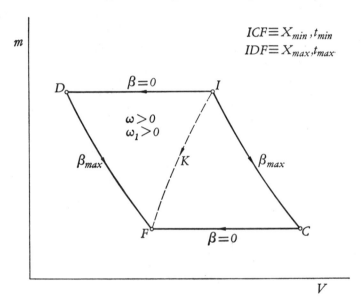

$ICF \equiv X_{min}, t_{min}$
$IDF \equiv X_{max}, t_{max}$

Fig. 8.   Arcs extremizing the range and the time.

is composed only of subarcs flown along the boundary of the admissible domain. Hence, the following conclusions arise (Fig. 8):

(a) The path ICF, which is composed of a subarc IC flown with the maximum thrust and a subarc CF flown with zero thrust, *minimizes the range* (this can be seen by comparing the trajectory ICF with an arbitrary admissible path IKF and applying Green's theorem).

(b) The path IDF, which is composed of a subarc ID flown with zero thrust and a subarc DF flown with maximum thrust, *maximizes the range* (this can be seen by comparing the trajectory IDF with an arbitrary admissible path IKF and applying Green's theorem).

3.54 Extremization of the Time

After the propellant mass flow is eliminated from the third and the fifth of Eqs. (3.28), the following differential relationship can be obtained:

$$dt = \varphi_1 \, dV + \psi_1 \, dm \qquad (3.39)$$

where

$$\varphi_1 = -\frac{m}{KV^2}, \qquad \psi_1 = -\frac{c}{KV^2} \qquad (3.40)$$

Consequently, after it is assumed that $t_i = 0$ and $t_f = t$, the total time is given by the linear integral

$$t = \int_i^f (\varphi_1 \, dV + \psi_1 \, dm) \qquad (3.41)$$

which depends on the integration path $m(V)$. In this connection, the problem of the optimum burning program is formulated as follows: *In the class of functions $m(V)$ which satisfy the prescribed end values of the velocity and the mass and which are consistent with Ineq. (3.29), determine that particular function which extremizes the integral (3.41).*

The fundamental function for this extremal problem is defined as

$$\omega_1(V, m) = \frac{\partial \psi_1}{\partial V} - \frac{\partial \varphi_1}{\partial m} \qquad (3.42)$$

and, after simple manipulations, becomes

$$\omega_1(V, m) = \frac{V + 2c}{KV^3} > 0 \qquad (3.43)$$

Since this function is positive everywhere, the extremal arc is composed only of subarcs flown along the boundary of the admissible region. Therefore, by applying the same reasoning as in the previous example, it is seen that the trajectory ICF of Fig. 8 *minimizes the time*, while the trajectory IDF *maximizes the time*.

3.55 Extremization of the Range for a Given Time

From the results of the preceding analyses, it is seen that the maximum range trajectory simultaneously maximizes the time. Since this characteristic may not be a desirable one, it is of interest to investigate the class of flight paths which extremize the range for the case where the flight time as well as the end values of the velocity and the mass are prescribed.

This problem is of the linear isoperimetric type and is governed by the theory developed in Section 3.3. Hence, the first step in the analysis is to investigate the distribution of signs of the augmented fundamental function within the admissible domain. This function is given by

$$\omega_*(V, m, \lambda) = \frac{\partial \psi_*}{\partial V} - \frac{\partial \varphi_*}{\partial m} \tag{3.44}$$

where λ is a constant Lagrange multiplier and where

$$\varphi_* = \varphi + \lambda \varphi_1 = -\frac{m}{KV^2}(V + \lambda)$$

$$\psi_* = \psi + \lambda \psi_1 = -\frac{c}{KV^2}(V + \lambda) \tag{3.45}$$

After the augmented fundamental function is rewritten in the form

$$\omega_*(V, m, \lambda) = \frac{V^2 + (\lambda + c)V + 2\lambda c}{KV^3} \tag{3.46}$$

it is seen that, for each given λ, the function is zero along the *constant velocity line* defined by

$$V^2 + (\lambda + c)V + 2\lambda c = 0 \tag{3.47}$$

Since positive solutions for the velocity modulus exist for $\lambda < 0$ only, the

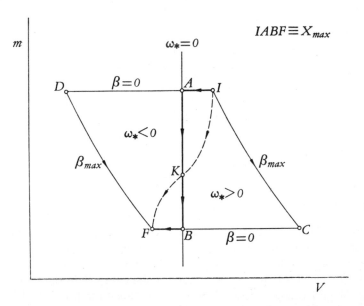

FIG. 9.   Distribution of signs for the augmented fundamental function.

fundamental function is negative to the left of any constant velocity line and positive to the right (Fig. 9) and, hence, changes sign within the admissible domain. Consequently, the extremal arc is composed of subarcs flown along the boundary of the admissible domain and subarcs satisfying the condition $\omega_* = 0$, that is,

$\qquad$ (a) subarcs $\beta = 0$

$\qquad$ (b) subarcs $\beta = \beta_{\max}$

$\qquad$ (c) subarcs $V = \text{const}$

The way in which these different subarcs must be combined is to be determined from the prescribed boundary conditions and the given isoperimetric constraint. In this connection, a particular example is indicated in Fig. 10.

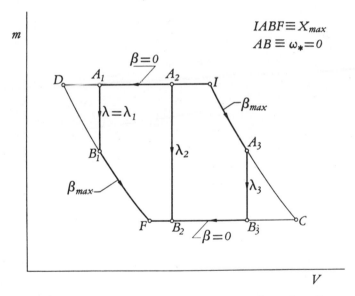

FIG. 10.   Totality of arcs extremizing the range for a given time.

The totality of extremal arcs associated with prescribed end values of the velocity and the mass is represented by the family of paths $IABF$, whose generic member can be characterized by the value of the Lagrange multiplier λ which defines the constant velocity subarc.* Consequently, by cal-

---

* For simplicity and for the sake of brevity, it is assumed that Ineq. (3.29) is satisfied everywhere along the constant velocity subarc defined by Eq. (3.47). Should this inequality be violated along some portion of the subarc in question (this would occur if the aerodynamic drag is larger than the maximum available thrust), the composition of the extremal arc would be somewhat different from that indicated in Fig. 10.

culating the over-all range and flight time, one obtains the following functional relationships (Fig. 11):

$$X = A(\lambda)$$

$$t = B(\lambda) \tag{3.48}$$

the second of which determines the Lagrange multiplier, while the first supplies the distance traveled by the missile in the prescribed time interval.

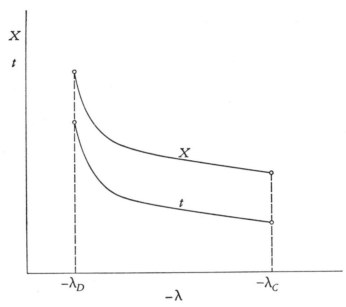

Fig. 11.   Determination of the Lagrange multiplier and solution of the boundary-value problem.

This distance is a *maximum*, as can be seen by comparing the extremal trajectory $IABF$ with any arbitrary admissible path flown in the same time IKF and applying Green's theorem (Fig. 9).

3.6 Optimum Drag Modulation Program for the Re-Entry of a Variable-Geometry Ballistic Missile

As another application of the previous theory, this section considers the re-entry trajectory of a variable-geometry ballistic missile under the assumption that the distribution of the atmospheric properties versus the altitude is arbitrarily specified. For simplicity, a vertical re-entry is considered, even though the results can be applied to arbitrarily inclined, rectilinear paths by a simple coordinate transformation. The following hypotheses are employed: (a) the earth is flat and nonrotating and the acceleration of gravity is constant; (b) the trajectory is vertical so that the lift is zero at all time instants; (c) the weight is negligible with respect to the drag; and (d) the drag function has the form

$$D = \tfrac{1}{2}C_D \, \rho(h) \, SV^2 \tag{3.49}$$

where S is a reference surface, ρ the air density, h the altitude, and where the drag coefficient C_D is ideally independent of both the Mach number and the Reynolds number in the hypervelocity regime.

In the light of these hypotheses, the motion of the ballistic missile is governed by the differential equations

$$\dot{h} + V = 0$$

$$\dot{V} + \frac{gC_D \, \rho(h) \, SV^2}{2W} = 0 \tag{3.50}$$

which, after the altitude is selected as the new independent variable, can be rewritten in the form

$$\frac{dt}{dh} = -\frac{1}{V}$$

$$\frac{dV}{dh} = g\,\frac{C_D \, \rho(h) \, SV}{2W} \tag{3.51}$$

It is now assumed that the missile has a variable-geometry arrangement (for instance, spoilers or dive brakes), so that the drag coefficient can be controlled in flight. Consequently, Eqs. (3.51) involve one independent variable (h), three dependent variables (t, V, C_D), and, therefore, one degree of freedom. This means that, for each given set of initial conditions, infinite trajectories exist which are physically and mathematically possible, more specifically, one trajectory for each arbitrarily prescribed drag modulation program $C_D(h)$. However, there exist limitations to the choice of this program, since the missile can only develop instantaneous drag coefficients bounded by a lower limit and an upper limit. Thus, the following inequality must be satisfied at all points of the flight path:

$$C_{D\,\min} \le C_D \le C_{D\,\max} \tag{3.52}$$

where the lower limit corresponds to the spoilers fully retracted and the upper limit to the spoilers fully extended. This inequality has a considerable influence on the solution of the extremal problems of variable-geometry missiles in that it defines both the class of admissible displacements and the region of admissible paths for the vehicle.

3.61 Class of Admissible Displacements

Consider a missile which, at a given time instant, has the velocity V and the altitude h, and let P be its associated point in the velocity-altitude plane (Fig. 12). After an infinitesimal time interval, the new velocity of

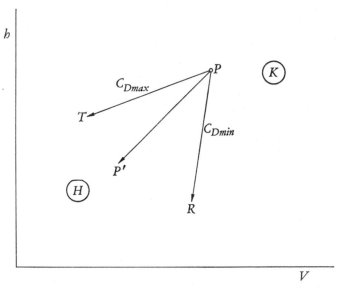

FIG. 12.   Class of admissible displacements in the velocity-altitude plane.

the missile is $V' = V + dV$, the new altitude is $h' = h + dh$, and the new position in the velocity-altitude plane is represented by point P'. Consequently, the vector $\overline{PP'}$ is the infinitesimal displacement of the missile in the Vh-plane.

As the second of Eqs. (3.51) indicates, there exists one infinitesimal displacement for each drag coefficient C_D. However, because of Ineq. (3.52), not every displacement is physically possible. More specifically, the *class of admissible displacements* is bounded by two limiting conditions: a displacement $\overline{PR}$ corresponding to the spoilers fully retracted and a displacement $\overline{PT}$ corresponding to the spoilers fully extended. In conclusion, the two limiting displacements $\overline{PR}$ and $\overline{PT}$ divide the velocity-altitude domain into two regions: a region H whose points are accessible to the missile and a region K which is forbidden by the physics of the motion.

3.62 Region of Admissible Paths

Consider a missile which must be transferred from the initial state of flight V_i, h_i to the final state V_f, h_f. Observe that, if the drag modulation program $C_D(h)$ is specified, the second of Eqs. (3.51) can be integrated by separation of variables. In particular, if the drag coefficient is constant, the following solution is obtained:

$$V \exp\left[-\frac{gC_D S}{2W} \int_0^h \rho(h)\, dh\right] = \text{const} \tag{3.53}$$

By calculating the integration constant in terms of the known initial conditions, one can trace the two limiting lines $C_D = C_{D\,min}$ (spoilers fully retracted) and $C_D = C_{D\,max}$ (spoilers fully extended) which begin at point I; on the other hand, by calculating the constant in terms of the known final conditions, one can trace the other two limiting lines $C_D = C_{D\,min}$ and $C_D = C_{D\,max}$ which arrive at point F. These four limiting lines identify the curve $IDFCI$ which encloses the *region of admissible paths* (Fig. 13), that is, the region of the Vh-plane containing all the trajectories which are consistent with the prescribed end values of the velocity and the altitude. No trajectory connecting the end points I and F may cross the boundary of this region without violating the inequality constraint (3.52). Conversely, every trajectory internal to the region under consideration is physically possible, providing that the drag coefficient constraint (3.52) is satisfied at each point.

3.63 Extremization of the Heat Transfer

In accordance with the accepted engineering practice, the following generalized heat transfer law is assumed for hypervelocity flight:

$$\dot{H} = K\rho^x V^y \tag{3.54}$$

which implies that

$$\frac{dH}{dh} = -K\rho^x V^{y-1} \tag{3.55}$$

where H denotes the heat transferred from the boundary layer to some specific area of the missile, K is a characteristic constant of the missile, and x and y are dimensionless exponents. If the area under consideration is the entire wetted surface of the missile (excluding the spoilers), appropriate values of the exponents are

$$x = 1, \qquad y = 3 \tag{3.56}$$

On the other hand, if the area under consideration is a small region immediately surrounding the nose, representative values of the exponents are

$$x = 0.5, \qquad y = 3 \tag{3.57}$$

In the light of Eq. (3.55), the infinitesimal amount of heat transferred from the boundary layer to the missile is written in the form

$$dH = \psi \, dh \tag{3.58}$$

where

$$\psi = -K\rho^x V^{y-1} \tag{3.59}$$

Consequently, after it is assumed that $H_i = 0$ and $H_f = H$, the over-all heat transferred during re-entry is given by

$$H = \int_i^f \psi \, dh \tag{3.60}$$

and depends on the integration path $V(h)$. In this connection, the problem of the optimum drag modulation program is formulated as follows: *In the class of functions $V(h)$ which satisfy the prescribed end values of the velocity and the altitude and which are consistent with Ineq. (3.52), determine that particular function which extremizes the integral (3.60).*

Because of the inequality constraint (3.52), the class of admissible arcs is contained in the region bounded by the closed contour $IDFCI$ of

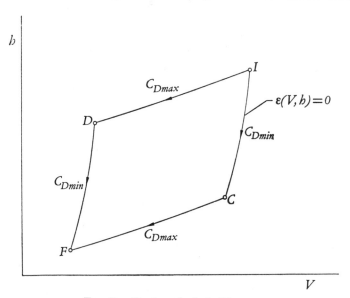

FIG. 13.   Region of admissible arcs.

Fig. 13, whose equation can be symbolically written as

$$\epsilon(V, h) = 0 \tag{3.61}$$

Furthermore, the initial and final points belong to the boundary of this region and, hence, satisfy the conditions

$$\epsilon(V_i, h_i) = \epsilon(V_f, h_f) = 0 \tag{3.62}$$

Since the problem represented by Eqs. (3.60)–(3.62) is mathematically identical with the linear problem represented by Eqs. (3.1)–(3.3), the results of Section 3.2 are applicable to the present problem.

Thus, the first step in the analysis is to investigate the sign of the fundamental function which is defined as

$$\omega(V, h) = \frac{\partial \psi}{\partial V} \tag{3.63}$$

and, after simple manipulations, becomes

$$\omega = -K(y - 1)\rho^x V^{y-2} < 0 \tag{3.64}$$

Since $y = 3$, the fundamental function is negative everywhere; therefore, the extremal arc is composed only of subarcs flown along the boundary of the admissible domain. Hence, the following conclusions arise (Fig. 14):

(a) The path ICF, which is composed of a subarc IC flown with the

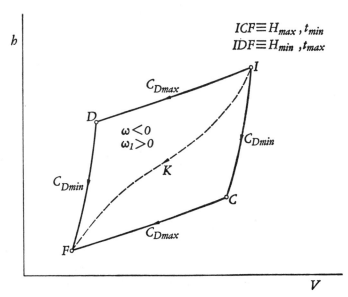

FIG. 14. Arcs extremizing the heat transfer and the time.

spoilers fully retracted followed by a subarc CF flown with the spoilers fully extended, *maximizes the heat transfer* (this can be seen by comparing the trajectory ICF with an arbitrary admissible path IKF and applying Green's theorem).

(b) The path IDF, which is composed of a subarc ID flown with the spoilers fully extended followed by a subarc DF flown with the spoilers fully retracted *minimizes the heat transfer* (this can be seen by comparing the trajectory IDF with the arbitrary admissible path IKF and applying Green's theorem).

3.64 Extremization of the Time

Because of the first of Eqs. (3.51), the infinitesimal time interval is written in the form

$$dt = \psi_1 \, dh \tag{3.65}$$

where

$$\psi_1 = -\frac{1}{V} \tag{3.66}$$

Consequently, after it is assumed that $t_i = 0$ and $t_f = t$, the total time is given by the linear integral

$$t = \int_i^f \psi_1 \, dh \tag{3.67}$$

which depends on the integration path $V(h)$. In this connection, the problem of the optimum drag modulation program is formulated as follows: *In the class of functions $V(h)$ which satisfy the prescribed end values of the velocity and the altitude and which are consistent with Ineq. (3.52), determine that particular function which extremizes the integral (3.67).*

The fundamental function for this extremal problem is defined as

$$\omega_1(V, h) = \frac{\partial \psi_1}{\partial V} \tag{3.68}$$

and, after simple manipulations, becomes

$$\omega_1(V, h) = \frac{1}{V^2} > 0 \tag{3.69}$$

Since this function is positive everywhere, the extremal arc is composed only of subarcs flown along the boundary of the admissible region. Therefore, by applying the same reasoning as in the previous example, it is seen that the trajectory *ICF* of Fig. 14 *minimizes the time,* while the trajectory *IDF maximizes the time.*

3.65 Extremization of the Heat Transfer for a Given Time

From the results of the previous analyses, it is seen that the trajectory of minimum heat transfer simultaneously maximizes the time. Since this characteristic may not be a desirable one, it is of interest to investigate the class of flight paths which extremize the heat transfer for the case where the flight time as well as the end values of the velocity and the mass are prescribed.

This problem is of the linear isoperimetric type and is governed by the theory developed in Section 3.3. Hence, the first step in the analysis is to investigate the distribution of signs of the augmented fundamental function within the admissible domain. This function is given by

$$\omega_*(V, h, \lambda) = \frac{\partial \psi_*}{\partial V} \tag{3.70}$$

where λ is a constant Lagrange multiplier and where

$$\psi_* = \psi + \lambda \psi_1 = -\left(K\rho^x V^{y-1} + \frac{\lambda}{V}\right) \tag{3.71}$$

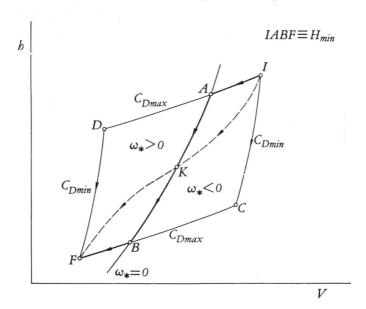

FIG. 15.   Distribution of signs for the augmented fundamental function.

After the augmented fundamental function is rewritten in the form

$$\omega_* = -K(y - 1)\rho^x V^{y-2} + \frac{\lambda}{V^2} \tag{3.72}$$

it is seen that, for each given λ, this function is zero along the *constant time rate of heat transfer line* defined by

$$\rho^x V^y = \frac{\lambda}{K(y - 1)} \tag{3.73}$$

Since the Lagrange multiplier is positive, the fundamental function is positive to the left of any constant time rate of heat transfer line and negative to the right (Fig. 15) and, hence, changes sign within the admissible domain. Consequently, the extremal arc is composed of subarcs flown along the boundary of the admissible domain and subarcs satisfying the condition $\omega_* = 0$, that is,

(a) subarcs $C_D = C_{D\,min}$

(b) subarcs $C_D = C_{D\,max}$

(c) subarcs $\rho^x V^y = \text{const}$

The way in which these different subarcs must be combined is to be de-

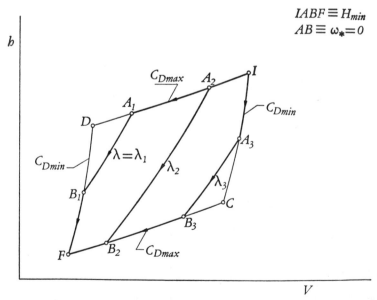

FIG. 16. Totality of arcs extremizing the heat transferred in a given time.

termined from the prescribed boundary conditions and the given iso-perimetric condition. In this connection, a particular example is indicated in Fig. 16. The totality of extremal arcs associated with prescribed end values of the velocity and the altitude is represented by the family of paths $IABF$, whose generic member is characterized by the value of the Lagrange multiplier λ which defines the constant time rate of heat transfer subarc.* Consequently, by calculating the over-all heat transferred and the

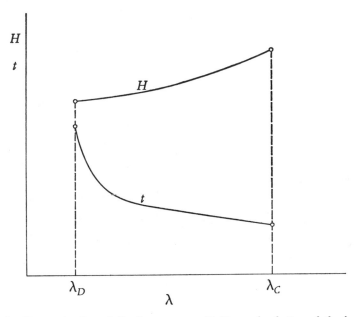

Fig. 17. Determination of the Lagrange multiplier and solution of the boundary-value problem.

flight time, one obtains the following functional relationships (Fig. 17):

$$H = H(\lambda)$$

$$t = t(\lambda)$$

(3.74)

the second of which determines the Lagrange multiplier, while the first supplies the heat transferred by the boundary layer to the missile in the

---

* For simplicity and for the sake of brevity, it is assumed that the inequality constraint (3.52) is satisfied everywhere along the constant time rate of heat transfer subarc defined by Eq. (3.73). Should this inequality be violated along some portion of the subarc in question, the composition of the extremal arc would be somewhat different from that indicated in Fig. 16.

prescribed time interval. This heat transferred is a *minimum*, as can be shown by comparing the extremal trajectory $IABF$ with any other admissible path IKF flown in the same time and applying Green's theorem (Fig. 15).

REFERENCES

1. A. Miele, Problemi di minimo tempo nel volo non-stazionario degli aeroplani, *Atti accad. sci. Torino, Classe sci. fis. mat. e nat.* 85 (1950–1951).
2. A. Miele, General solutions of optimum problems in non-stationary flight, *NACA, Tech. Memo No.* 1388 (1955).
3. A. Miele, Optimum climbing technique for a rocket-powered aircraft, *ARS Journal* 25, No. 8 (1955).
4. A. Miele, Flight mechanics and variational problems of a linear type, *J. Aero/Space Sci.* 25, No. 9 (1958).
5. A. Miele, Minimality for arbitrarily inclined rocket trajectories, *ARS Journal* 28, No. 7 (1958).
6. A. Miele, Application of Green's theorem to the extremization of linear integrals, Boeing Scientific Research Laboratories, Flight Sciences Laboratory, TR No. 40 (1961).
7. A. Miele, The relation between the Green's theorem approach and the indirect methods for extremal problems of a linear type, Boeing Scientific Research Laboratories, Flight Sciences Laboratory, TR No. 47 (1961).

GENERAL REFERENCE

1. A. Miele, "Flight Mechanics," Vol. 1: Theory of Flight Paths. Addison-Wesley, Reading, Massachusetts, 1962.
2. A. Miele, "Flight Mechanics," Vol. 2: Theory of Optimum Flight Paths. Addison-Wesley, Reading, Massachusetts (in preparation).
3. P. Cicala and A. Miele, Generalized theory of the optimum thrust programming for the level flight of a rocket-powered aircraft, *ARS Journal* 26, No. 6 (1956).
4. A. Miele and C. R. Cavoti, Generalized variational approach to the optimum thrust programming for the vertical flight of a rocket, Part 2, Application of Green's theorem to the development of sufficiency proofs for particular classes of solutions, *ZFW* 6, No. 4 (1958).
5. A. Miele and C. R. Cavoti, Variational approach to the re-entry of a ballistic missile, Part 2, Purdue University, School of Aeronautical Engineering, Rept. No. A–59–3 (1959).
6. A. Miele, An extension of the theory of the optimum burning program for the level flight of a rocket-powered aircraft, *J. Aero/Space Sci.* 24, No. 12 (1957).

—4—

The Calculus of Variations in Applied Aerodynamics and Flight Mechanics

ANGELO MIELE

Boeing Scientific Research Laboratories, Seattle, Washington

4.1 Introduction

The calculus of variations is that branch of calculus in which extremal problems are investigated under more general conditions than those considered in the ordinary theory of maxima and minima. More specifically, the calculus of variations is concerned with the maxima and minima of functional expressions where entire functions must be determined. Thus, the unknown of the calculus of variations is not a discrete number of points but rather the succession or assembly of an infinite set of points, all those which identify a curve, a surface, or a hypersurface, depending on the nature of the problem.[1]

Applications of the calculus of variations occur in several fields of science and engineering, for instance: classical geometry, dynamics, elasticity, optics, electromagnetic theory, and fluid dynamics. With particular regard to aeronautics and astronautics, the use of variational techniques was almost unheard of only a decade ago. In recent times, however, the calculus of variations has become increasingly popular, two fields of problems being mainly responsible for this: applied aerodynamics through the study of the optimum shapes of aircraft and missile components and flight mechanics through the study of the optimum trajectories of aircraft, missiles, and spaceships.[2]

In the following sections, the most general problem of the calculus of variations in one independent variable, the problem of Bolza, is reviewed; then, a particular case of the Bolza problem is considered, that is, the problem of Mayer; finally, the application of the Mayer formulation to several engineering problems is demonstrated. Because of the extent of the available literature and the impossibility of surveying it in a systematic fashion, only a few typical problems are considered here. More specifically, concerning applied aerodynamics, the theory of the optimum bodies of revolution in Newtonian flow and that of the optimum wings in linearized supersonic flow are derived. Furthermore, concerning flight mechanics, the theory of the optimum two-dimensional paths of a rocket vehicle in both a vacuum and a resisting medium is presented.

4.2 The Problem of Bolza

The most general problems of the calculus of variations in one independent variable are the problems of Bolza, Mayer, and Lagrange. Even though these problems are theoretically equivalent in that any one of them can be transformed into another by a change of coordinates, the simplest approach consists of studying the problem of Bolza first and then deriving the other two as particular cases. Referring, for the sake of brevity, to the case where the end-conditions are separated, one can formulate the *problem of Bolza* as follows: *Consider the class of functions*

$$y_k(x), \qquad k = 1, \cdots, n \tag{4.1}$$

*satisfying the constraints**

$$\varphi_j(x, y_k, \dot{y}_k) = 0, \qquad j = 1, \cdots, p < n \tag{4.2}$$

which involve $f = n - p$ *degrees of freedom.† Assuming that these functions must be consistent with the end-conditions‡*

$$\omega_r(x_i, y_{ki}) = 0, \qquad r = 1, \cdots, q$$

$$\omega_r(x_f, y_{kf}) = 0, \qquad r = q + 1, \cdots, s \leq 2n + 2 \tag{4.3}$$

find that special set which minimizes the functional form

$$\psi \equiv [G(x, y_k)]_i^f + \int_{x_i}^{x_f} H(x, y_k, \dot{y}_k) \, dx \tag{4.4}$$

4.21 Euler-Lagrange Equations

The problem formulated above can be treated in a simple and elegant manner if a set of variable *Lagrange multipliers*

$$\lambda_j(x), \qquad j = 1, \cdots, p \tag{4.5}$$

is introduced and if the following expression, called the *augmented function*, is formed:

$$F = H + \sum_{j=1}^{p} \lambda_j \varphi_j \tag{4.6}$$

It is known that the *extremal arc* (the special curve extremizing ψ) must satisfy not only Eqs. (4.2) but also the *Euler-Lagrange equations*[1-5]

$$\frac{d}{dx}\left(\frac{\partial F}{\partial \dot{y}_k}\right) - \frac{\partial F}{\partial y_k} = 0, \qquad k = 1, \cdots, n \tag{4.7}$$

---

* The dot sign denotes a derivative with respect to the independent variable.
† By definition, the number of degrees of freedom of a differential system is the difference between the number of dependent variables and the number of equations.
‡ The subscript i stands for initial point, and the subscript f, for final point.

The differential system composed of the constraining equations and the Euler-Lagrange equations includes $n + p$ equations and unknowns; consequently, its solution yields the n dependent variables and the p Lagrange multipliers simultaneously. Generally speaking, approximate methods of integration are needed, since analytical solutions are possible only in special cases. An additional complication arises from the fact that the variational problems of interest in engineering are always of the mixed boundary-value type, that is, problems with conditions prescribed in part at the initial point and in part at the final point. Consequently, in the case where closed-form solutions cannot be obtained, trial-and-error techniques must be employed; they consist of guessing the missing initial conditions, integrating numerically the set of Euler-Lagrange equations and constraining equations, and then determining the difference between the resulting final conditions and the specified final conditions. Since these differences are in general not zero, the process must be repeated several times until these differences vanish, that is, until the specified final conditions are met; in this connection, it is worth mentioning that analytical schemes have been developed (see, for instance, Kulakowski and Stancil[6]) in order to contain the number of iterations within reasonable limits.*

4.22 First Integral

A mathematical consequence of the Euler-Lagrange equations is the differential relationship[1]

$$\frac{d}{dx}\left(-F + \sum_{k=1}^{n} \frac{\partial F}{\partial \dot{y}_k}\, \dot{y}_k\right) + \frac{\partial F}{\partial x} = 0 \qquad (4.8)$$

Consequently, for problems where the augmented function is formally independent of x, the following *first integral* is valid:

$$-F + \sum_{k=1}^{n} \frac{\partial F}{\partial \dot{y}_k}\, \dot{y}_k = C \qquad (4.9)$$

where C is an integration constant.

---

* An alternative possibility consists of abandoning the indirect methods considered here and employing direct procedures, for instance, those discussed by Bryson and Denham[7] and Kelley.[8] These direct procedures, which have been developed primarily in order to circumvent the mixed boundary value difficulties, have many computational merits; however, they only yield numerical solutions valid for particular problems. On the other hand, the indirect methods enable one to obtain general results valid for entire classes of problems providing analytical solutions can be found; furthermore, even in the case where such solutions cannot be found, the indirect methods often supply important qualitative information on the nature of the extremal path, information which cannot be obtained by any of the existing direct procedures.

4.23 Corner Conditions

There are many variational problems which are characterized by discontinuous solutions, that is, solutions in which one or more of the derivatives $\dot{y}_k$ experience a jump at a finite number of points.* These points are called *corner points*; the entire solution is still called the *extremal arc*, while each component portion is called a *subarc*. When discontinuities occur, a mathematical criterion is needed to join the different portions of the extremal arc. This criterion is supplied by the *Erdmann-Weierstrass corner conditions*[1]

$$\left(\frac{\partial F}{\partial \dot{y}_k}\right)_- = \left(\frac{\partial F}{\partial \dot{y}_k}\right)_+, \qquad k = 1, \cdots, n \tag{4.10}$$

$$\left(- F + \sum_{k=1}^{n} \frac{\partial F}{\partial \dot{y}_k} \dot{y}_k\right)_- = \left(- F + \sum_{k=1}^{n} \frac{\partial F}{\partial \dot{y}_k} \dot{y}_k\right)_+ \tag{4.11}$$

in which the negative and positive signs denote conditions immediately before and after a corner point, respectively. For the particular case in which the fundamental function is formally independent of x, Eqs. (4.9) and (4.11) imply that

$$(C)_- = (C)_+ \tag{4.12}$$

which means that the integration constant C has the same value for all the subarcs composing the extremal arc.

4.24 Transversality Condition

The system composed of the constraining equations and the Euler-Lagrange equations is subjected to $2n + 2$ boundary conditions. Of these, s are supplied by Eqs. (4.3) and $2n + 2 - s$ by the *transversality condition*[1]

$$\left[dG + \left(F - \sum_{k=1}^{n} \frac{\partial F}{\partial \dot{y}_k} \dot{y}_k\right) dx + \sum_{k=1}^{n} \frac{\partial F}{\partial \dot{y}_k} dy_k\right]_i^t = 0 \tag{4.13}$$

which is to be satisfied identically for all systems of infinitesimal displacements consistent with Eqs. (4.3). For the particular case in which the

---

* Discontinuous solutions are of particular importance in engineering. In fact, while nature forbids discontinuities on a macroscopic scale, it is not infrequent that the process of idealization which is intrinsic to all engineering applications leads to a mathematical scheme which forces a discontinuity into the solution.

fundamental function is formally independent of x, the transversality condition reduces to

$$\left[dG - C \, dx + \sum_{k=1}^{n} \frac{\partial F}{\partial \dot{y}_k} \, dy_k \right]_i^f = 0 \qquad (4.14)$$

4.25 Legendre-Clebsch and Weierstrass Conditions

After an extremal arc has been determined, it is necessary to investigate whether the function ψ attains a maximum or a minimum value. In this connection, the necessary conditions due to Weierstrass and to Legendre-Clebsch are of considerable assistance. Even though both of these conditions have a local nature, they differ insofar as the former refers to a system of *strong variations* and the latter, to a system of *weak variations*. Hence, the Legendre-Clebsch condition is a consequence of the Weierstrass condition.

Analytically, the *Weierstrass condition* states that the functional ψ attains a minimum if the following inequality is satisfied at all points of the extremal arc[1]:

$$\Delta F - \sum_{k=1}^{n} \frac{\partial F}{\partial \dot{y}_k} \Delta \dot{y}_k \geq 0 \qquad (4.15)$$

for all systems of strong variations $\Delta \dot{y}_k$ consistent with the constraining equations (4.2). On the other hand, if a system of weak variations $\delta \dot{y}_k$ is considered and a Maclaurin expansion is employed, inequality (4.15) reduces to the *Legendre-Clebsch condition*

$$\sum_{k=1}^{n} \sum_{j=1}^{n} \frac{\partial^2 F}{\partial \dot{y}_k \partial \dot{y}_j} \delta \dot{y}_k \delta \dot{y}_j \geq 0 \qquad (4.16)$$

which is to be satisfied for all systems of weak variations consistent with the constraining equations (4.2), that is, with

$$\sum_{k=1}^{n} \frac{\partial \varphi_j}{\partial \dot{y}_k} \delta \dot{y}_k = 0, \qquad j = 1, \cdots, p \qquad (4.17)$$

It must be noted that the Weierstrass condition and the Legendre-Clebsch condition are only *necessary conditions* for the extremum and that the development of the complete sufficiency proof for a relative minimum requires that the further necessary condition due to Jacobi-Mayer be met.[1] It must also be noted that, for most problems having engineering interest, the Legendre-Clebsch condition yields the same information as the Weierstrass condition*; furthermore, the investigation of the *Jacobi-Mayer condition* is not easily accomplished. Consequently, the practicing engineer is often forced to rely on the Legendre-Clebsch condition alone in order to distinguish a relative minimum from a relative maximum. Even though the results obtained in this way are by no means complete, physical reasoning in combination with the numerical investigation of neighboring paths allows one in most cases to be certain that the solution obtained by the combined use of the Euler-Lagrange equations and the Legendre-Clebsch condition yields a relative minimum for the function under consideration.

4.26 The Problem of Mayer

The problem of Mayer is the particular case of the Bolza problem which occurs when the integrand of Eq. (4.4) is identically zero, that is, when

$$H \equiv 0 \qquad (4.18)$$

For this problem, Eqs. (4.7)–(4.16) are still valid, with the further simplification that

$$F = 0 \qquad (4.19)$$

for any admissible path and, hence, for the extremal arc. Incidentally, the number of end-conditions s is to be less than $2n + 2$.

4.27 The Problem of Lagrange

The problem of Lagrange is the particular case of the Bolza problem which occurs when

$$G \equiv 0 \qquad (4.20)$$

that is, when the functional to be extremized appears entirely in integral form. For this problem, Eqs. (4.7)–(4.16) are still valid. In particular, the transversality condition is simplified by the fact that $dG = 0$.

4.28 First Example

As an application of the previous theory, the problem of determining the curve which minimizes the distance between two given end-points is

---

* This statement is not necessarily true for every problem.⁹

now considered. The curvilinear abscissa s is assumed to be the independent variable, while the Cartesian coordinates x, y, z are regarded to be the dependent variables. Consequently, if the dot sign denotes a derivative with respect to the curvilinear abscissa and if the seven coordinates s_i, x_i, y_i, z_i, x_f, y_f, z_f are specified, the minimum distance problem can be formulated as follows: *In the class of arcs* $x(s)$, $y(s)$, $z(s)$ *which satisfy the constraint*

$$\varphi \equiv \dot{x}^2 + \dot{y}^2 + \dot{z}^2 - 1 = 0 \tag{4.21}$$

as well as the specified end-conditions, find that particular arc which minimizes the difference $\Delta G = G_f - G_i$, *where* $G = s$.

Clearly, this is a Mayer problem with separated end-conditions. Consequently, after a Lagrange multiplier λ is introduced and the augmented function is written in the form

$$F = \lambda(\dot{x}^2 + \dot{y}^2 + \dot{z}^2 - 1) \tag{4.22}$$

the Euler-Lagrange equations become

$$\frac{d}{ds}(\lambda\dot{x}) = \frac{d}{ds}(\lambda\dot{y}) = \frac{d}{ds}(\lambda\dot{z}) = 0 \tag{4.23}$$

and admit the first integral

$$2\lambda(\dot{x}^2 + \dot{y}^2 + \dot{z}^2) = C \tag{4.24}$$

where C is a constant. Because of the constraining equation (4.21), this first integral implies that

$$\lambda = C/2 \tag{4.25}$$

which shows that the Lagrange multiplier is constant. Furthermore, if the transversality condition is written in the form

$$[(1 - C)\, ds + 2\lambda(\dot{x}\, dx + \dot{y}\, dy + \dot{z}\, dz)]_i^f = 0 \tag{4.26}$$

and if it is observed that the end-coordinates are fixed except for s_f, the following result is obtained:

$$C = 1, \qquad \lambda = \tfrac{1}{2} \tag{4.27}$$

The next step consists of rewriting the Euler-Lagrange equations in the differential form

$$\ddot{x} = \ddot{y} = \ddot{z} = 0 \tag{4.28}$$

which can be integrated to give

$$x = C_1 s + C_2, \qquad y = C_3 s + C_4, \qquad z = C_5 s + C_6 \qquad (4.29)$$

that is, the parametric equations of a straight line.* Incidentally, the solution obtained minimizes the distance. One can prove this statement by applying the Legendre-Clebsch condition†

$$2\lambda[(\delta\dot{x})^2 + (\delta\dot{y})^2 + (\delta\dot{z})^2] \geq 0 \qquad (4.30)$$

and observing that it is satisfied, since $\lambda > 0$.

4.29 Second Example

As another application of the previous theory, the problem of determining the curve which lies on the surface of a sphere having unit radius and joins two given end-points with the minimum distance is now considered. Again, the curvilinear abscissa s is assumed to be the independent variable, while the Cartesian coordinates x, y, z are regarded to be the dependent variables. Consequently, if the dot sign denotes a derivative with respect to the curvilinear abscissa and if the seven coordinates s_i, x_i, y_i, z_i, x_t, y_t, z_t are specified, the minimum distance problem is formulated as follows: *In the class of arcs $x(s)$, $y(s)$, $z(s)$ which satisfy the constraints‡*

$$\varphi_1 \equiv x^2 + y^2 + z^2 - 1 = 0$$

$$\qquad (4.31)$$

$$\varphi_2 \equiv \dot{x}^2 + \dot{y}^2 + \dot{z}^2 - 1 = 0$$

as well as the specified end-conditions, determine that particular arc which minimizes the difference $\Delta G = G_t - G_i$, *where* $G = s$.

Clearly, this is also a Mayer problem with separated end-conditions. Consequently, after the Lagrange multipliers λ_1, λ_2 are introduced and the fundamental function is written in the form

$$F = \lambda_1(x^2 + y^2 + z^2 - 1) + \lambda_2(\dot{x}^2 + \dot{y}^2 + \dot{z}^2 - 1) \qquad (4.32)$$

the Euler-Lagrange equations are given by

$$\frac{d}{ds}(\lambda_2\dot{x}) - \lambda_1 x = \frac{d}{ds}(\lambda_2\dot{y}) - \lambda_1 y = \frac{d}{ds}(\lambda_2\dot{z}) - \lambda_1 z = 0 \qquad (4.33)$$

---

* The symbols C_1 through C_6 denote integration constants.
† The variations $\delta\dot{x}$, $\delta\dot{y}$, $\delta\dot{z}$ must be consistent with the constraint (4.21).
‡ It is assumed that the center of the sphere is the origin of the coordinate system.

and, in view of the transversality condition and of the existence of a first integral identical with Eq. (4.24), imply that $\lambda_2 = \frac{1}{2}$.

The next step consists of differentiating the first constraining equation twice with respect to the curvilinear abscissa. Simple manipulations yield the relationship

$$x\ddot{x} + y\ddot{y} + z\ddot{z} + 1 = 0 \tag{4.34}$$

which is compatible with Eqs. (4.33) if, and only if,

$$\lambda_1 = -\tfrac{1}{2} \tag{4.35}$$

Hence, after the Euler-Lagrange equations are rewritten in the form

$$\ddot{x}/x = \ddot{y}/y = \ddot{z}/z = -1 \tag{4.36}$$

it becomes apparent that the direction of the normal to the sphere is identical with the direction of the principal normal to the curve. Consequantly, the curve in question is a *geodesic* of the sphere, and its general integral is given by the parametric equations

$$x = C_1 \sin s + C_2 \cos s$$

$$y = C_3 \sin s + C_4 \cos s \tag{4.37}$$

$$z = C_5 \sin s + C_6 \cos s$$

in which C_1 through C_6 denote integration constants. Notice that these parametric equations can be satisfied for every value of the curvilinear abscissa if, and only if,

$$\begin{vmatrix} x & C_1 & C_2 \\ y & C_3 & C_4 \\ z & C_5 & C_6 \end{vmatrix} = 0 \tag{4.38}$$

Thus, the geodesic of a sphere lies in a plane passing through the origin of the coordinate system, that is, a great-circle plane. Clearly, there exists two great-circle arcs joining the prescribed end-points. While the Legendre-Clebsch condition is satisfied for both of these arcs ($\lambda_2 > 0$), only the shorter yields a true relative minimum. The longer arc corresponds to a solution which is neither a minimum nor a maximum, but merely stationary. Thus, the geodesic example should be a warning to the reader of the pitfalls involved when studying extremal problems with the aid of the Euler-Lagrange equations and the Legendre-Clebsch and Weierstrass conditions alone.

4.3 Transformation of Variational Problems

In this section, several mathematical artifices which can be of assistance in the solution of practical variational problems are illustrated. In the first place, it is emphasized that there exists nothing sacrosanct in the use of the formulations of Bolza, Mayer, or Lagrange; one can always introduce some auxiliary variables which transform a Lagrange problem into a Bolza problem or a Mayer problem, and vice versa. In the second place, it is stressed that, while there are many engineering problems which do not seem to be covered by any of these formulations, one can always resort to some analytical artifice which reduces the initial scheme to one of those considered in the previous section. These concepts are now illustrated with several examples.

4.31 Transformation of a Lagrange Problem into a Mayer Problem

Consider the problem of minimizing the functional form

$$\psi \equiv \int_{x_i}^{x_f} F(x, y, \dot{y}) \, dx \tag{4.39}$$

assuming that the end-values for the coordinates x, y are specified. This problem is of the Lagrange type, but it can be reduced to a Mayer problem if the auxiliary variable z satisfying the differential constraint

$$\dot{z} - F(x, y, \dot{y}) = 0 \tag{4.40}$$

is introduced. In fact, after the integral (4.39) is rewritten as

$$\psi \equiv z_f - z_i \tag{4.41}$$

it becomes clear that the problem previously formulated is identical with that of finding, in the class of arcs $y(x)$, $z(x)$ which satisfy the constraint (4.40), that particular set which minimizes the difference (4.41). This new problem is one of the Mayer type.

4.32 Problems Involving Higher Derivatives

In this section, the problem of minimizing the functional form

$$\psi \equiv \int_{x_i}^{x_f} H(x, y, \dot{y}, \ddot{y}) \, dx \tag{4.42}$$

is considered under the assumption that the end-values for x, y, $\dot{y}$ are specified. Since this functional form involves the second derivative of the unknown function, it is not covered by the formulations of Bolza, Mayer, and Lagrange. However, it can be reduced to the mathematical scheme of a Lagrange problem if the auxiliary variable z satisfying the different constraint

$$\varphi \equiv \dot{y} - z = 0 \tag{4.43}$$

is introduced. In fact, after the integral (4.42) is rewritten as

$$\psi \equiv \int_{x_i}^{x_f} H(x, y, z, \dot{z}) \, dx \tag{4.44}$$

it becomes obvious that the problem under consideration is equivalent to that of finding, in the class of arcs $y(x)$, $z(x)$ which satisfy the constraint (4.43), that particular set which minimizes the integral (4.44). This new problem involves first-order derivatives only and, therefore, is of the Lagrange type.

4.33 Problems Not Involving Derivatives

Consider the problem of minimizing the functional form

$$\psi \equiv \int_{x_i}^{x_f} H(x, y) \, dx \tag{4.45}$$

and assume that the end-values for x are specified but that the end-values for y are free. Since this functional form does not contain the derivative of the unknown function, the associated Euler-Lagrange equation is written as

$$\partial H/\partial y = 0 \tag{4.46}$$

Furthermore, since the left-hand side of relationship (4.16) vanishes, the Legendre-Clebsch condition seems to provide no information on the minimal or maximal nature of the extremal arc. One can bypass this apparent difficulty by (a) introducing the auxiliary variable z satisfying the differential constraint $\dot{z} - y = 0$, (b) transforming the problem from the

xy-plane into the xz-plane, and (c) observing that the problem previously formulated is identical with that of minimizing the functional form

$$\psi \equiv \int_{x_i}^{x_f} H(x, \dot{z}) \, dx \qquad (4.47)$$

under the assumption that z_i, z_f are free.

The Euler-Lagrange equation associated with this new problem is given by

$$(d/dx)(\partial H/\partial \dot{z}) = 0 \qquad (4.48)$$

and can be integrated to give

$$\partial H/\partial \dot{z} = \text{const} \qquad (4.49)$$

where the constant is zero because of the transversality condition. Consequently, if this relationship is transformed from the xz-plane back into the xy-plane, one can arrive once more at the result expressed by Eq. (4.46).

The Legendre-Clebsch condition leads to the inequality

$$(\partial^2 H/\partial \dot{z}^2)(\delta \dot{z})^2 \geq 0 \qquad (4.50)$$

which, after the transformation from the xz-plane back into the xy-plane is performed, can be written in the form

$$(\partial^2 H/\partial y^2)(\delta y)^2 \geq 0 \qquad (4.51)$$

Thus, the following rule is deduced: *In any variational problem not involving derivatives, the Legendre-Clebsch condition can still supply some useful information on the minimal or maximal nature of the extremal path providing that the variation of the derivative is replaced by the variation of the function itself.*

4.34 Problems Involving Inequalities

In this section, the problem of minimizing the functional form

$$\psi \equiv \int_{x_i}^{x_f} F(x, y, \dot{y}) \, dx \qquad (4.52)$$

is considered under the assumptions that the end-values for the Cartesian coordinates are specified and that the class of arcs investigated is subjected to the inequality constraint

$$\dot{y} \geq K \qquad (4.53)$$

where K is a prescribed constant. This problem can be reduced to the same mathematical model useful in solving problems where all the constraints are represented by equalities if the real variable z defined by[5]

$$\varphi \equiv \dot{y} - K - z^2 = 0 \qquad (4.54)$$

is introduced.* In fact, because of the equivalence of expressions (4.53) and (4.54), the problem under consideration becomes identical with that of finding, in the class of arcs $y(x)$, $z(x)$ which satisfy the constraint (4.54), that special arc which minimizes the integral (4.52).

A modification of the previous problem arises when the integral to be minimized is subjected to a two-sided inequality constraint having the form

$$K_1 \leq \dot{y} \leq K_2 \qquad (4.55)$$

In this case, the transformation into a Lagrange problem is accomplished by replacing the above inequality constraint with the equality constraint

$$\varphi \equiv (\dot{y} - K_1)(K_2 - \dot{y}) - z^2 = 0 \qquad (4.56)$$

where z is a real variable.

4.4 The Calculus of Variations in Applied Aerodynamics

An important application of the calculus of variations is the study of the optimum shapes of aircraft and missile components, that is, shapes which embody some especially desirable aerodynamic characteristic, such as, minimum drag or maximum lift-to-drag ratio.[11-15] The techniques employed and the results obtained depend, to a large degree, on the class of bodies being investigated (bodies of revolution, two-dimensional wings, three-dimensional wings) as well as the flow regime (subsonic, transonic, supersonic, hypersonic, free molecular). In fact, the flow regime determines the distribution of pressure coefficients and, therefore, the aerodynamic forces acting on the body.

Since the literature on the subject is quite extensive, it is not possible in this short space to survey every possible problem which has been treated thus far. Consequently, only two classes of problems are discussed here, that is, (a) the determination of the body of revolution having minimum

---

* An alternative possibility is to use the device of parametric representation of the bounded variable developed by Miele.[2,10]

pressure drag in Newtonian flow and (b) the determination of the two-dimensional wing having minimum pressure drag in linearized supersonic flow.

4.5 Bodies of Revolution Having Minimum Pressure Drag in Newtonian Flow

In this section, the problem of determining the body of revolution having minimum pressure drag in Newtonian flow is considered. With the purpose of gradually introducing the reader to the applications of the theory, the generalized treatment is preceded by a preliminary example in which the length and the diameter of the body are prescribed.

4.51 Preliminary Example

The problem of determining the body of revolution having minimum pressure drag was originally investigated by Newton under the assumptions that the tangential velocity component of the molecules impinging on the body is unchanged, while the normal velocity component is reduced to zero. Hence, Newton's inelastic model approximates that of a hypersonic inviscid flow; furthermore, if the angle of attack is assumed to be zero, this model yields the following expression for the pressure coefficient[11]:

$$C_p = 2 \sin^2 \theta = 2\dot{y}^2/(1 + \dot{y}^2) \tag{4.57}$$

where θ denotes the angle of inclination of the body profile with respect to its axis (Fig. 1), x an axial coordinate, y a radial coordinate, and $\dot{y}$ the derivative dy/dx. This expression simplifies to

$$C_p = 2\dot{y}^2 \tag{4.58}$$

if the slender body approximation is used, that is, if the hypothesis

$$\dot{y}^2 \ll 1 \tag{4.59}$$

is employed.

In this section, the Newtonian point of view is retained but, in order to simplify the discussion, the slender body approximation is used. Consequently, the aerodynamic drag associated with the portion of the fuselage

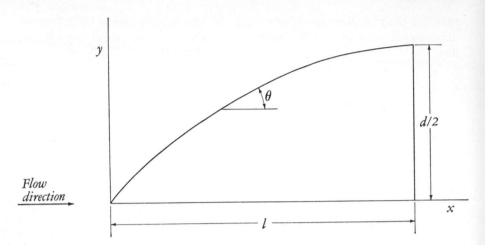

FIG. 1.   Coordinate system for the analysis of a body of revolution.

included between stations 0 and x is written in the form

$$D(x) = 2\pi q \int_0^x C_p y \dot{y} \, dx = 4\pi q \int_0^x y \dot{y}^3 \, dx \qquad (4.60)$$

where q is the free-stream dynamic pressure. After introducing the definition

$$\alpha = D/4\pi q \qquad (4.61)$$

and differentiating both sides of Eq. (4.60) with respect to the independent variable, one can arrive at the relationship

$$\varphi \equiv \dot{\alpha} - y \dot{y}^3 = 0 \qquad (4.62)$$

which is necessary in order to treat the minimum drag problem as a problem of Mayer type.

The previous differential equation has one independent variable (x), two dependent variables (y, α), and one degree of freedom; hence, some optimum requirement can be imposed on the body profile. In this connection, after the length is denoted by l, the diameter is denoted by d, and the end-conditions

$$x_i = y_i = \alpha_i = 0, \qquad x_f = l, \qquad y_f = d/2 \qquad (4.63)$$

are assumed, the minimum drag problem is formulated as follows: *In the class of functions $y(x)$, $\alpha(x)$ which are consistent with the differential* *constraint* (4.62) *and the end-conditions* (4.63), *find that special set which minimizes the difference* $\Delta G = G_f - G_i$, *where* $G = \alpha$.

Clearly, the proposed problem is of the Mayer type with separated end-conditions. Consequently, after the augmented function is written as

$$F = \lambda(\dot\alpha - y\dot y^3) \tag{4.64}$$

the Euler-Lagrange equations become

$$(d/dx)(3\lambda y\dot y^2) = \lambda\dot y^3, \qquad \dot\lambda = 0 \tag{4.65}$$

and admit the first integral

$$-2\lambda y\dot y^3 = C \tag{4.66}$$

where C is a constant. If the transversality condition is written in the form

$$[-C\,dx - 3\lambda y\dot y^2\,dy + (\lambda + 1)\,d\alpha]_i^f = 0 \tag{4.67}$$

and if it is observed that the end-coordinates are fixed with the exception of α_f, one concludes that $\lambda_f = -1$. Hence, the second Euler-Lagrange equation can be integrated to give $\lambda = -1$ everywhere. In addition, after the variables are separated and a further integration is performed, the first integral (4.66) leads to the following general solution for the extremal arc:

$$y = (C_1 x + C_2)^{3/4} \tag{4.68}$$

where C_1, C_2 are appropriate constants. If these constants are evaluated in terms of the given end-conditions and if the dimensionless coordinates

$$\xi = x/l, \qquad \eta = 2y/d \tag{4.69}$$

are introduced, one obtains the result

$$\eta = \xi^{3/4} \tag{4.70}$$

which means that *the contour of the body of revolution having minimum drag for a given diameter and a given length is a parabola satisfying the $\frac{3}{4}$-power law*. This result was empirically found by Eggers *et al.*,[11] who used the exact expression (4.57) of the pressure coefficient, integrated the equation of the optimum shape in parametric form, and realized by a graphical procedure that the difference between their solution and the $\frac{3}{4}$-power body is negligible. Actually, the previous analysis shows that the $\frac{3}{4}$-power body is not an empirical optimum but rather an analytical optimum; in fact, it is a solution of the Euler-Lagrange equations if the slender body approximation is used. In closing, the following remarks are pertinent:

(a) The Legendre-Clebsch condition can be written in the form

$$6y\dot{y}(\delta\dot{y})^2 \geq 0 \tag{4.71}$$

and, consequently, is satisfied at every point of the extremal arc.

(b) If $\tau = d/l$ denotes the thickness ratio and if $\dot{\eta}$ indicates the derivative $d\eta/d\xi$, the drag coefficient of the optimum body of revolution is given by

$$C_\mathrm{D} = \frac{4D(l)}{q\pi d^2} = \tau^2 \int_0^1 \eta\dot{\eta}^3 d\xi = \frac{27}{64}\tau^2 \tag{4.72}$$

and, therefore, is proportional to the square of the thickness ratio.

(c) For the body of revolution described by the $\frac{3}{4}$-power law, the derivative $\dot{y}$ becomes infinitely large at $x = 0$; hence, the slender body approximation becomes locally invalid in the region which immediately surrounds the nose. For the sake of discussion, let this region be defined as the *critical region*, and let it be identified by the inequality $\dot{y} \geq \tau$. With this hypothesis in mind, it is possible to show that the frontal area associated with the critical region is less than 3% of the over-all cross-sectional area, while the corresponding drag is less than 2% of the over-all drag. For these reasons, the shape predicted with the slender body approximation is very close to the shape predicted with the exact Newtonian expression for the pressure coefficient.

(d) While the result expressed by Eq. (4.70) has been derived for the Newtonian flow regime, it also holds for the free molecular flow regime as long as a specular reflection is assumed. This is due to the fact that the pressure coefficient in free molecular flow is then proportional to (twice) that in Newtonian flow; consequently, the equation of extremal arc is unchanged.

4.52 Generalized Approach

A generalization of the previous problem arises when the body of revolution having minimum drag is to be determined under certain additional conditions imposed on the wetted area and/or the volume. This new problem is of the isoperimetric type, but it can be reduced to a Mayer problem with the procedure indicated below.

First, the drag, the wetted area, and the volume of that portion of the body which is included between stations 0 and x are written in the form*

$$D(x) = 4\pi q \int_0^x y\dot{y}^3 \, dx, \qquad S(x) = 2\pi \int_0^x y \, dx, \qquad V(x) = \pi \int_0^x y^2 \, dx$$

$$(4.73)$$

Then, the definitions

$$\alpha = D/4\pi q, \qquad \beta = S/2\pi, \qquad \gamma = V/\pi \qquad (4.74)$$

are introduced. Finally, after differentiating both sides of Eqs. (4.73) with respect to the independent variable, one can arrive at the differential constraints

$$\varphi_1 \equiv \dot{\alpha} - y\dot{y}^3 = 0$$

$$\varphi_2 \equiv \dot{\beta} - y = 0 \qquad (4.75)$$

$$\varphi_3 \equiv \dot{\gamma} - y^2 = 0$$

which are necessary in order to treat the minimum drag problem as a problem of the Mayer type.

The previous differential system involves one independent variable (x), four dependent variables $(y, \alpha, \beta, \gamma)$, and one degree of freedom; hence, some optimum requirement can be imposed on the body profile. In this connection, after assuming that $x_i = y_i = \alpha_i = \beta_i = \gamma_i = 0$ and that some, but not all, of the final coordinates are given, one can formulate the minimum drag problem as follows: *In the class of functions* $y(x)$, $\alpha(x)$, $\beta(x)$, $\gamma(x)$ *which are consistent with the differential constraints* (4.75) *and the prescribed end-conditions, find that special set which minimizes the difference* $\Delta G = G_f - G_i$, *where* $G = \alpha$.

After three Lagrange multipliers are introduced and the augmented function is written in the form

$$F = \lambda_1(\dot{\alpha} - y\dot{y}^3) + \lambda_2(\dot{\beta} - y) + \lambda_3(\dot{\gamma} - y^2) \qquad (4.76)$$

---

* The expressions for the drag and the wetted area are subjected to the slender body approximation (4.59).

the extremal arc is described by the Euler-Lagrange equations

$$(d/dx)(3\lambda_1 y\dot{y}^2) = \lambda_1\dot{y}^3 + \lambda_2 + 2\lambda_3 y$$

$$\dot{\lambda}_1 = \dot{\lambda}_2 = \dot{\lambda}_3 = 0$$

(4.77)

Hence, the Lagrange multipliers are constant, as is logical owing to the basically isoperimetric nature of the problem under consideration; furthermore, since the fundamental function is formally independent of x, the following first integral is valid:

$$-2\lambda_1 y\dot{y}^3 + \lambda_2 y + \lambda_3 y^2 = C$$

(4.78)

where C is a constant. In addition, the transversality condition is written in the form

$$[-C\,dx - 3\lambda_1 y\dot{y}^2\,dy + (\lambda_1 + 1)\,d\alpha + \lambda_2\,d\beta + \lambda_3\,d\gamma]_i^f = 0 \quad (4.79)$$

This condition and the second Euler-Lagrange equation imply that $\lambda_1 = -1$ everywhere for the minimum drag problem. Consequently, the Legendre-Clebsch condition is still expressed by Eq. (4.71) and, therefore, is satisfied as long as the body contour is such that $\dot{y} \geq 0$.

While the previous discussion is general, the extremal arc is now determined for several particular cases, that is, for different sets of boundary conditions. Then, the results are summarized in Fig. 2.

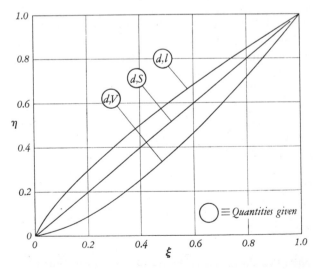

FIG. 2. Bodies of revolution having minimum pressure drag in Newtonian flow.

4.521 Given Diameter and Length

If the diameter and the length are prescribed, while the wetted area and the volume are free, the transversality condition and the Euler-Lagrange equations imply that

$$\lambda_1 = -1, \qquad \lambda_2 = \lambda_3 = 0 \tag{4.80}$$

everywhere. Consequently, after the variables are separated and a further integration is performed, the first integral (4.78), in combination with the appropriate end-conditions, leads once more to the result expressed by Eq. (4.70).

4.522 Given Diameter and Wetted Area

If the diameter and the wetted area are given, while the length and the volume are free, the transversality condition and the Euler-Lagrange equations lead to

$$\lambda_1 - -1, \qquad \lambda_3 = C = 0 \tag{4.81}$$

everywhere. Consequently, after the first integral (4.78) is rewritten in the form

$$2\dot{y}^3 + \lambda_2 = 0 \tag{4.82}$$

the following general solution is obtained:

$$y = C_1 x + C_2 \tag{4.83}$$

where C_1, C_2 are constant. If the prescribed end-conditions are considered, one obtains the relationship

$$\eta = \xi \tag{4.84}$$

which means that *the body of revolution having the minimum drag for a given diameter and a given wetted area is a cone.* The thickness ratio of this cone is given by

$$\tau = \frac{\pi}{2} \frac{d^2}{S(l)} \tag{4.85}$$

and the associated drag coefficient by

$$C_{\mathrm{D}} = \tau^2/2 \tag{4.86}$$

4.523 Given Diameter and Volume

If the diameter and the volume are prescribed, while the length and the wetted area are free, the transversality condition and the Euler-Lagrange equations lead to

$$\lambda_1 = -1, \qquad \lambda_2 = C = 0 \tag{4.87}$$

everywhere. Consequently, the first integral (4.78) can be rewritten in the form

$$2\dot{y}^3 + \lambda_3 y = 0 \tag{4.88}$$

which, after further integration, implies that

$$y = (C_1 x + C_2)^{3/2} \tag{4.89}$$

where C_1, C_2 are constant. If the prescribed end-conditions are considered, one obtains the result

$$\eta = \xi^{3/2} \tag{4.90}$$

which means that *the contour of the body of revolution having the minimum drag for a given diameter and a given volume is a parabola satisfying the $\frac{3}{2}$-power law.* The thickness ratio of this body of revolution is given by

$$\tau = \frac{\pi}{16} \frac{d^3}{V(l)} \tag{4.91}$$

and the associated drag coefficient by

$$C_D = 27\tau^2/32 \tag{4.92}$$

4.6 Wings Having Minimum Pressure Drag in Linearized Supersonic Flow

The problem of determining the two-dimensional wing having minimum pressure drag in supersonic flow has attracted considerable interest in recent years. Worthy of particular mention is the work by Drougge[12] which can be employed in connection with Ackeret's linearized theory and the more general analysis by Chapman[13] which can be employed in connection with either linearized, second-order, hypersonic, or shock-expansion theory. For simplicity, the linearized theory is considered here, and the pressure coefficient law for a supersonic, two-dimensional, sym-

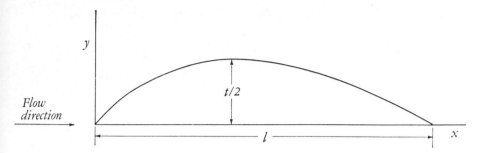

Fig. 3. Coordinate system for the analysis of a two-dimensional wing.

metric airfoil operating at zero lift in an inviscid, nonconducting, perfect gas is written in the form

$$C_p = 2\dot{y}/\sqrt{M^2 - 1} \tag{4.93}$$

where M is the free-stream Mach number, x a chordwise coordinate, y the ordinate of the generic point of the upper half of the airfoil (Fig. 3), and $\dot{y}$ the derivative dy/dx. Consequently, the aerodynamic drag per unit span associated with the portion of the airfoil included between stations 0 and x is given by

$$D(x) = 2q \int_0^x C_p \dot{y} \, dx = \frac{4q}{\sqrt{M^2 - 1}} \int_0^x \dot{y}^2 \, dx \tag{4.94}$$

Furthermore, if the definition

$$\alpha = D\sqrt{M^2 - 1}/4q \tag{4.95}$$

is introduced, the following differential constraint is obtained:

$$\varphi_1 \equiv \dot{\alpha} - \dot{y}^2 = 0 \tag{4.96}$$

Next, attention is focused on the area enclosed by the airfoil contour (profile area) as well as the moments of inertia of the contour and of the profile area with respect to the x-axis. With reference to the portion of the airfoil included between stations 0 and x, these quantities are defined by

$$S(x) = 2 \int_0^x y \, dx, \quad I_c(x) = 2 \int_0^x y^2 \, dx, \quad I_s(x) = \tfrac{2}{3} \int_0^x y^3 \, dx \tag{4.97}$$

so that, after the definitions

$$\beta = S/2, \quad \gamma = I_c/2, \quad \epsilon = 3I_s/2 \tag{4.98}$$

are introduced, the following differential constraints are obtained:

$$\varphi_2 \equiv \dot\beta - y = 0$$

$$\varphi_3 \equiv \dot\gamma - y^2 = 0 \qquad\qquad (4.99)$$

$$\varphi_4 \equiv \dot\epsilon - y^3 = 0$$

The differential system composed of Eqs. (4.96) and (4.99) involves one independent variable (x), five dependent variables $(y,\ \alpha,\ \beta,\ \gamma,\ \epsilon)$, and one degree of freedom; hence, some optimum requirement can be imposed on the airfoil shape. In this connection, after assuming that $x_i = y_i = \alpha_i = \beta_i = \gamma_i = \epsilon_i = 0$, that $x_f = l$, $y_f = 0$, and that some, but not all, of the remaining final coordinates are given, one can formulate the minimum drag problem as follows: *In the class of functions* $y(x)$, $\alpha(x)$, $\beta(x)$, $\gamma(x)$, $\epsilon(x)$ *which are consistent with Eqs.* (4.96) *and* (4.99) *and with the prescribed end-conditions, find that special set which minimizes the difference* $\Delta G = G_f - G_i$, *where* $G = \alpha$.

After four Lagrange multipliers are introduced and the augmented function is written in the form

$$F = \lambda_1(\dot\alpha - \dot y^2) + \lambda_2(\dot\beta - y) + \lambda_3(\dot\gamma - y^2) + \lambda_4(\dot\epsilon - y^3) \quad (4.100)$$

the extremal arc is described by the Euler-Lagrange equations

$$(d/dx)(2\lambda_1\dot y) = \lambda_2 + 2\lambda_3 y + 3\lambda_4 y^2$$

$$\dot\lambda_1 = \dot\lambda_2 = \dot\lambda_3 = \dot\lambda_4 = 0 \qquad\qquad (4.101)$$

Hence, the Lagrange multipliers are constant, a result which stresses the basically isoperimetric nature of the problem being investigated; furthermore, since the fundamental function is formally independent of x, the following first integral can be written:

$$-\lambda_1\dot y^2 + \lambda_2 y + \lambda_3 y^2 + \lambda_4 y^3 = C \qquad\qquad (4.102)$$

where C is a constant. In addition, the transversality condition is given by

$$[-C\,dx - 2\lambda_1\dot y\,dy + (\lambda_1 + 1)\,d\alpha + \lambda_2\,d\beta + \lambda_3\,d\gamma + \lambda_4\,d\epsilon]_i^f = 0$$

$$(4.103)$$

This condition and the second Euler-Lagrange equation imply that $\lambda_1 = -1$

everywhere for the minimum drag problem. Consequently, the Legendre-Clebsch condition becomes

$$2(\delta\dot{y})^2 \geq 0 \tag{4.104}$$

and, therefore, is satisfied by any of the shapes which are consistent with the constraining equations and the Euler-Lagrange equations.

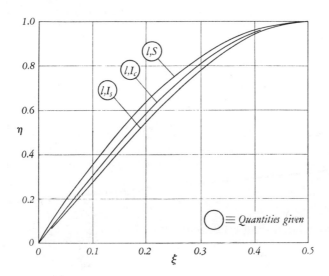

Fig. 4. Airfoils having minimum pressure drag in linearized supersonic flow.

While the previous discussion is general, the extremal arc is now determined for several particular cases, that is, for different types of boundary conditions. Then, the results are summarized in Fig. 4.

4.61 Given Profile Area

If the profile area is prescribed,* while its moment of inertia as well as the moment of inertia of the contour are free, the transversality condition and the Euler-Lagrange equations lead to

$$\lambda_1 = -1, \qquad \lambda_3 = \lambda_4 = 0 \tag{4.105}$$

---

* Prescribing the profile area is equivalent to prescribing the torsional stiffness of a thin-skin structure.

everywhere. Consequently, the first Euler-Lagrange equation becomes

$$\ddot{y} = K \tag{4.106}$$

(where K is a negative constant) and admits the following general integral:

$$y = \tfrac{1}{2}Kx^2 + C_1 x + C_2 \tag{4.107}$$

where C_1, C_2 are constant. If these constants are evaluated in terms of the prescribed end-conditions, if it is observed that $C_1 = -Kl/2$, $C_2 = 0$, and $K = -4t/l^2$ (where t denotes the maximum thickness), and if the dimensionless coordinates

$$\xi = x/l , \qquad \eta = 2y/t \tag{4.108}$$

are introduced, one obtains the result

$$\eta = 4\xi(1 - \xi) \tag{4.109}$$

which means that, under the slender body approximation, *the optimum airfoil is a circular arc airfoil*. The thickness ratio of such an airfoil is given by

$$\tau = t/l = \tfrac{3}{2}S(l)/l^2 \tag{4.110}$$

and the associated drag coefficient by

$$C_D = \frac{D(l)}{ql} = \frac{\tau^2}{\sqrt{M^2 - 1}} \int_0^1 \dot{\eta}^2 \, d\xi = \frac{16}{3} \frac{\tau^2}{\sqrt{M^2 - 1}} \tag{4.111}$$

in which the sumbol $\dot{\eta}$ denotes the derivative $d\eta/d\xi$.

4.62 Given Moment of Inertia of the Contour

If the moment of inertia of the contour is prescribed* while the profile area and its moment of inertia are free, the transversality condition and the Euler-Lagrange equations lead to

$$\lambda_1 = -1, \qquad \lambda_2 = \lambda_4 = 0 \tag{4.112}$$

everywhere. Consequently, the first Euler-Lagrange equation reduces to

$$\ddot{y} + Ky = 0 \tag{4.113}$$

---

* Prescribing the moment of inertia of the contour is the same as prescribing the bending stiffness of a thin-skin structure.

(where K is a positive constant) and admits the general integral

$$y = C_1 \sin (\sqrt{K}x) + C_2 \cos (\sqrt{K}x) \qquad (4.114)$$

where C_1, C_2 are constants. If these constants are evaluated in terms of the prescribed end-conditions and if it is observed that $C_1 = t/2$, $C_2 = 0$, and $K = (\pi/l)^2$, one obtains the result

$$\eta = \sin (\pi\xi) \qquad (4.115)$$

which means that *the optimum airfoil has a sinusoidal shape.* The thickness ratio of such an airfoil is given by

$$\tau = 2\sqrt{I_c/l^3} \qquad (4.116)$$

and the associated drag coefficient by

$$C_D = \frac{\pi^2}{2} \frac{\tau^2}{\sqrt{M^2 - 1}} \qquad (4.117)$$

4.63 Given Moment of Inertia of the Profile Area

If the moment of inertia of the profile area is prescribed,* while the area itself and the moment of inertia of the contour are free, the transversality condition and the Euler-Lagrange equations lead to

$$\lambda_1 = -1, \qquad \lambda_2 = \lambda_3 = 0 \qquad (4.118)$$

everywhere. Consequently, the first Euler-Lagrange equation reduces to

$$\ddot{y} + Ky^2 = 0 \qquad (4.119)$$

(where K is a positive constant) and admits the first integral

$$\tfrac{1}{2}\dot{y}^2 + \tfrac{1}{3}Ky^3 = C_1 \qquad (4.120)$$

where $C_1 = Kt^3/24$ is another positive constant. After separating the variables and performing a further integration, one can arrive at the result

$$\xi = \frac{1}{2} \left\{ 1 \mp \frac{F[\varphi(\eta), k]}{F[\varphi(0), k]} \right\} \qquad (4.121)$$

where the upper sign holds for the first half of the airfoil, the lower sign

---

* Prescribing the moment of inertia of the profile area is the same as prescribing the bending stiffness or the torsional stiffness of a solid-section structure.

holds for the second half, and where symbol F denotes the incomplete elliptic integral of the first kind, whose argument $\varphi(\eta)$ and parameter k are defined as

$$\varphi(\eta) = \arccos \frac{\sqrt{3} - 1 + \eta}{\sqrt{3} + 1 - \eta}$$

(4.121a)

$$k = \sqrt{\frac{2 + \sqrt{3}}{4}}$$

The thickness ratio of such an airfoil is given by[12]

$$\tau = \sqrt[3]{60 I_s / l^4}$$

(4.122)

and the associated drag coefficient by

$$C_D = 5\pi \Gamma^2(4/3) \tau^2 / 3\Gamma^2(11/6) \sqrt{M^2 - 1}$$

$$= 4.72\tau^2 / \sqrt{M^2 - 1}$$

(4.123)

where $\Gamma(x)$ denotes the gamma function of argument x.

4.7 The Calculus of Variations in Flight Mechanics

Another important application of the calculus of variations is the study of the optimum trajectories of aircraft, missiles, and spaceships, that is, trajectories which embody some especially desirable characteristic, such as maximum range, minimum propellant consumption, or minimum heat transfer. Even though this application is quite recent, it is of interest to note that Goddard[16] recognized the calculus of variations as an important tool in the performance analysis of rockets in a paper published nearly 40 years ago. Hamel,[17] on the other hand, formulated the problem of the optimum burning program for vertical flight more than 30 years ago.

Despite these sporadic attempts, the need for an entirely new approach to the problem of optimum aircraft performance was realized by the Germans only during World War II; in particular, Lippisch[18] investigated the most economic climb of a rocket-powered aircraft and shed considerable light on a new class of problems of the mechanics of flight. In the years following World War II, the optimum climbing program of turbojet aircraft attracted considerable interest and was investigated in a highly simplified form by Lush[19] and Miele[20] with techniques other than the indirect methods of the calculus of variations.

A short time later, a rigorous variational formulation of the problem of the optimum flight paths became possible due to the work of Cicala,[21,22] Garfinkel,[23] and Hestenes[24] on the formulations of Bolza, Mayer, and Lagrange. Subsequently, a general theory of these problems was formulated by Breakwell,[25] Fried,[26] Lawden,[27,28] Leitmann,[29,30] and Miele.[31,32] It must be noted that, while the indirect methods of the calculus of variations are of fundamental importance in solving extremal problems, several other optimization techniques have been employed in recent years; more specifically, Bellman's theory of dynamic programming,[33] Kelley's gradient theory of optimum flight paths[8], and Miele's theory of linear integrals by Green's theorem.[34-36] It must also be noted that, for the limiting case of flight with negligible acceleration, the calculus of variations and the ordinary theory of maxima and minima yield identical results[37]; consequently, a greatly simplified approach to the problem of the optimum quasi-steady flight paths is possible if the method of the Lagrange multipliers is employed.[38]

Since the literature on the subject is quite extensive, it is not possible in this short space to present a detailed account of every problem which has been treated thus far. Consequently, only two classes of problems are discussed here, that is, (a) the determination of the optimum thrust program for flight in a vacuum in a constant gravitational field, and (b) the determination of the optimum thrust program and angle of attack program for flight in a resisting medium in a constant gravitational field. Except for a number of preliminary examples, the following analysis emphasizes only statements of a broad engineering nature with regard to the necessary conditions for the extremum. Detailed topics, such as discontinuities arising from staging or methods of solution of special types of boundary-value problems, are excluded. For these problems as well as for problems of flight in a nonuniform (for instance, central) gravitational field, the reader is referred to the continuously growing specialized literature on the subject (see General References).

4.8 Optimum Trajectories for Rocket Flight in a Vacuum

In this section, the problem of determining optimum trajectories for rocket flight in a vacuum is considered. In order to introduce the reader gradually to the applications of the theory, the generalized treatment is preceded by a preliminary example relative to vertical flight.

4.81 Preliminary Example

The problem of determining optimum burning programs for a rocket in vertical flight has received considerable attention in recent years. Following the initial work by Hamel[17] and by Tsien and Evans[39] several types of boundary-value problems were investigated by Leitmann[40-43] and Miele.[44-47] While these papers considered the effect of the aerodynamic forces, this section is confined to the limiting case in which these forces are negligible, so that the rocket moves under the combined effect of its thrust and weight only. More specifically, the following hypotheses are employed: (a) the earth is flat and the acceleration of gravity is constant; (b) the flight takes place in a vacuum; (c) the trajectory is vertical; (d) the thrust is tangent to the flight path; (e) the equivalent exit velocity of the rocket engine is constant; and (f) the engine is capable of delivering all mass flows between a lower limit and an upper limit. Under these assumptions, the motion of the rocket vehicle is governed by the differential equations

$$\varphi_1 \equiv \dot{h} - V = 0$$

$$\varphi_2 \equiv \dot{V} + g - \frac{c\beta}{m} = 0 \tag{4.124}$$

$$\varphi_3 \equiv \dot{m} + \beta = 0$$

where h is the altitude, V the velocity, m the mass, g the acceleration of gravity, c the equivalent exit velocity, and β the propellant mass flow. The dot sign denotes a derivative with respect to the time t. Because of hypothesis (f), the mass flow must satisfy the inequality constraint

$$0 \le \beta \le \beta_{max} \tag{4.125}$$

which, in accordance with the discussion of Section 4.34, can be replaced by the equality constraint

$$\varphi_4 \equiv \beta(\beta_{max} - \beta) - \alpha^2 = 0 \tag{4.126}$$

where α is a real variable. The effect of this new constraint is to reduce a variational problem involving a two-sided inequality constraint to the mathematical model which is useful for solving problems in which all the constraints are represented by equalities.

The differential system composed of Eqs. (4.124) and (4.126) involves one independent variable (t), five dependent variables (h, V, m, β, α), and one degree of freedom; hence, some optimum requirement can be imposed on the burning program $\beta(t)$. In this connection, after the end-conditions

$$t_i = 0; \qquad h_i, \ V_i, \ m_i \equiv \text{given}; \qquad V_f, \ m_f \equiv \text{given} \qquad (4.127)$$

are specified, the problem of the maximum altitude increase is formulated as follows: *In the class of functions $h(t)$, $V(t)$, $m(t)$, $\beta(t)$, $\alpha(t)$ which are consistent with the constraints (4.124) and (4.126) and the end-conditions (4.127), find that special set which minimizes* the difference $\Delta G = G_f - G_i$, where $G = -h$.

After four Lagrange multipliers are introduced and the augmented function is written in the form

$$F = \lambda_1(\dot{h} - V) + \lambda_2\left(\dot{V} + g - \frac{c\beta}{m}\right)$$

$$+ \lambda_3(\dot{m} + \beta) + \lambda_4[\beta(\beta_{\max} - \beta) - \alpha^2] \qquad (4.128)$$

the extremal arc is governed by the Euler-Lagrange equations

$$\dot{\lambda}_1 = 0$$

$$\dot{\lambda}_2 = -\lambda_1$$

$$\dot{\lambda}_3 = \lambda_2(c\beta/m^2) \qquad (4.129)$$

$$0 = -K + \lambda_4(\beta_{\max} - 2\beta)$$

$$0 = \lambda_4\alpha$$

where, by definition,

$$K = \lambda_2(c/m) - \lambda_3 \qquad (4.130)$$

Hence, the Lagrange multiplier λ_1 is constant; furthermore, since the augmented function is formally independent of the time, the following first integral is obtained:

$$\lambda_1 V - \lambda_2 g + K\beta = C \qquad (4.131)$$

---

* It is recalled that the problem of maximizing Δh is identical with that of minimizing $-\Delta h$.

where C is a constant. In addition, the transversality condition is written in the form

$$[-C\,dt + (\lambda_1 - 1)\,dh + \lambda_2\,dV + \lambda_3\,dm]_i^f = 0 \qquad (4.132)$$

which implies that

$$\lambda_1 = 1, \qquad C = 0 \qquad (4.133)$$

Finally, if both sides of Eq. (4.130) are differentiated with respect to the time and the resulting expression is then combined with the transversality condition and the Euler-Lagrange equations, the following result holds everywhere along the extremal arc:

$$\dot{K} = -c/m \qquad (4.134)$$

4.811 Totality of Subarcs

As the fifth Euler-Lagrange equation indicates, the extremal arc is discontinuous and is composed of subarcs governed by either of the conditions

$$\alpha = 0 \quad \text{or} \quad \lambda_4 = 0 \qquad (4.135)$$

Along the subarcs $\alpha = 0$, the mass flow can take either of the following constant values:

$$\beta = 0 \quad \text{or} \quad \beta = \beta_{\max} \qquad (4.136)$$

On the other hand, along the subarc $\lambda_4 = 0$, the fourth Euler-Lagrange equation leads to

$$K = 0, \qquad \dot{K} = 0 \qquad (4.137)$$

Since this result is incompatible with Eq. (4.134), there exists no subarc along which $\lambda_4 = 0$, that is, *there is no subarc flown with variable thrust.*[44] Thus, *the totality of extremal arcs includes only two kinds of subarcs, that is, coasting subarcs and subarcs flown with maximum engine output.*

4.812 Sequences of Subarcs

The next step consists of determining what sequences of subarcs may compose the extremal arc. More specifically, the following questions are posed: What is the maximum number of subarcs composing the extremal arc? Should the coasting subarc precede or follow the subarc flown with the maximum thrust? Considerable light can be shed on this problem if the Erdmann-Weierstrass conditions are employed in combination with the Legendre-Clebsch condition.

Because of the corner conditions, the multipliers λ_1, λ_2, λ_3 are continuous at each junction point; also, the integration constant C has the same value for all the subarcs composing the extremal arc. Since the velocity is continuous, the first integral (4.131) indicates that a discontinuity in the mass flow is possible if, and only if,

$$(K)_- = (K)_+ = 0 \qquad (4.138)$$

Because of the Legendre-Clebsch condition and the fourth Euler-Lagrange equation, the altitude increase is a maximum (that is, its negative is a minimum) providing that the following inequality is satisfied everywhere along the extremal arc:

$$\frac{2K}{2\beta - \beta_{\max}} \left[(\delta\alpha)^2 + (\delta\beta)^2 \right] \geq 0 \qquad (4.139)$$

where the variations $\delta\alpha$ and $\delta\beta$ must be consistent with the constraining equation (4.126). After this inequality is restated in the form

$$K \geq 0, \qquad \beta = \beta_{\max}$$

$$\qquad (4.140)$$

$$K \leq 0, \qquad \beta = 0$$

it appears that the function K plays a dominant role in determining the composition of the extremal arc, since it is positive for the subarc flown with maximum engine output, zero at a corner point, and negative for the coasting subarc. For these reasons, the function K is called the *switching function*.*

Notice that the time rate of variation of the switching function along the extremal arc is governed by Eq. (4.134). Hence, if this differential equation is integrated and the boundary conditions (4.138) are applied, the following relationships are derived†:

$$K = (c/\beta_{\max}) \log(m/m_c), \qquad \beta = \beta_{\max}$$

$$\qquad (4.141)$$

$$K = (c/m_c)(t_c - t), \qquad \beta = 0$$

---

* Historically speaking, the first use of the switching function in aeronautical engineering can be found in the papers by Cicala[22] and Garfinkel.[23]

† The subscript c refers to the corner point.

and show that the function K can be zero only once (Fig. 5). Consequently, the extremal arc includes at most one corner point and, hence, two subarcs. Notice that the Legendre-Clebsch condition is satisfied along a subarc flown with maximum engine output providing $m \geq m_c$, that is, providing

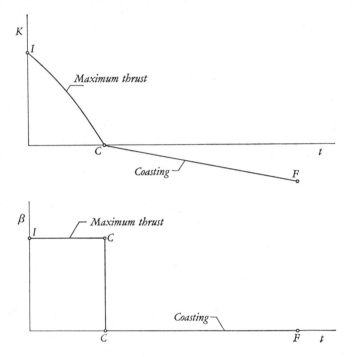

FIG. 5.   Switching function and mass flow rate versus time.

this subarc *precedes* the corner point; furthermore, it is satisfied along a coasting subarc providing $t \geq t_c$, that is, providing this subarc *follows* the corner point. In conclusion, the extremal arc associated with the problem of the maximum increase in altitude includes at most two subarcs in the following sequence:

$$\beta = \beta_{\max} \rightarrow \beta = 0 \tag{4.142}$$

which is indicated in Fig. 5.

4.813 Totality of Extremal Arcs

If the equations of motion are integrated subject to the condition that the mass flow is either maximum or zero, the following results are ob-

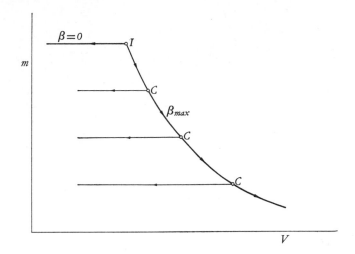

FIG. 6. Family of extremal arcs departing from a given initial point.

tained:

$$m \exp \left(\frac{V}{c} - \frac{mg}{c\beta_{\max}} \right) = \text{const} , \qquad \beta = \beta_{\max}$$

$$(4.142a)$$

$$m = \text{const} , \qquad \beta = 0$$

the first of which reduces to

$$m \exp (V/c) = \text{const} \qquad (4.142b)$$

for an infinitely large propellant mass flow (pulse-burning). It is then possible to determine in the velocity-mass plane the family of extremal arcs issuing from a given initial point (Fig. 6) and the family of extremal arcs arriving at a given final point (Fig. 7).

4.814 Maximum Altitude Increase

After the optimum burning program has been determined, the equations of motion can be integrated. For example, assume that the initial altitude, the initial velocity, and the final velocity are zero, and denote the final dimensionless altitude, the initial thrust-to-weight ratio, and the propellant mass ratio by

$$\eta_{\mathrm{f}} = h_{\mathrm{f}} g/c^2, \qquad \tau_{\mathrm{i}} = c\beta_{\max}/m_{\mathrm{i}} g , \qquad \zeta = (m_{\mathrm{i}} - m_{\mathrm{f}})/m_{\mathrm{i}} \qquad (4.143)$$

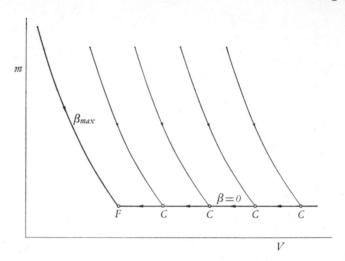

Fig. 7. Family of extremal arcs arriving at a given final point.

Under these conditions, rather laborious manipulations yield the following expression for the peak altitude reached by the rocket[48]:

$$\eta_f = \tfrac{1}{2} \log^2 (1 - \zeta) + \frac{\zeta + \log (1 - \zeta)}{\tau_i} \tag{4.144}$$

which is plotted in Fig. 8 versus the initial thrust-to-weight ratio for a propellant mass ratio of 0.7.

It is of interest to compare the optimum burning program with a constant acceleration-zero thrust program, that is, the program

$$\beta \sim m \rightarrow \beta = 0 \tag{4.145}$$

For such a program, the integration of the equations of motion yields the following expression for the peak altitude[48]:

$$\eta_f = \frac{\tau_i - 1}{2\tau_i} \log^2 (1 - \zeta) \tag{4.146}$$

which is plotted in Fig. 8 versus the initial thrust-to-weight ratio for a propellant mass ratio of 0.7.

Clearly, for the same initial thrust-to-weight ratio, the constant thrust-zero thrust program is superior to the constant acceleration-zero thrust program; for example, if the initial thrust-to-weight ratio is 2, the peak altitude of the optimum burning program is 30% higher than that of the alternate program. As the initial thrust-to-weight ratio increases, the

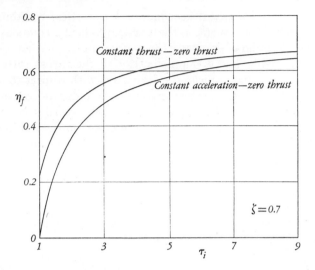

FIG. 8. Peak altitude reached by a rocket versus the initial thrust-to-weight ratio.

relative difference between these programs decreases; in particular, for the limiting case where $\tau_i = \infty$ (pulse burning), these programs yield the same increase in altitude, that is,

$$\eta_f = \tfrac{1}{2} \log^2 (1 - \zeta) \tag{4.147}$$

4.82 Generalized Approach

A generalization of the former problem arises when hypotheses (c) and (d) of the previous section are eliminated and the simultaneous programming of the thrust modulus and the thrust direction is investigated for general two-dimensional paths in a vertical plane. After the kinematical and dynamical relationships are projected on the horizontal and vertical directions, the equations of motion are written as

$$
\begin{aligned}
&\varphi_1 \equiv \dot{X} - u = 0 \\
&\varphi_2 \equiv \dot{h} - v = 0 \\
&\varphi_3 \equiv \dot{u} - c\beta \cos \psi/m = 0 \\
&\varphi_4 \equiv \dot{v} + g - c\beta \sin \psi/m = 0 \\
&\varphi_5 \equiv \dot{m} + \beta = 0 \\
&\varphi_6 \equiv \beta(\beta_{\max} - \beta) - \alpha^2 = 0
\end{aligned}
\tag{4.148}
$$

where X denotes a horizontal coordinate, h a vertical coordinate, u the horizontal velocity component, v the vertical velocity component, m the mass, g the acceleration of gravity, c the equivalent exit velocity, β the mass flow, α a real variable, and ψ the inclination of the thrust with respect to the horizon. The dot sign indicates a derivative with respect to time.

The previous differential system involves one independent variable (t), eight dependent variables $(X, h, u, v, m, \beta, \alpha, \psi)$, and two degrees of freedom; hence, some optimum requirement can be imposed on the burning program $\beta(t)$ and the thrust direction program $\psi(t)$. In this connection, the variational problem is formulated as follows: *In the class of functions $X(t)$, $h(t)$, $u(t)$, $v(t)$, $m(t)$, $\beta(t)$, $\alpha(t)$, $\psi(t)$ which are consistent with Eqs. (4.148) and certain prescribed end-conditions,* find that particular set which minimizes the difference $\Delta G = G_f - G_i$, where $G = G(t, X, h, u, v, m)$.

After six variable Lagrange multipliers are introduced and the augmented function is written in the form

$$F = \lambda_1(\dot{X} - u) + \lambda_2(\dot{h} - v) + \lambda_3[\dot{u} - c\beta \cos \psi/m]$$

$$+ \lambda_4[\dot{v} + g - c\beta \sin \psi/m] + \lambda_5(\dot{m} + \beta)$$

$$+ \lambda_6[\beta(\beta_{\max} - \beta) - \alpha^2] \quad (4.149)$$

the extremal arc is described by the Euler-Lagrange equations

$$\dot{\lambda}_1 = 0$$

$$\dot{\lambda}_2 = 0$$

$$\dot{\lambda}_3 = -\lambda_1$$

$$\dot{\lambda}_4 = -\lambda_2$$

$$\dot{\lambda}_5 = (c\beta/m^2) K_\psi \quad (4.150)$$

$$0 = -K_\beta + \lambda_6(\beta_{\max} - 2\beta)$$

$$0 = \lambda_6 \alpha$$

$$0 = \lambda_3 \sin \psi - \lambda_4 \cos \psi$$

---

* The total number of such conditions is less than 12.

where, by definition,

$$K_\beta = (c/m)(\lambda_3 \cos \psi + \lambda_4 \sin \psi) - \lambda_5$$

$$(4.151)$$

$$K_\psi = \lambda_3 \cos \psi + \lambda_4 \sin \psi$$

Hence, the Lagrange multipliers λ_1, λ_2 are constant; furthermore, since the augmented function is formally independent of the time, the following first integral is valid:

$$\lambda_1 u + \lambda_2 v - \lambda_4 g + K_\beta \beta = C \qquad (4.152)$$

In addition, the transversality condition is given by

$$[dG - C \, dt + \lambda_1 \, dX + \lambda_2 \, dh + \lambda_3 \, du + \lambda_4 \, dv + \lambda_5 \, dm]_i^f = 0 \quad (4.153)$$

Finally, if both sides of the first of Eqs. (4.151) are differentiated with respect to time and the resulting expression is then combined with the Euler-Lagrange equations, the following result holds everywhere along the extremal arc:

$$\dot{K}_\beta = -(c/m)(\lambda_1 \cos \psi + \lambda_2 \sin \psi) \qquad (4.154)$$

4.821 Burning Program

As the seventh Euler-Lagrange equation indicates, the extremal arc is discontinuous and is composed of subarcs along which $\alpha = 0$ and subarcs along which $\lambda_6 = 0$. Along the subarcs $\alpha = 0$, the mass flow can take either of the following constant values:

$$\beta = 0 \quad \text{or} \quad \beta = \beta_{max} \qquad (4.155)$$

On the other hand, along the subarc $\lambda_6 = 0$, the sixth Euler-Lagrange equation leads to

$$K_\beta = 0, \qquad \dot{K}_\beta = 0 \qquad (4.156)$$

It can be shown that this result is incompatible with Eq. (4.154); consequently, there exists no subarc along which $\lambda_6 = 0$, that is, *no subarc is flown with variable thrust.*[29]

4.822 Thrust Direction Program

Inspection of the system of Euler-Lagrange equations shows that the first four equations can be integrated as follows:

$$\lambda_1 = C_1$$

$$\lambda_2 = C_2$$

$$\lambda_3 = C_3 - C_1 t \tag{4.157}$$

$$\lambda_4 = C_4 - C_2 t$$

where C_1 through C_4 are constants. Since the eighth Euler-Lagrange equation is solved by

$$\tan \psi = \lambda_4/\lambda_3 \tag{4.158}$$

the following solution is obtained:

$$\tan \psi = (C_4 - C_2 t)/(C_3 - C_1 t) \tag{4.159}$$

meaning that *the tangent of the inclination of the thrust with respect to the horizon is a bilinear function of the time,* a result due to Lawden.[49] While this conclusion is general, several particular cases are now considered.

(a) If the functional to be minimized is such that $\partial G/\partial u = \partial G/\partial v = 0$ and if the final velocity components are free, the transversality condition yields the relationships

$$\lambda_{3f} = \lambda_{4f} = 0 \tag{4.160}$$

which imply that

$$C_3 = C_1 t_f, \qquad C_4 = C_2 t_f \tag{4.161}$$

and that

$$\tan \psi = \text{const} \tag{4.162}$$

Thus, *the inclination of the thrust with respect to the horizon is constant,* a result due to Fried and Richardson.[50]

(b) If the functional under consideration is such that $\partial G/\partial u = \partial G/\partial v = \partial G/\partial t = 0$, if the final velocity components as well as the time are free, and if the final point is reached by coasting, the transversality condition and the first integral (4.152) yield the relationships

$$\lambda_{3f} = \lambda_{4f} = C = 0, \qquad (\lambda_1 u + \lambda_2 v)_f = 0 \qquad (4.163)$$

which imply that

$$\tan \psi = -(u/v)_f \qquad (4.164)$$

Hence, *the inclination of the thrust during powered flight is constant and perpendicular to the final velocity.*[51]

(c) If the G-function is such that $\partial G/\partial u = \partial G/\partial v = 0$ and if the initial velocity modulus is specified while its direction is free, the transversality condition leads to

$$\begin{vmatrix} \lambda_3 & \lambda_4 \\ u & v \end{vmatrix}_i = 0 \qquad (4.165)$$

which implies that

$$\tan \psi_i = (v/u)_i \qquad (4.166)$$

Hence, *the optimum initial velocity is parallel to the thrust.*[51]

(d) If the functional to be minimized is such that $\partial G/\partial X = 0$ and if the final horizontal coordinate is free, the transversality condition leads to

$$\lambda_{1f} = 0 \qquad (4.167)$$

which implies that $C_1 = 0$ and that

$$\tan \psi = C_4/C_3 - (C_2/C_3)t \qquad (4.168)$$

Hence, *the tangent of the inclination of the thrust with respect to the horizon is a linear function of the time,* a result due to Fried.[52]

(e) If the G-function is such that $\partial G/\partial h = 0$ and if the final altitude is free, the transversality condition leads to

$$\lambda_{2f} = 0 \qquad (4.169)$$

which implies that $C_2 = 0$ and that

$$\cot \psi = C_3/C_4 - (C_1/C_4)t \qquad (4.170)$$

Hence, *the cotangent of the inclination of the thrust with respect to the horizon is a linear function of time.*

4.823 Sequences of Subarcs

The next step is to determine what sequences of subarcs may compose the extremal arc. More specifically, the following questions arise: What is the maximum number of subarcs composing the extremal arc? Should the coasting subarc precede or follow the subarc flown with the maximum thrust? Are discontinuities in the thrust direction possible? Considerable light can be shed on this problem if the Erdmann-Weierstrass corner conditions are employed in combination with the Legendre-Clebsch condition.

Because of the corner conditions, the multipliers λ_1 through λ_5 as well as the integration constant C are continuous at each junction point. Hence, after considering the first integral (4.152) and observing that the velocity components and the mass are continuous functions of the time, one concludes that a discontinuity in the mass flow is possible if, and only if,

$$(K_\beta)_- = (K_\beta)_+ = 0 \qquad (4.171)$$

while a discontinuity (by π) in the thrust direction is possible if, and only if,

$$(K_\psi)_- = (K_\psi)_+ = 0 \qquad (4.172)$$

Because of the Legendre-Clebsch condition and the sixth Euler-Lagrange equation, the functional ΔG is a minimum if the following condition is satisfied everywhere along the extremal arc:

$$\frac{2K_\beta}{2\beta - \beta_{max}} \left[(\delta\beta)^2 + (\delta\alpha)^2 \right] + \frac{c\beta}{m} K_\psi (\delta\psi)^2 \geq 0 \qquad (4.173)$$

where the variations $\delta\alpha$, $\delta\beta$ must be consistent with the sixth constraining equation. Consequently, the burning program is optimum if

$$K_\beta \geq 0, \qquad \beta = \beta_{max}$$

$$\qquad (4.174)$$

$$K_\beta \leq 0, \qquad \beta = 0$$

while the thrust direction program is optimum if, and only if,

$$K_\psi \geq 0 \qquad (4.175)$$

From these results, it appears that the functions K_β and K_ψ play a dominant role in determining the composition of the extremal arc. Hence, these functions can be called the *mass flow switching function* and the *thrust direction switching function*, respectively. In particular, if these functions are employed in combination with the procedure described by Leitmann,[29] it can be shown that (a) *no more than three subarcs may enter into the extremal arc* and (b) *a discontinuity in the thrust direction may occur if, and only if,* $\lambda_3 = \lambda_4 = 0$.

4.824 Maximum Range

As an application of the previous theory, the problem of maximizing the range $(G = -X)$ is now considered in connection with the end-conditions

$$t_i = X_i = h_i = u_i = v_i = 0 , \qquad m_i \equiv \text{given}$$

$$h_f = 0 , \qquad m_f \equiv \text{given} \tag{4.176}$$

Making use of the Euler-Lagrange equations, the transversality condition, and the properties of the switching functions, one obtains the following conclusions: (a) the extremal arc includes at most one corner point and, hence, two subarcs; (b) the maximum thrust subarc precedes the coasting subarc; (c) the thrust direction during powered flight is constant and perpendicular to the velocity at the end of the coasting phase. Furthermore, if the equations of motion are integrated and the dimensionless range, the initial thrust-to-weight ratio, and the propellant mass ratio are denoted by

$$\xi_f = X_f g/c^2, \qquad \tau_i = c\beta_{\max}/m_i g , \qquad \zeta = (m_i - m_f)/m_i \tag{4.177}$$

respectively, the optimum thrust direction can be shown to be a solution of the transcendental equation[48]

$$\frac{2 \sin^3 \psi}{2 \sin^2 \psi - 1} + \frac{\tau_i \log^2 (1 - \zeta)}{\zeta + \log (1 - \zeta)} = 0 \tag{4.178}$$

while the corresponding range is given by

$$\xi_f = \frac{\cos \psi}{2 \sin^3 \psi} \log^2 (1 - \zeta) \tag{4.179}$$

Elimination of the parameter ψ from these equations leads to a functional relationship of the form

$$\xi_f = A (\tau_i, \zeta) \tag{4.180}$$

which is plotted in Fig. 9 versus the initial thrust-to-weight ratio for a propellant mass ratio of 0.7.

It is of interest to compare the optimum burning program with a constant acceleration-zero thrust program. For the latter, the optimum thrust direction can be shown to be a solution of the equation[48]

$$\sin^3 \psi / (2 \sin^2 \psi - 1) - \tau_i = 0 \qquad (4.181)$$

while the corresponding range is still supplied by Eq. (4.179). Consequently, after the parameter ψ is eliminated, a functional relationship of the form

$$\xi_f = B(\tau_i, \zeta) \qquad (4.182)$$

is obtained and is plotted in Fig. 9 versus the initial thrust-to-weight ratio for a propellant mass ratio of 0.7.

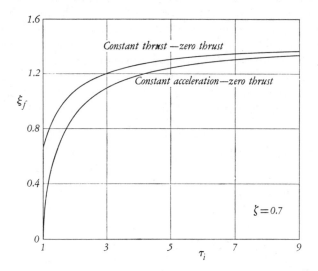

Fig. 9. Maximum range versus the initial thrust-to-weight ratio.

Clearly, the constant thrust-zero thrust program is superior to the constant acceleration-zero thrust program; for example, if the initial thrust-to-weight ratio is 2, the range of the optimum burning program is 20% greater than that of the alternate program. As the initial thrust-to-weight ratio increases, the relative difference between these programs decreases;

in particular, for the limiting case where $\tau_i = \infty$ (pulse burning), these programs yield the same range,* that is,

$$\xi_f = \log^2 (1 - \zeta) \qquad (4.183)$$

4.9 Optimum Trajectories for Rocket Flight in a Resisting Medium

In this section, the problem of determining optimum trajectories for rocket flight in a resisting medium is considered. For didactic purposes, the generalized treatment is preceded by a preliminary example relative to level flight.

4.91 Preliminary Example

The problem of determining optimum burning programs for a rocket-powered aircraft in level flight was initially investigated by Hibbs[53] and then extended by Cicala and Miele.[10,54] It was assumed that: (a) the earth is flat and the acceleration of gravity is constant; (b) the flight takes place in a resisting medium; (c) the trajectory is horizontal; (d) the thrust is tangent to the flight path; (e) the equivalent exit velocity of the rocket engine is constant; and (f) the engine is capable of delivering all mass flows bounded by a lower value and an upper value. In this section, the above hypotheses are retained, and the equations of motion are written as follows†:

$$\varphi_1 \equiv \dot{X} - V = 0$$

$$\varphi_2 \equiv \dot{V} + [D(V, m) - c\beta]/m = 0$$

$$\varphi_3 \equiv \dot{m} + \beta = 0 \qquad (4.184)$$

$$\varphi_4 \equiv \beta(\beta_{\max} - \beta) - \alpha^2 = 0$$

where X denotes the horizontal distance, V the velocity, m the mass, D the drag, c the equivalent exit velocity of the rocket engine, β the pro-

---

* For $\tau_i \to \infty$, the optimum thrust direction tends to $\pi/4$.

† Generally speaking, the drag function has the form $D = D(h, V, L)$, where h is the altitude, V the velocity, and L the lift. However, if it is considered that the altitude is constant and that $L = mg$, the drag function can be rewritten in the form $D(V, m)$, which is employed here.

pellant mass flow, and α a real variable. The dot sign denotes a derivative respect to the time.

The previous differential system involves one independent variable (t), five dependent variables (X, V, m, β, α), and one degree of freedom; hence, some optimum requirement can be imposed on the burning program $\beta(t)$. In this connection, after the end-conditions

$$t_i = X_i = 0; \qquad V_i, m_i \equiv \text{given}; \qquad V_f, m_f \equiv \text{given} \quad (4.185)$$

are specified, the maximum range problem is formulated as follows: *In the class of functions $X(t)$, $V(t)$, $m(t)$, $\beta(t)$, $\alpha(t)$ which are consistent with Eqs. (4.184) and the end-conditions (4.185), find that special set which minimizes the difference $\Delta G = G_f - G_i$, where $G = -X$.*

After four variable Lagrange multipliers are introduced and the augmented function is written in the form

$$F = \lambda_1(\dot{X} - V) + \lambda_2[\dot{V} + (D - c\beta)/m]$$

$$+ \lambda_3(\dot{m} + \beta) + \lambda_4[\beta(\beta_{\max} - \beta) - \alpha^2] \quad (4.186)$$

the Euler-Lagrange equations become

$$\dot{\lambda}_1 = 0$$

$$\dot{\lambda}_2 = -\lambda_1 + \frac{\lambda_2}{m} \frac{\partial D}{\partial V}$$

$$\dot{\lambda}_3 = \frac{\lambda_2}{m} \left(\frac{c\beta - D}{m} + \frac{\partial D}{\partial m} \right) \quad (4.187)$$

$$0 = -K + \lambda_4(\beta_{\max} - 2\beta)$$

$$0 = \lambda_4\alpha$$

where, by definition,

$$K = \lambda_2(c/m) - \lambda_3 \quad (4.188)$$

Hence, the Lagrange multiplier λ_1 is constant; furthermore, since the fundamental function is formally independent of the time, the following first integral can be written:

$$\lambda_1 V - \lambda_2(D/m) + K\beta = C \quad (4.189)$$

where C is a constant. In addition, the transversality condition becomes

$$[-C\,dt + (\lambda_1 - 1)\,dX + \lambda_2\,dV + \lambda_3\,dm]_i^f = 0 \qquad (4.190)$$

and implies that

$$\lambda_1 = 1, \qquad C = 0 \qquad (4.191)$$

Finally, if both sides of Eq. (4.188) are differentiated with respect to the time and the resulting expression is then combined with the Euler-Lagrange equations, the first integral (4.189), and the transversality condition, the following result holds everywhere along the extremal arc:

$$\dot{K} = \epsilon(V, m, \beta)K + \omega(V, m) \qquad (4.192)$$

where, by definition,

$$\epsilon(V, m, \beta) = (\beta/mD)(D + c\,\partial D/\partial V - m\,\partial D/\partial m) \qquad (4.193)$$

$$\omega(V, m) = (1/mD)[(V - c)D + V(c\,\partial D/\partial V - m\,\partial D/\partial m)]$$

4.911 Totality of Subarcs

As the fifth Euler-Lagrange equation indicates, the extremal arc is discontinuous and is composed of subarcs along which $\alpha = 0$ and subarcs along which $\lambda_4 = 0$. Along the subarcs $\alpha = 0$, the mass flow can take either of the following constant values:

$$\beta = 0 \quad \text{or} \quad \beta = \beta_{max} \qquad (4.194)$$

On the other hand, along the subarcs $\lambda_4 = 0$, both K and $\dot{K}$ vanish. Consequently, Eq. (4.192) leads to

$$\omega(V, m) = 0 \qquad (4.195)$$

which implies that

$$(V - c)D + V(c\,\partial D/\partial V - m\,\partial D/\partial m) = 0 \qquad (4.196)$$

In conclusion, *the extremal arc is composed of coasting subarcs, subarcs flown with maximum engine output, and variable thrust subarcs.*[54] Along the latter, the engine is to be throttled in such a way that Eq. (4.196) is satisfied at every time instant. For example, if the parabolic approximation is employed for the drag polar, that is, if

$$D = AV^2 + B(m^2/V^2) \tag{4.197}$$

where A and B are constants, Eq. (4.196) can be rewritten in the form

$$m = V^2\sqrt{A/B}\sqrt{(V + c)/(V + 3c)} \tag{4.198}$$

which shows that the mass is a monotonic function of the velocity; more specifically, any decrease in the mass due to the propellant consumption is accompanied by a corresponding decrease in the velocity. Hence, the acceleration is negative, and the variable thrust subarc must be flown with a thrust less than the drag at all time instants.

4.912 Sequences of Subarcs

The next step is to determine what combinations of subarcs are consistent with the corner conditions and the Legendre-Clebsch condition. Because of the Erdmann-Weierstrass corner conditions, the multipliers $\lambda_1, \lambda_2, \lambda_3$ as well as the integration constant C must be continuous at each junction point. Since the velocity and the mass are continuous, the first integral (4.189) shows that a discontinuity in the mass flow rate is possible providing the following relationships are satisfied:

$$(K)_- = (K)_+ = 0 \tag{4.199}$$

which imply that

$$(\dot{K})_- = (\dot{K})_+ = \omega \tag{4.200}$$

Furthermore, if the Legendre-Clebsch condition is combined with the Euler-Lagrange equations, the conditions

$$K \gtrless 0 \tag{4.201}$$

can be shown to hold for the maximum thrust subarc, the variable thrust subarc, and the coasting subarc, respectively. As indicated by Miele,[36] it appears that the function ω (*fundamental function*) and the function K (*switching function*) play a dominant role in the solution of the maximum range problem since, by knowing the fundamental function, it is possible to calculate the switching function and, hence, to predict those sequences of subarcs which do not violate the Legendre-Clebsch condition. More specifically, if the switching function is developed into a Taylor

TABLE I

SEQUENCES OF SUBARCS

Location of the corner point	Sequence of subarcs
$\omega_c > 0$	$\beta = 0 \rightarrow \beta = \beta_{max}$
$\omega_c < 0$	$\beta = \beta_{max} \rightarrow \beta = 0$
$\omega_c = 0$	$\omega = 0 \rightleftarrows \beta = 0$
	$\omega = 0 \rightleftarrows \beta = \beta_{max}$

series in the immediate neighborhood of a corner point and if relationships (4.199)–(4.201) are combined, the conditions*

$$\omega_c(t - t_c) \gtrless 0 \qquad (4.202)$$

can be shown to hold for the maximum thrust subarc, the variable thrust subarc, and the coasting subarc, respectively. Therefore, the only sequences of subarcs which do not violate the Legendre-Clebsch test are those indicated in Table I and Fig. 10.

4.913 Composition of the Extremal Arc

The final step is to determine the extremal arc connecting two given end-points, for instance, an initial point I located in the region where $\omega > 0$ and a final point F located in the region where $\omega < 0$. Such an ex-

---

* The subscript c refers to a corner point.

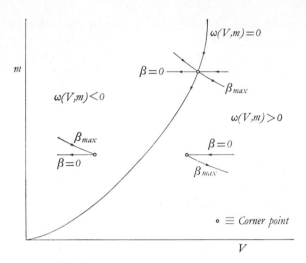

FIG. 10.   Sequence of subarcs consistent with the Erdmann-Weierstrass corner conditions and the Legendre-Clebsch condition.

tremal arc is the trajectory $IMNF$ of Fig. 11, which is composed of the sequence of subarcs

$$\beta = 0 \rightarrow \omega = 0 \rightarrow \beta = 0 \qquad\qquad (4.203)$$

This statement can be verified by examining a number of alternate com-

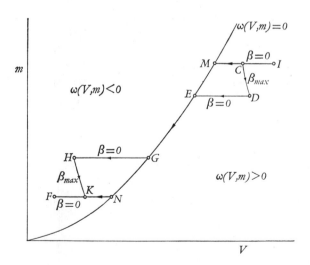

FIG. 11.   Particular extremal arc.

binations of subarcs and showing that each of these violates the Legendre-Clebsch condition at some point. For example, consider the path $ICDENF$, which is composed of the sequence of subarcs

$$\beta = 0 \to \beta = \beta_{\max} \to \beta = 0 \to \omega = 0 \to \beta = 0 \qquad (4.204)$$

Although each of these subarcs satisfies the Euler-Lagrange equations, the resulting trajectory must be discarded, since the partial sequence

$$\beta = \beta_{\max} \to \beta = 0 \qquad (4.205)$$

with corner point D located in the region where $\omega > 0$ violates the Legendre-Clebsch condition. By the same reasoning, the path $IMGHKF$ must be discarded, since the Legendre-Clebsch condition is violated in the neighborhood of corner point H. In conclusion, *while there are infinite combinations of subarcs which satisfy the Euler-Lagrange equations, there exists only one combination which does not violate the Legendre-Clebsch condition at any point.* This unique combination is the path $IMNF$ of Fig. 11.

4.914 Totality of Extremal Arcs

After the time is eliminated from the second and the third of Eqs. (4.184), the following differential relationship is obtained:

$$\frac{dm}{dV} = \frac{m\beta}{D - c\beta} \qquad (4.205a)$$

and holds for every subarc composing the extremal arc. For the coasting subarc, the above equation can be integrated to give

$$m = \text{const} \qquad (4.205b)$$

On the other hand, for the subarc flown with maximum engine output, approximate methods of integration are necessary; only for the ideal case of an infinite propellant flow rate (pulse-burning), the following analytical solution:

$$m \exp(V/c) = \text{const} \qquad (4.205c)$$

is possible. Finally, for the variable-thrust subarc, the velocity-mass relationahip is represented by

$$(V - c)D + V(c\,\partial D/\partial V - m\,\partial D/\partial m) = 0 \qquad (4.205d)$$

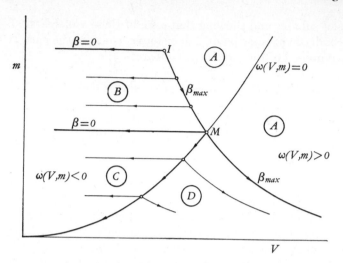

Fig. 12. Family of extremal arcs departing from a given initial point ($\omega_i < 0$).

It is then possible to determine in the mass-velocity plane the family of extremal arcs issuing from a given initial point (Figs. 12 and 13) and the family of extremal arcs arriving at a given final point (Figs. 14 and 15). As an example, consider the case where the initial point is given and belongs to the region where $\omega < 0$ (Fig. 12). Denote with M the point where the subarc $\beta = \beta_{max}$ issuing from the initial point intersects the

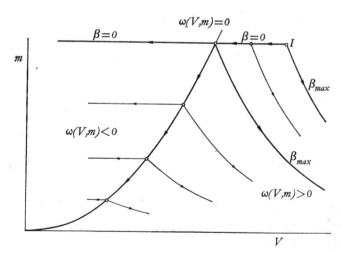

Fig. 13. Family of extremal arcs departing from a given initial point ($\omega_i > 0$).

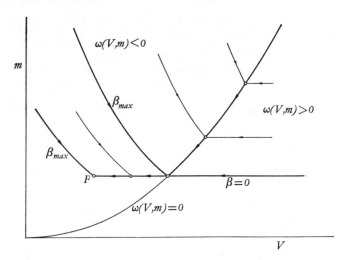

FIG. 14. Family of extremal arcs arriving at a given final point ($\omega_f < 0$).

line $\omega = 0$; furthermore, determine the subarc $\beta = 0$ issuing from point M. It appears that the velocity-mass plane can be divided in the following regions: (a) a region A located above the line $\beta = \beta_{\max}$ issuing from the initial point; (b) a region B located between this line, the m-axis, and the line $\beta = 0$ issuing from point M; (c) a region C located between this line, the m-axis, and the line $\omega = 0$; and (d) a region D located between the

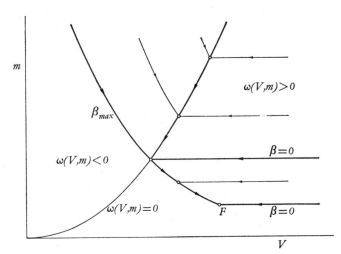

FIG. 15. Family of extremal arcs arriving at a given final point ($\omega_f > 0$).

line $\omega = 0$, the V-axis, and the line $\beta = \beta_{max}$ issuing from point M. Clearly, the variational problem has no physical solution if the final point belongs to the region A; it admits the solution $\beta = \beta_{max} \to \beta = 0$ if the final point belongs to the region B; it admits the solution $\beta = \beta_{max} \to \omega = 0 \to \beta = 0$ if the final point belongs to the region C; and it admits the solution $\beta = \beta_{max} \to \omega = 0 \to \beta = \beta_{max}$ if the final point belongs to the region D. If a similar procedure is employed, the cases indicated in Figs. 13–15 can be discussed. At any rate, it appears that (a) no more than three subarcs may compose the extremal arc and (b) the solution of the variational problem depends strongly on the boundary conditions.

4.915 Remark

It is emphasized that the conclusions of the previous sections relative to the composition of the extremal arc are valid providing that (a) the mass-velocity relationship corresponding to $\omega = 0$ is monotonic and (b) the mass flow rate required along the line $\omega = 0$ is smaller than the maximum available. Should any of these conditions be violated, that is, should the mass-velocity relationship corresponding to $\omega = 0$ be nonmonotonic and/or should the mass flow required be greater than the maximum available, then some modification would appear in the composition of the extremal arc. More specifically, the extremal arc satisfying the given boundary conditions might include more than three subarcs (in some cases, five), even though each of them is flown by coasting, with maximum thrust, or along the line $\omega = 0$. For the sake of brevity, the analytical treatment of this case is not considered here, and the reader is referred to the specialized literature on the subject. However, it can be anticipated that, by the combined use of the Erdmann-Weierstrass corner conditions and the Legendre-Clebsch condition, the solution of this problem can be found and is usually unique.

4.92 Generalized Approach

A generalization of the former problem arises when hypotheses (c) and (d) of the previous section are eliminated, and the simultaneous programming of the thrust modulus, the thrust direction, and the lift is investigated for general two-dimensional paths in a vertical plane. After the kinematical relationships are projected on the horizontal and vertical directions and the dynamical relationships are projected on the tangent and the normal to the flight path, the equations of motion are written as follows:

$$\varphi_1 \equiv \dot{X} - V \cos \gamma = 0$$

$$\varphi_2 \equiv \dot{h} - V \sin \gamma = 0$$

$$\varphi_3 \equiv \dot{V} + g \sin \gamma + [D(h, V, L) - c\beta \cos \epsilon]/m = 0$$

$$\varphi_4 \equiv \dot{\gamma} + \frac{g \cos \gamma}{V} - (L + c\beta \sin \epsilon)/mV = 0 \tag{4.206}$$

$$\varphi_5 \equiv \dot{m} + \beta = 0$$

$$\varphi_6 \equiv \beta(\beta_{\max} - \beta) - \alpha^2 = 0$$

where X denotes a horizontal coordinate, h a vertical coordinate, V the velocity, γ the inclination of the flight path with respect to the horizon, m the mass, g the acceleration of gravity, c the equivalent exit velocity of the rocket engine, β the mass flow, α a real variable, ϵ the inclination of the thrust with respect to the velocity, D the drag, L the lift, and the dot sign a derivative with respect to time.

The previous differential system involves one independent variable (t), nine dependent variables $(X, h, V, \gamma, m, \beta, \alpha, \epsilon, L)$, and three degrees of freedom; hence, some optimum requirement can be imposed on the burning program $\beta(t)$, the thrust direction program $\epsilon(t)$, and the lift program $L(t)$. In this connection, the Mayer problem is formulated as follows: *In the class of functions* $X(t), h(t), V(t), \gamma(t), m(t), \beta(t), \alpha(t), \epsilon(t), L(t)$ *which are consistent with Eqs.* (4.206) *and certain prescribed end-conditions,* * *find that special set which minimizes the difference* $\Delta G = G_f - G_i$, *where* $G = G(X, h, V, \gamma, m, t)$.

After six variable Lagrange multipliers are introduced and the augmented function is written in the form

$$F = \lambda_1(\dot{X} - V \cos \gamma) + \lambda_2(\dot{h} - V \sin \gamma)$$

$$+ \lambda_3 \left(\dot{V} + g \sin \gamma + \frac{D - c\beta \cos \epsilon}{m} \right) + \lambda_4 \left(\dot{\gamma} + \frac{g \cos \gamma}{V} - \frac{L + c\beta \sin \epsilon}{mV} \right)$$

$$+ \lambda_5(\dot{m} + \beta) + \lambda_6[\beta(\beta_{\max} - \beta) - \alpha^2] \tag{4.207}$$

---

* The total number of such conditions is less than 12.

the extremal arc is described by the Euler-Lagrange equations[31]

$$\dot{\lambda}_1 = 0$$

$$\dot{\lambda}_2 = (\lambda_3/m)\ \partial D/\partial h$$

$$\dot{\lambda}_3 = -\lambda_1 \cos \gamma - \lambda_2 \sin \gamma + (\lambda_3/m)\ \partial D/\partial V$$

$$- (\lambda_4 g/V^2) \cos \gamma + (\lambda_4/mV^2)(L + c\beta \sin \epsilon)$$

$$\dot{\lambda}_4 = \lambda_1 V \sin \gamma - \lambda_2 V \cos \gamma + \lambda_3 g \cos \gamma - \lambda_4 \frac{g}{V} \sin \gamma$$

$$\dot{\lambda}_5 = (1/m^2)(c\beta K_\epsilon - K_L) \qquad (4.208)$$

$$0 = -K_\beta + \lambda_6(\beta_{\max} - 2\beta)$$

$$0 = \lambda_6 \alpha$$

$$0 = \lambda_3 \sin \epsilon - \lambda_4 \cos \epsilon/V$$

$$0 = \lambda_3\ \partial D/\partial L - \lambda_4/V$$

where, by definition,

$$K_\beta = \frac{c}{m}\ [\lambda_3 \cos \epsilon + (\lambda_4/V) \sin \epsilon] - \lambda_5$$

$$K_\epsilon = \lambda_3 \cos \epsilon + (\lambda_4/V) \sin \epsilon \qquad (4.209)$$

$$K_L = \lambda_3 D - (\lambda_4/V) L$$

Hence, the Lagrange multiplier λ_1 is constant; furthermore, since the augmented function is formally independent of the time, the first integral

$$V(\lambda_1 \cos \gamma + \lambda_2 \sin \gamma) - g\left(\lambda_3 \sin \gamma + \frac{\lambda_4}{V} \cos \gamma\right) + \beta K_\beta - \frac{K_L}{m} = C$$

$$(4.210)$$

is valid. In addition, the transversality condition is given by

$$[dG - C\ dt + \lambda_1\ dX + \lambda_2\ dh + \lambda_3\ dV + \lambda_4\ d\gamma + \lambda_5\ dm]_i^f = 0 \qquad (4.211)$$

4.921 Burning Program

As the seventh Euler-Lagrange equation indicates, the extremal arc is discontinuous and is composed of subarcs along which $\alpha = 0$ and subarcs along which $\lambda_6 = 0$. Along the subarcs $\alpha = 0$, the mass flow is constant and is given by either

$$\beta = 0 \quad \text{or} \quad \beta = \beta_{\max} \tag{4.212}$$

On the other hand, along the subarc $\lambda_6 = 0$ the mass flow varies in such a way that

$$K_\beta = 0, \qquad \dot{K}_\beta = 0 \tag{4.213}$$

Thus, *the extremal arc is composed of coasting subarcs, subarcs flown with maximum engine output, and variable thrust subarcs.*[31]

4.922 Thrust Direction Program

After the eighth and ninth Euler-Lagrange equations are considered, it is seen that nontrivial solutions exist for the Lagrange multipliers if, and only if,

$$\begin{vmatrix} \sin \epsilon & \cos \epsilon \\ \partial D/\partial L & 1 \end{vmatrix} = 0 \tag{4.214}$$

Hence, the optimum inclination of the thrust with respect to the velocity satisfies the relationship

$$\epsilon = \arctan (\partial D/\partial L) \tag{4.215}$$

which, for the particular case of a drag polar having the form

$$D = A(V, h) + B(V, h)L^2 \tag{4.216}$$

reduces to

$$\epsilon = \arctan (2BL) \tag{4.217}$$

Since $B > 0$, the thrust must be tilted in the direction of the lift; this result is logical, since the creation of a normal component of the thrust reduces the amount of aerodynamic lift necessary to perform a certain maneuver and, therefore, reduces the induced drag associated with that lift. For the particular case in which $2BL \ll 1$, the previous relationship simplifies to

$$\epsilon = 2BL \qquad (4.218)$$

which, for the low subsonic flight, is susceptible to a simple physical interpretation: *the optimum inclination of the thrust axis is twice the downwash angle BL associated with the particular flight condition under consideration.*

4.923 Sequences of Subarcs

The next step is to determine what sequences of subarcs may enter into the extremal arc. The available knowledge on the problem with the aerodynamic forces included is not as complete as that relative to flight in a vacuum. Despite this, some rather general criteria can be formulated with the aid of the corner conditions and the Legendre-Clebsch condition.

Because of the corner conditions, the multipliers λ_1 through λ_5 as well as the integration constant C are continuous at each junction point. Hence, after considering the first integral (4.210), one concludes that a discontinuity in the mass flow is possible if, and only if,

$$(K_\beta)_- = (K_\beta)_+ = 0 \qquad (4.219)$$

On the other hand, a discontinuity (by π) in the thrust direction is possible if

$$(K_\epsilon)_- = (K_\epsilon)_+ = 0 \qquad (4.220)$$

Finally, a discontinuity in the lift is possible providing that

$$(K_L)_- = (K_L)_+ = 0 \qquad (4.221)$$

that is, providing that

$$(L/D)_- = (L/D)_+ \qquad (4.222)$$

and that (see the ninth Euler-Lagrange equation)

$$(\partial D/\partial L)_- = (\partial D/\partial L)_+ \qquad (4.223)$$

After it is observed that the simultaneous equations (4.222) and (4.223) admit the solution

$$(L)_- = (L)_+ \qquad (4.224)$$

discontinuities in the lift are ruled out; hence, *the optimum lift program is a continuous function of time.*

Because of the Legendre-Clebsch condition and the sixth Euler-Lagrange equation, the functional ΔG is a minimum if the following inequality is satisfied everywhere along the extremal arc:

$$\frac{2K_\beta}{2\beta - \beta_{\max}} \left[(\delta\alpha)^2 + (\delta\beta)^2 \right] + \frac{c\beta}{m} K_\epsilon(\delta\epsilon)^2 + \frac{\lambda_3}{m} \frac{\partial^2 D}{\partial L^2} (\delta L)^2 \geq 0 \quad (4.225)$$

where the variations $\delta\alpha$, $\delta\beta$ must be consistent with the sixth constraining equation. Consequently, the burning program is optimum if

$$K_\beta \gtreqless 0 \qquad (4.226)$$

for the maximum, variable, and zero thrust subarcs, respectively. Furthermore, the thrust direction program is optimum if

$$K_\epsilon \geq 0 \qquad (4.227)$$

Finally, after observing that, for a parabolic drag polar,

$$\partial^2 D / \partial L^2 = 2B > 0 \qquad (4.228)$$

one concludes that the lift program is optimum providing that

$$\lambda_3 \geq 0 \qquad (4.229)$$

everywhere along the extremal arc.

It is apparent from the previous discussion that the functions K_β and K_ϵ play a dominant role in determining the composition of the extremal arc. For this reason, these functions can be called the *mass flow switching function* and the *thrust direction switching function*, respectively. Incidentally, a discontinuity in the thrust direction may occur if, and only if, $\lambda_3 = \lambda_4 = 0$.

4.93 Additional Constraints

In the previous section, optimum rocket trajectories in a resisting medium were investigated with the assumption that, in addition to the well-known kinematic and dynamic relationships, a two-sided inequality constraint relative to the propellant mass flow must be satisfied. In this section, the case where the flight path is subjected not only to the previous constraints but also to two *additional constraints* of the form*

$$\varphi(X, h, V, \gamma, m, \beta, \epsilon, L, t) = 0$$

$$(4.230)$$

$$\psi(X, h, V, \gamma, m, \beta, \epsilon, L, t) = 0$$

is considered. Because of these additional constraints, the number of degrees of freedom is reduced to one; consequently, the Euler-Lagrange equations are modified and, hence, the resulting optimum trajectories are modified. The analytical procedure is analogous to that of the previous section and, hence, it is not repeated here; only the main results are summarized for several classes of flight paths.

4.931 Vertical Paths

For the category of vertical paths flown with the thrust tangent to the flight path, the additional constraints become

$$\varphi \equiv \gamma - \pi/2 = 0$$

$$(4.231)$$

$$\psi \equiv \epsilon = 0$$

If the G-function has the form $G = G(h, V, m, t)$, the totality of extremal

---

* This is the most general problem encountered in the theory of the optimum flight paths.[31] In fact, it contains the following problems as particular cases: (a) the problem with one degree of freedom, which occurs when both the additional constraints are present; (b) the problem with two degrees of freedom, which occurs when one of the additional constraints is absent; and (c) the problem with three degrees of freedom, which occurs when both the additional constraints are absent.

arcs includes subarcs $\beta = 0$, subarcs $\beta = \beta_{max}$, and variable thrust subarcs along which[31]

$$mg = D\left(\frac{V}{c} - 1\right) + V \frac{\partial D}{\partial V} - A \exp\left(-\frac{V + gt}{c}\right) \qquad (4.232)$$

where A is a constant.

An important subcase occurs when the G-function has the form $G = G(h, V, m)$ and no time condition is imposed; for this subcase, the transversality condition yields $A = 0$, and the equation to be satisfied along the variable thrust subarc becomes[41]

$$mg = D[(V/c) - 1] + V \, \partial D/\partial V \qquad (4.233)$$

Incidentally, should the aerodynamic forces be absent, this equation would have no physical solution; consequently, the optimum thrust program would include coasting subarcs and maximum thrust subarcs only, in accordance with the result of Section 4.811.

4.932 Level Paths

For the category of level paths flown with the thrust tangent to the flight path, the additional constraints are written as

$$\varphi \equiv \gamma = 0$$
$$\qquad (4.234)$$
$$\psi \equiv \epsilon = 0$$

If the G-function has the form $G = G(X, V, m, t)$, the totality of extremal arcs includes coasting subarcs, maximum thrust subarcs, and variable thrust subarcs along which[31]

$$mg = \frac{D(V - c - A) + c(V - A) \, \partial D/\partial V}{(V - A) \, \partial D/\partial L} \qquad (4.235)$$

where A is a constant.

An important subcase occurs when the G-function has the form $G = G(X, V, m)$ and no time condition is imposed; for this subcase, the transversality condition leads to $A = 0$, and the equation to be satisfied along the variable thrust subarc becomes[31]

$$mg = \frac{D(V - c) + cV\, \partial D/\partial V}{V\, \partial D/\partial L} \qquad (4.236)$$

in accordance with the result of Section 4.91.

Another interesting subcase occurs when the G-function has the form $G = G(t, V, m)$ and no condition is imposed on the horizontal distance; for this subcase, the transversality condition yields $A = \infty$, and the relationship governing the variable thrust subarc becomes[10]

$$mg = \frac{D + c\, \partial D/\partial V}{\partial D/\partial L} \qquad (4.237)$$

4.933 Arbitrarily Inclined Rectilinear Paths

For the category of rectilinear paths flown with the thrust tangent to the flight path, the additional constraints become

$$\varphi \equiv \gamma - \text{const} = 0$$
$$\qquad (4.238)$$
$$\psi \equiv \epsilon = 0$$

If the G-function has the form $G = G(X, h, V, m)$ and if no time condition is prescribed, the totality of extremal arcs includes subarcs $\beta = 0$, subarcs $\beta = \beta_{max}$, and variable thrust subarcs along which[31]

$$mg = \frac{D(V - c) + cV\, \partial D/\partial V}{c \sin \gamma + V \cos \gamma\, \partial D/\partial L} \qquad (4.239)$$

This equation reduces to Eq. (4.233) for vertical flight and to Eq. (4.236) for level flight.

4.934 Trajectories Flown with Constant Mass Flow and Negligible Induced Drag

For a rocket engine operating with constant mass flow and with the thrust tangent to the flight path, the additional constraints are given by

$$\varphi \equiv \beta - \text{const} = 0$$
$$\qquad (4.240)$$
$$\psi \equiv \epsilon = 0$$

If the induced drag is negligible with respect to the zero-lift drag, if the G-function has the form $G = G(h, V, m, t)$, and if no condition is imposed on the horizontal distance, the totality of extremal arcs includes subarcs along which[31]

$$\cos \gamma = 0 \tag{4.241}$$

and subarcs along which

$$\beta c = D + V\, \partial D/\partial V - (V^2/g)\, \partial D/\partial h \tag{4.242}$$

While the former subarcs are flown vertically (dive or zoom), the latter subarcs are flown with a continuously variable path inclination.

4.935 Nonlifting Paths

For the category of nonlifting paths flown with the thrust tangent to the flight path, the additional constraints are given by

$$\psi = L - 0$$

$$\tag{4.243}$$

$$\varphi \equiv \epsilon = 0$$

The totality of extremal arcs includes coasting subarcs, maximum thrust subarcs, and variable thrust subarcs. Along the latter subarcs, the optimum instantaneous acceleration can be readily calculated if an isothermal atmosphere is assumed; the result can be found in Bryson and Ross[55] for problems not involving time and in Miele[31] for problems where some time condition is imposed on the flight path.

4.936 Gliding Paths

For the category of glide paths, the thrust is zero, so that the propellant mass flow is zero. Clearly, the variational problem has only one degree of freedom, that associated with the optimization of the lift program. For simplicity, the class of smooth, shallow paths is now considered, that is, the assumptions

$$\sin \gamma \cong \gamma, \qquad \cos \gamma \cong 1, \qquad V\dot{\gamma}/g \ll 1 \tag{4.244}$$

are employed. Under these hypotheses, the condition to be satisfied along the extremal arc is given by

$$\frac{\partial D/\partial V - (V/g)\, \partial D/\partial h}{\partial D/\partial V + D/V - (V/g)\partial D/\partial h} = A/V \qquad (4.245)$$

where A is a constant which depends on the boundary conditions of the problem and on the function $G = G(t, X, h, V)$ to be extremized.

An important subcase occurs if the G-function has the form $G = G(X, h, V)$ and no time condition is imposed. For this subcase, the transversality condition yields $A = 0$, and the equation governing the optimum lift program becomes[56]

$$\frac{\partial D}{\partial V} - \frac{V}{g}\frac{\partial D}{\partial h} = 0 \qquad (4.246)$$

If $H = h + V^2/2g$ denotes the energy height and the drag function is rewritten in the form $D = D(H, V, L)$, the previous equation becomes

$$[\partial D/\partial V]_{H,L} = 0 \qquad (4.247)$$

meaning that *the optimum flight program is achieved when the aerodynamic drag has a minimum with respect to the velocity for constant values of the energy height and the lift.* For the low subsonic regime, this particular program is flown with constant dynamic pressure and, hence, with constant angle of attack.

Another interesting subcase occurs when the G-function has the form $G = G(t, h, V)$ and no condition is imposed on the horizontal distance. For this subcase, the transversality condition yields $A = \infty$, and the equation governing the optimum lift program becomes[56]

$$\frac{\partial (DV)}{\partial V} - \frac{V}{g}\frac{\partial (DV)}{\partial h} = 0 \qquad (4.248)$$

which is equivalent to

$$[\partial (DV)/\partial V]_{H,L} = 0 \qquad (4.249)$$

Hence, *the optimum flight program is achieved when the power required to overcome the aerodynamic drag has a minimum with respect to the velocity for constant values of the energy height and the lift.* For the low subsonic regime this particular program requires that the dynamic pressure be kept constant, so that the angle of attack is constant.

4.10 Conclusions

This chapter considers the indirect methods of the calculus of variations with particular emphasis on the problems of Bolza, Mayer, and Lagrange. After the Euler-Lagrange equations, the corner conditions, the transversality condition, the Legendre-Clebsch condition, and the Weierstrass condition are reviewed, the difficulties inherent to the solution of the mixed boundary-value problem are pointed out. Furthermore, some mathematical artifices are introduced which enable one to reduce engineering problems originally not covered by the formulations of Bolza, Mayer, and Lagrange (that is, problems involving higher derivatives, problems not involving derivatives, and problems involving inequality constraints) to the mathematical scheme considered in these formulations.

The use of variational techniques in applied aerodynamics is reviewed with particular regard to the determination of the geometry of the slender body of revolution having minimum pressure drag in Newtonian flow as well as the two-dimensional wing having minimum pressure drag in linearized supersonic flow. Also, the use of variational techniques in flight mechanics is reviewed with particular regard to the determination of the optimum two-dimensional paths for a rocket vehicle flying in either a vacuum or a resisting medium. Discontinuous solutions are discussed and the use of the switching function for predicting the composition of the extremal arc is demonstrated.

References

1. G. A. Bliss, "Lectures on the Calculus of Variations." Univ. of Chicago Press, Chicago, 1946.
2. A. Miele, "Flight Mechanics," Vol. 2: Theory of Optimum Flight Paths. Addison-Wesley, Reading, Massachusetts (in preparation).
3. O. Bolza, "Lectures on the Calculus of Variations." Stechert, New York, 1946.
4. P. Cicala, "An Engineering Approach to the Calculus of Variations." Levrotto & Bella, Torino, Italy, 1957.
5. F. A. Valentine, *in* "Contributions to the Calculus of Variations, 1933–1937." The Problem of Lagrange with Differential Inequalities as Added Side Conditions. Univ. of Chicago Press, Chicago, 1937.
6. L. J. Kulakowski and R. T. Stancil, Rocket boost trajectories for maximum burnout velocity, *ARS Journal* **30**, No. 7 (1960).

7. A. E. Bryson and W. F. Denham, A steepest-ascent method for solving optimum programming problems, Ratheon Company, Missile and Space Division, Rept. No. BR-1303 (1961).

8. H. J. Kelley, Gradient theory of optimal flight paths, *ARS Journal* **30**, No. 10 (1960).

9. G. Leitmann, An elementary derivation of the optimal control conditions, *Proc. 12th Intern. Astronaut. Congr. Washington* (1961).

10. A. Miele, An extension of the theory of the optimum burning program for the level flight of a rocket-powered aircraft, *J. Aero/Space Sci.* **24**, No. 12 (1957).

11. A. J. Eggers, M. M. Resnikoff and D. H. Dennis, Bodies of revolution having minimum drag at high supersonic airspeeds NACA TR No. 1306 (1958).

12. G. Drougge, Wing sections with minimum drag at supersonic speeds, The Aeronautical Research Institute of Sweden Rept. No. 26 (1949).

13. D. R. Chapman, Airfoil profiles for minimum pressure drag at supersonic velocities. General analysis with application to linearized supersonic flow, NACA TR No. 1063 (1952).

14. A. Miele, Optimum slender bodies of revolution in Newtonian flow, Boeing Scientific Research Laboratories, Flight Sciences Laboratory, TR No. 56 (1962).

15. A. Miele, The extremization of functionals involving products of powers of integrals and its application to aerodynamics, Boeing Scientific Research Laboratories, Flight Sciences Laboratory, TR No. 57 (1962).

16. R. H. Goddard, A method of reaching extreme altitudes, *Smithsonian Inst. Publs. Misc. Collections* **71**, No. 2 (1919).

17. G. Hamel, "Über eine mit dem Problem der Rakete zusammenhängende Aufgabe der Variationsrechnung, *Z. angew. Math. Mech.* **7**, No. 6 (1927).

18. A. Lippisch, Performance theory of airplanes with jet propulsion, Headquarters, Air Matériel Command, Translation Rept. No. F-TS-685-RE (1946).

19. K. J. Lush. A review of the problem of choosing a climb technique with proposals for a new climb technique for high performance aircraft, Aeronautical Research Council, RM No. 2557 (1951).

20. A. Miele, Problemi di Minimo Tempo nel Volo Non Stazionario degli Aeroplani, *Atti accad. sci. Torino, Classe sci. fis. mat. e nat.* **85**, (1950–1951).

21. P. Cicala, Optimum airplane flight paths, NASA TT No. F-4 (1959).

22. P. Cicala, Piecemeal solutions in the programming of optimal flight trajectories, NASA TT No. F-3 (1959).

23. B. Garfinkel, Minimal problems in airplane performance, *Quart. Appl. Math.* **9**, No. 2 (1951).

24. M. R. Hestenes A general problem in the calculus of variations with applications to paths of least time, The RAND Corporation, Rept. No. RM-100 (1950).

25. J. V. Breakwell, The optimization of trajectories, *SIAM Journal* **7**, No. 2 (1959).

26. B. D. Fried, *in* "Space Technology" Trajectory optimization for powered flight in two or three dimensions, Chap. 4. Wiley, New York, 1959.

27. D. F. Lawden, Dynamic problems of interplanetary flight, *Aeronaut. Quart.* **6**, No. 3 (1955).

28. D. F. Lawden, Interplanetary trajectories, *Advances in Space Sci.* **1**, No. 1 (1959).

29. G. Leitmann, On a class of variational problems in rocket flight, *J. Aero/Space Sci.* **26**, No. 9 (1959).

30. G. Leitmann, Extremal rocket trajectories in position and time dependent force fields, AAS Preprint No. 61-30 (1961).

31. A. Miele, General variational theory of the flight paths of rocket-powered aircraft, missiles, and satellite carriers, *Astronaut. Acta* **4**, No. 4 (1958).
32. A. Miele, Minimal maneuvers of high-performance aircraft in a vertical plane, NASA TN No. D-155 (1959).
33. R. Bellman, "Dynamic Programming." Princeton Univ. Press, Princeton, New Jersey, 1957.
34. A. Miele, Flight mechanics and variational problems of a linear type, *J. Aero/Space Sci.* **25**, No. 9 (1958).
35. A. Miele, Application of Green's theorem to the extremization of linear integrals, Boeing Scientific Research Laboratories, Flight Sciences Laboratory, TR No. 40 (1961).
36. A. Miele, The relation between the Green's theorem approach and the indirect methods for extremal problems of a linear type, Boeing Scientific Research Laboratories, Flight Sciences Laboratory, TR No. 47 (1961).
37. A. Miele, Interrelationship of calculus of variations and ordinary theory of maxima and minima for flight mechanics applications, *ARS Journal* **29**, No. 1 (1959).
38. A. Miele, Lagrange multipliers and quasi-steady flight mechanics, *J. Aero/Space Sci.* **26**, No 9 (1959).
39. H. S. Tsien and R. C. Evans, Optimum thrust programming for a sounding rocket, *ARS Journal* **21**, No. 5 (1951).
40. G. Leitmann, A calculus of variations solution of Goddard's problem, *Astronaut. Acta* **2**, No. 2 (1956).
41. G. Leitmann, Stationary trajectories for a high-altitude rocket with drop-away booster, *Astronaut. Acta* **2**, No. 3 (1956).
42. G. Leitmann, Optimum thrust programming for high-altitude rockets, *Aero/Space Eng.* **16**, No. 6 (1957).
43. G. Leitmann, A note on Goddard's problem, *Astronaut. Acta* **3**, No. 4 (1957).
44. A. Miele, Generalized variational approach to the optimum thrust programming for the vertical flight of a rocket. Part I. Necessary conditions for the extremum, *ZFW* **6**, No. 3 (1958).
45. A. Miele, Minimality for arbitrarily inclined rocket trajectories, *ARS Journal* **28**, No. 7 (1958).
46. A. Miele, Stationary conditions for problems involving time associated with vertical rocket trajectories, *J. Aero/Space Sci.* **25**, No. 7 (1958).
47. A. Miele, On the brachistocronic thrust program for a rocket-powered missile traveling in an isothermal medium, *ARS Journal* **28**, No. 10 (1958).
48. A. Miele, "Flight Mechanics," Vol. 1: Theory of Flight Paths. Addison-Wesley, Reading, Massachusetts, 1962.
49. D. F. Lawden, Optimal rocket trajectories, *ARS Journal* **27**, No. 12 (1957).
50. B. D. Fried and J. M. Richardson, Optimum rocket trajectories, *J. Appl. Phys.* **27**, No. 8 (1956).
51. A. Miele and J. O. Cappellari, Topics in dynamic programming for rockets, *ZFW* **7**, No. 1 (1959).
52. B. D. Fried, On the powered flight trajectory of an earth satellite, *ARS Journal* **27**, No. 6 (1957).
53. A. R. Hibbs, Optimum burning program for horizontal flight, *ARS Journal* **22**, No. 4 (1952).
54. P. Cicala and A. Miele, Generalized theory of the optimum thrust programming for the level flight of a rocket-powered aircraft, *ARS Journal* **26**, No. 6 (1956).

55. A. E. Bryson and S. E. Ross, Optimum rocket trajectories with aerodynamic drag, *ARS Journal* **28**, No. 7 (1958).
56. A. Miele, General solutions of optimum problems in nonstationary flight, NACA TM No. 1388 (1955).

GENERAL REFERENCES

Baker, G. A., Ford, K. W., and Porter, C. E., Optimal accuracy rocket trajectories, *J. Appl. Phys.* **30**, No. 12 (1959).

Baker, R. M. L., Jr., Recent advances in astrodynamics, 1960, *ARS Journal* **30**, No. 12 (1960).

Behrbohm, H., Brachystochrone Flugbahnen im Raum bei Zeitlich Veränderlichem Fluggewicht, *Jahrb. WGL* (1954).

Behrbohm, H., Optimal trajectories in the horizontal plane, SAAB TN No. 33 (1955).

Behrbohm, H., Optimal trajectories in the vertical plane, SAAB TN No. 34 (1955).

Bellman, R., and Dreyfus, S., An application of dynamic programming to the determination of optimal satellite trajectories, *J. Brit. Interplanet. Soc.* **17**, Nos. 3–4 (1959).

Bergqvist, B., The optimization problem for rocket vehicles subjected to medium and high accelerations: A literature survey, *Astronautik* **1**, No. 3 (1959).

Breakwell, J. V., Fuel requirements for crude interplanetary guidance, AAS Preprint No. 59–5 (1959).

Breakwell, J. V., The spacing of corrective thrusts in interplanetary navigation, AAS Preprint No. 60–76 (1960).

Breakwell, J. V., Gillespie, R. W., and Ross, S. E., Researches in interplanetary transfer, ARS, Preprint No. 954–59 (1959).

Bryson, A. E., Denham, W. F., Carroll, F. J., and Mikami, K., Determination of the lift or drag program that minimizes re-entry heating with acceleration or range constraints using a steepest descent computation procedure, IAS Preprint No. 61–6 (1961).

Burns, R. E., Correlative survey report on powered flight trajectory optimization including an extensive critical bibliography, ARS Preprint No. 2071-61 (1961).

Carstoiu, J., On a minimum-time flight path of a jet aircraft, *J. Aero/Space Sci.* **24**, No. 9 (1957).

Cartaino, T. F., and Dreyfus, S. E., Application of dynamic programming to the airplane minimum time-to-climb problem, *Aero/Space Eng.* **16**, No. 6 (1957).

Carter, W. J., Optimum nose shapes for missiles in the superaerodynamic region, *J. Aero/Space Sci.* **24**, No. 7 (1957).

Chang, I. D., On optimum nose shapes for missiles in the superaerodynamic region, *J. Aero/Space Sci.* **25**, No. 1 (1958).

Cicala, P., and Miele, A., Evoluzioni Brachistocrone di un Aereo, *Atti accad. sci. Torino, Classe sci. fis. mat. e nat.* **89**, (1954–1955).

Cicala, P., and Miele, A., Brachistocronic maneuvers of a constant mass aircraft in a vertical plane, *J. Aero/Space Sci.* **22**, No. 4 (1955).

Cicala, P., and Miele, A., Brachistocronic maneuvers of a variable mass aircraft in a vertical plane, *J. Aero/Space Sci.* **22**, No. 8 (1955).

Dennis, D. H., On optimum nose shapes for missiles in the superaerodynamic region, *J. Aero/Space Sci.* **25**, No. 3 (1958).

Ewing, G. M., A fundamental problem of navigation in free space, *Quart. Appl. Math.* **18**, No. 4 (1961).

Faulders, C. R., Minimum-time steering programs for orbital transfer with low-thrust rockets, North American Aviation, Inc., Missile Division, Rept. No. MD 60-280 (1960).

Faulders, C. R., Optimum thrust programming of electrically powered rocket vehicles in a gravitational field, *ARS Journal* **30**, No. 10 (1960).

Faulkner, F. D., Homing in a vacuum with minimum fuel consumption, Univ. of Michigan, Aeronautical Research Center, Rept. No. UMM 18 (1949).

Faulkner, F. D., The problem of Goddard and optimum thrust programming, *Proc. 3rd Ann. Meeting Am. Astronaut. Soc.* (1956).

Faulkner, F. D., Some results from direct methods applied to optimum rocket trajectories, *Proc. 9th Intern. Astronaut. Congr. Amsterdam* (1958).

Ferrari, C., Sulla determinazione del proietto di minima resistenza d'onda, *Atti accad. Sci. Torino, Class sci. fis. mat. e nat.* **74**, (1939–1940).

Foote, J. R., Butler, T., Adney, J. E., and Thacher, H. C., Direct variational methods and brachistochrone problems, AFOSR TR No. 101 (1961).

Fox, R. H., Optimum exhaust velocity programming and propulsion efficiency, *J. Astronaut. Sci.* **6**, No. 1 (1959).

Fox, R. H., The payload capabilities of ion propulsion rocket systems, *J. Astronaut. Sci.* **6**, No. 3 (1959).

Foy, W. H., Steering of an ascent rocket for maximum cut-off velocity, *Proc. 4th Ann Meeting Am. Astronaut. Soc.* (1958).

Fraeijs de Veubeke, B., Méthodes Variationnelles et Performances Optimales en Aéronautique, *Bull. Soc. Math. Belgique* **8**, No. 2 (1956).

Fraeijs de Veubeke, B., Le Problème du Maximum de Rayon d'Action dans un Champ de Gravitation Uniforme, *Astronaut. Acta* **4**, No. 1 (1958).

Fraeijs de Veubeke, B., *in* "Rocket Propulsion," Variational methods in optimizing rocket performance, Chap. 12. Elsevier, New York, 1960.

Garbell, M. A., Optimum climbing techniques for high performance aircraft, Garbell Research Foundation, Rept. No. 8 (1953).

Graham, E. W., and Beane, B. J., Optimum trajectory problems: Some special cases, Douglas Aircraft Company, Inc. Santa Monica Division, Rept. No. SM-23687 (1959).

Haack, W., Projectile forms of minimum wave resistance, Douglas Aircraft Company, Inc., Translation Rept. No. 288 (1946).

Irving, J. H., *in* "Space Technology," Low-thrust flight: Variable exhaust velocity in gravitational fields, Chap. 10. Wiley, New York, 1959.

Irving, J. H., and Blum, E. K., *in* "Vistas in Astronautics," Vol. 2, Comparative performance of ballistic and low-thrust vehicles for flight to Mars. Pergamon, New York, 1959.

Jurovics, S., Optimum steering program for the entry of a multistage vehicle into a circular orbit, *ARS Journal* **31**, No. 4 (1961).

Jurovics, S. A., and McIntyre, J. E., The adjoint method and its application to trajectory optimization, North American Aviation, Inc., Missile Division, Rept. No. MD 60-334 (1960).

Kaiser, F., The climb of jet-propelled aircraft. Part I. Speed along the path in optimum climb, Ministry of Supply (Gt. Brit.), RTP/TIB Translation No. GDC/15/148T (1944).

Kelley, H. J., An investigation of Optimal Zoom Climb Techniques, *J. Aero/Space Sci.* **26**, No. 12 (1959).

Kelley, H. J., Variational treatment of three-dimensional boost-turn performance. Grumman Aircraft Engineering Corp., RM No. 162 (1959).

Kelly, L., Optimum climb technique for a jet-propelled aircraft, The College of Aeronautics, Cranfield, Rept. No. 57 (1952).

Lawden, D. F., Minimal trajectories, *J. Brit. Interplanet. Soc.* **9**, No. 4 (1950).

Lawden, D. F., Entry into circular orbits, *J. Brit. Interplanet. Soc.* **10**, No. 1 1951).

Lawden, D. F., The determination of minimal orbits, *J. Brit. Interplanet. Soc.* **11**, No. (1952).

Lawden, D. F., Interorbital transfer of a rocket, *Brit. Interplanet. Soc. Ann. Rept.* (1952).

Lawden, D. F., Orbital transfer via tangential ellipses, *J. Brit. Interplanet. Soc.* **11**, No. 6 (1952).

Lawden, D. F., Minimal rocket trajectories, *ARS Journal* **23**, No. 6 (1953).

Lawden, D. F., Stationary rocket trajectories, *Quart. J. Mech. and Appl. Math.* **7**, No. 4 (1954).

Lawden, D. F., Optimum launching of a rocket into an orbit about the earth. *Astronaut. Acta* **1**, No. 4 (1955).

Lawden, D. F., Optimal programming of rocket thrust direction, *Astronaut. Acta* **1**, No. 1 (1955).

Lawden, D. F., Optimal transfer between circular orbits about two planets, *Astronaut. Acta* **1**, No. 2 (1955).

Lawden, D. F., Transfer between circular orbits, *ARS Journal* **26**, No. 7 (1956).

Lawden, D. F., Mathematical problems of astronautics, *Math. Gazette* **41**, No. 337 (1957).

Lawden, D. F., Maximum ranges of intercontinental missiles, *Aeronaut. Quart.* **8**, No. 3 (1957).

Lawden, D. F., The employment of aerodynamic forces to obtain maximum range of a rocket missile, *Aeronaut. Quart.* **9**, No. 2 (1958).

Lawden, D. F., Optimal escape from a circular orbit, *Astronaut. Acta* **4**, No. 3 (1958).

Lawden, D. F., Discontinuous solutions of variational problems, *J. Australian Math. Soc.* **1**, No. 1 (1959).

Lawden, D. F., Necessary conditions for optimal rocket trajectories, *Quart. J. Mech. and Appl. Math.* **12**, No. 4 (1959).

Lawden, D. F., Optimal programme for correctional manoeuvres, *Astronaut. Acta* **6**, No. 4 (1960).

Leitmann, G., An optimum pursuit problem, *J. Franklin Inst.* **263**, No. 6 (1957).

Leitmann, G., Trajectory programming for maximum range, *J. Franklin Inst.* **264**, No. 6 (1957).

Leitmann G., Optimum thrust direction for maximum range, *J. Brit. Interplanet. Soc.* **16**, No. 9 (1958).

Leitmann, G., Some remarks on the optimum operation of a nuclear rocket, *Proc. 10th Intern. Astronaut. Congr., London* (1959).

Leitmann, G., Minimum transfer time for a power-limited rocket, *Proc. 11th Intern. Astronaut. Congr., Stockholm* (1960).

Leitmann, G., *in* "Progress in the Astronautical Sciences." The optimization of rocket trajectories. A survey, Chap. 5. North-Holland, Amsterdam, 1962.

Levinsky, E. S., Application of inequality constraints to variational problems of lifting re-entry, IAS Preprint No. 61-21 (1961).

Lush, K. J., Optimum climb theory and techniques of determining climb schedules from flight tests, AFFTC TN No. 56-13 (1956).

Miele, A., Optimum climbing technique for a rocket-powered aircraft, *ARS Journal* **25**, No. 8 (1955).

Miele, A., Optimum flight paths of turbojet aircraft, NACA TM No. 1389 (1955).

Miele, A., Optimum burning program as related to aerodynamic heating for a missile traversing the earth's atmosphere, *ARS Journal* **27**, No. 12 (1957).

Miele, A., Some recent advances in the mechanics of terrestrial flight, *ARS Journal* **28**, No. 9 (1958).

Miele, A., Variational approach to the stratospheric cruise of a turbojet-powered aircraft, *ZFW* **6**, No. 9 (1958).

Miele, A., On the flight path of a hypervelocity glider boosted by rockets, *Astronaut. Acta* **5**, No. 6 (1959).

Miele, A., Variational approach to problems of hypervelocity flight, Purdue University, School of Aeronautical Engineering, Rept. No. A-59-7 (1959).

Miele, A., A survey of the problem of optimizing flight paths of aircraft and missiles, Boeing Scientific Research Laboratories, Flight Sciences Laboratory, TR No. 27 (1960).

Miele, A., and Cappellari, J. O., Some variational solutions to rocket trajectories over a spherical earth, Purdue University, School of Aeronautical Engineering, Rept. No. A-58-9 (1958).

Miele, A., and Cappellari, J. O., Approximate solutions to the optimum climbing trajectory for a rocket-powered aircraft, NASA TN No. D-150 (1959).

Miele, A., and Capellari, J. O., Approximate solutions to optimum flight trajectories for a turbojet-powered aircraft, NASA TN No. D-152 (1959).

Miele, A., and Cavoti, C. R., Generalized variational approach to the optimum thrust programming for the vertical flight of a rocket, Part 2, Application of Green's theorem to the development of sufficiency proofs for particular classes of solutions, *ZFW* **6**, No. 4 (1958).

Miele, A., and Cavoti, C. R., Optimum thrust programming along arbitrarily inclined rectilinear paths, *Astronaut. Acta* **4**, No. 3 (1958).

Miele, A., and Cavoti, C. R., Variational approach to the reentry of a ballistic missile, Part 1, Purdue University, School of Aeronautical Engineering, Rept. No. A-59-1 (1959).

Miele, A., and Cavoti, C. R., Variational approach to the reentry of a ballistic missile, Part 2, Purdue University, School of Aeronautical Engineering, Rept. No. A-59-3 (1959).

Newton, R. R., On the optimum trajectory of a rocket, *J. Franklin Inst.* **266**, No. 3 (1958).

Okhotsimskii, D. E., and Eneev, T. M., Some variational problems connected with the launching of artificial satellites of the earth, *J. Brit. Interplanet. Soc.* **16**, No. 5 (1958).

Puckett, A. E., and Edwards, R. H., The optimum performance of short-range rocket-powered missiles, IAS Preprint No. 279 (1950).

Rosenberg, R. M., On optimum rocket trajectories and the calculus of variations, *Aero/Space Eng.* **19**, No. 10 (1960).

Ross, S. E., Minimality for problems in vertical and horizontal rocket flight, *ARS Journal* **28**, No. 1 (1958).

Ross, S. E., Composite trajectories yielding maximum coasting apogee velocity, *ARS Journal* **29**, No. 11 (1959).

Rutowski, E. S., Energy approach to the general aircraft performance problem, *J. Aero/Space Sci.* **21**, No. 3 (1954).

Santangelo, G., Sulla Virata Corretta Brachistocrona, *L'Aerotecnica* **33**, No. 2 (1953).

Sears, W. R., On projectiles of minimum wave drag, *Quart. Appl. Math.* **4,** No. 4 (1947).

Stancil, R. T., and Kulakowski, L. J., Rocket boost vehicle mission optimizations, *ARS* Preprint No. 1449-60 (1960).

Strand, T., Design of missile bodies for minimum drag at very high speeds. Thickness ratio, lift, and center of pressure given, *J. Aero/Space Sci.* **26**, No. 9 (1959).

Tan, H. S., On optimum nose curves for missiles in the superaerodynamic regime, *J. Aero/Space Sci.* **25,** No. 1 (1958).

Tan, H. S., Nose drag in free-molecule flow and its minimization, *J. Aero/Space Sci.* **26,** No. 6 (1959).

Theodorsen, T., Optimum path of an airplane—Minimum time to climb, *J. Aero/Space Sci.* **26,** No. 10 (1959).

Von Karman, T., The problem of resistance in compressible fluids, *Galcit Publ.* No. 75 (1936).

Ward, L. E., A calculus of variations problem in thrust programming, U.S. Naval Ordnance Test Station, TN No. 3503/2 (1955).

—5—

Variational Problems with Bounded Control Variables

G. LEITMANN

University of California, Berkeley, California

5.0 Introduction

The elements of the calculus of variations, particularly as they apply to problems in the optimization of missile systems and trajectories, were presented in Chapter 4. The theory takes on some rather special aspects whenever one or more of the control variables are subjected to inequality constraints (see Appendix and Chapter 7). It is the purpose of this chapter to treat a class of such problems in detail. In order to expose the underlying methods in some generality, and yet not to lose sight of the forest for the trees, the discussion will be limited to a class of problems which are sufficiently simple so as to be amenable to treatment by existing techniques and yet realistic enough to be of interest.

The discussion will be centered on the optimization of trajectories of rockets traveling in force fields which give rise to accelerations depending on position and time only, with gravitational force fields being of prime interest, of course.[1] Flight in an atmosphere leads to forces which are velocity dependent as well, and such problems are not included here. Their omission is not prompted by a lack of interest, but rather stems from a desire to demonstrate the techniques with a minimum of complications—and perhaps more importantly, because of the incomplete state of knowledge about optimum trajectories with velocity-dependent forces and linear control variables such as mass flow rate and propulsive power.

The control variables which will be considered subject to inequality constraints are mass flow rate, propulsive power, and thrust acceleration, respectively.

5.1 Statement of the Problem

It is desired to determine conditions resulting in the minimum value of a functional which is a function only of the end values of the state variables—position, velocity, mass, and time:

$$G = G(q_{ji}, q_{jt}) \tag{5.1}$$

where

$$q_j = x, y, u, v, m, t \tag{5.2}$$

The function G encompasses all quantities of interest such as time, mass, velocity, range, altitude, energy, angular momentum, etc.

The following assumptions are made concerning the rocket and its environment:

(a) The rocket is considered a particle of variable mass, i.e., the rocket's moments of inertia are assumed negligibly small.

(b) The thrust magnitude is taken as a linear function of the mass flow rate[2]

$$T = -c\dot{m} \tag{5.3}$$

(c) It is assumed that the thrust direction can be changed instantaneously, e.g., any time delays in controlling the gimbal angle of the motor are neglected.

(d) The external forces acting on the rocket give rise to accelerations which are functions of position and time only, i.e.,

$$X = X(x, y, t)$$

$$Y = Y(x, y, t) \tag{5.4}$$

The ensuing analysis is restricted to planar flight. This is done solely for the sake of simplicity and all results are readily extended to three-dimensional flight.

With assumptions (a)–(d) the equations of motion of the rocket, relative to inertial space, are

$$\dot{u} = X + \frac{c\beta}{m} \cos \psi$$

$$\dot{v} = Y + \frac{c\beta}{m} \sin \psi$$

$$\dot{x} = u \tag{5.5}$$

$$\dot{y} = v$$

$$\dot{m} = -\beta$$

The equations of motion, Eqs. (5.5), relate eight dependent variables, namely, x, y, u, v, m, c, β, and ψ. Since there are but five equations, three of the variables are arbitrary functions—the control variables $c(t)$, $\beta(t)$, and $\psi(t)$—to be chosen so as to obtain the desired optimum trajectory, i.e., one resulting in the minimum value of the "payoff" G.

The analysis of the class of problems posed above will be carried out, in turn, for rocket systems which are mass flow rate limited, power limited, and thrust-acceleration limited but operating at constant power. Bounds on these control variables have been considered, since without such bounds it is not possible to obtain a solution, for example, to problems in which the control variables enter linearly. Of course, inequality constraints on other control variables, such as thrust direction angle ψ,[3] can also be treated by the methods discussed in this chapter.

5.2 Mass Flow Rate Limited Systems

For most conventional rockets, e.g., chemical propulsion systems, the following constraints apply, in addition to Eqs. (5.5):

$$c = \text{const} \tag{5.6}$$

$$\beta_{\min} \leq \beta \leq \beta_{\max} \tag{5.7}$$

where $\beta_{\max}$ is specified and $\beta_{\min} = 0$, in general, to allow for coasting flight.

To permit the inclusion of inequality constraints, such as Ineq. (5.7), within the framework of the classical calculus of variations a real variable γ is introduced[4] such that

$$(\beta - \beta_{\min})(\beta_{\max} - \beta) = \gamma^2 \tag{5.8}$$

Equation (5.8) is equivalent to Ineq. (5.7).

For the rocket system under consideration the number of control variables is reduced to two, β and ψ, the former of which is bounded.

5.21 First Variation

In order that G possess an *extremum*, subject to constraints (5.5), (5.6), and (5.8), it is necessary that the first variation of the constrained functional vanish (see also Chapter 4). This leads to the Euler-Lagrange equations[5]

$$\dot{\lambda}_u + \lambda_x = 0$$

$$\dot{\lambda}_v + \lambda_y = 0$$

$$\dot{\lambda}_x + \lambda_u \partial X/\partial x + \lambda_v \partial Y/\partial x = 0$$

$$\dot{\lambda}_y + \lambda_u \partial X/\partial y + \lambda_v \partial Y/\partial y = 0 \tag{5.9}$$

$$\dot{\lambda}_m - \frac{c\beta}{m^2}(\lambda_u \cos \psi + \lambda_v \sin \psi) = 0$$

$$\frac{c\beta}{m}(\lambda_u \sin \psi - \lambda_v \cos \psi) = 0$$

$$\frac{c}{m}(\lambda_u \cos \psi + \lambda_v \sin \psi) - \lambda_m - \lambda_\gamma(\beta_{\max} + \beta_{\min} - 2\beta) = 0$$

$$\lambda_\gamma \gamma = 0$$

where the λ's are undetermined multipliers.

For a meaningful problem all but one of the end values of the state variables x, y, u, v, m, t may be specified. The remaining ones, together with those of the λ's may be found from the general transversality condition

$$dG + [\lambda_u \, du + \lambda_v \, dv + \lambda_x \, dx + \lambda_y \, dy + \lambda_m \, dm - C \, dt]_{t_i}^{t_f} = 0 \qquad (5.10)$$

where

$$C = \lambda_u \dot{u} + \lambda_v \dot{v} + \lambda_x \dot{x} + \lambda_y \dot{y} + \lambda_m \dot{m} \qquad (5.11)$$

If the external force accelerations X and Y are not explicit functions of the independent variable, here time t, then there exists a first integral

$$C = \text{constant} \qquad (5.12)$$

which may be used to replace any one of the differential Euler-Lagrange equations, thereby reducing the order of the system by one.

Equations (5.5), (5.6), (5.8), and (5.9) constitute a system of 15 equations which, together with the given and derived end conditions, are expected to yield the optimal solution, namely, the 15 functions of time x, y, u, v, m, c, β, ψ, γ, λ_u, λ_v, λ_x, λ_y, λ_m, and λ_γ. Since 10 of the equations are first-order ordinary differential equations, the system is of order 10, requiring 10 initial, or final, values of the state variables and multipliers, and the two end values of the independent variable, time.

Since half of the prescribed and derived values of the end conditions occur at $t = t_i$ and the other half at $t = t_f$, the problem is always of mixed end-value nature. From the computational point of view this requires an iterative procedure in which the unknown end values at the initial (or final) point are assumed, the integration is carried out, and an attempt is made to match the given and derived end conditions at the other terminal. Such a procedure is often time-consuming, sometimes nonconvergent.

Even if the difficulties posed by the mixed end-value nature of the problem can be surmounted—and they often can, see the numerical example, Section 5.6—there still exists a number of other questions left unresolved thus far.

5.22 Thrust Direction Program

The optimum thrust direction is given by Eq. (5.9)[6], namely,

$$\tan \psi = \lambda_v / \lambda_u \qquad (5.13)$$

that is,

$$\sin \psi = \pm \lambda_v / \sqrt{\lambda_u{}^2 + \lambda_v{}^2}$$
$$\cos \psi = \pm \lambda_u / \sqrt{\lambda_u{}^2 + \lambda_v{}^2} \qquad (5.14)$$

a result first found for flight in a constant gravitational field.[6]

As can be seen from Eqs. (5.13) or (5.14) there exists an ambiguity regarding the choice of principal value of the thrust direction angle, i.e., the solution of Eq. (5.13) is

$$\psi = \psi(t)$$

or   (5.15)

$$\psi = \psi(t) + \pi$$

In other words there exists no criterion, thus far, which prescribes the choice of the $+$ or $-$ sign in Eqs. (5.14). If the $+$ sign is chosen,[7] then λ_u and λ_v are in effect the direction numbers of the thrust vector. While this is indeed the proper choice, it needs to be proved. Here then is a question which, apparently, is not answered by considering only the conditions arising from the first variation. Since the answer to this question can be found together with the answer to another one, its resolution will be delayed for the moment.

5.23 Mass Flow Rate Program

If constraint (5.7) embodied in Eq. (5.8) is to be satisfied, then it is clear that flight must take place with maximum, minimum (coast), or intermediate mass flow rate. The Euler-Lagrange equation (5.9) arises from constraint (5.8). These equations result in the following conditions[8]:

$$\gamma \neq 0, \qquad \lambda_\gamma = 0 \quad \text{and} \quad \beta_{\min} < \beta < \beta_{\max}$$

$$\left.\begin{aligned} \gamma = 0, \qquad \lambda_\gamma \neq 0 \\ \gamma = 0, \qquad \lambda_\gamma = 0 \end{aligned}\right\} \quad \text{and} \quad \beta = \beta_{\min} \quad \text{or} \quad \beta = \beta_{\max} \quad (5.16)$$

While conditions (5.16) satisfy the Euler-Lagrange equation arising from the inequality constraint on mass flow rate β, they leave unanswered the crucial question of choosing the optimum mass flow rate regime. Here then is yet another problem apparently not solved by a consideration of the first variation. For a particular case, namely, maximum injection speed into a circular satellite orbit, ascent in a constant gravitational field, and unbounded mass flow rate, a solution can be obtained directly.[9] However, for the general problem considered here one must turn to stronger conditions than those arising from the vanishing of the first variation.[10]

Since the control variables ψ and β do not appear in derivated form, they may possess a finite number of discontinuities—and indeed do so, in general—so that accelerations $\dot{u}$ and $\dot{v}$ may also be discontinuous. Such discontinuities correspond to corners of the extremal arc, where the Weierstrass-Erdmann corner conditions apply.

5.24 Corner Conditions

For the problem under discussion the corner conditions are simply

$$\lambda_{q-} = \lambda_{q+}, \qquad q = x, y, u, v, m \tag{5.17}$$

and

$$C_- = C_+ \tag{5.18}$$

Thus, the multipliers associated with the state variables and expression (5.11) have equal values immediately prior to and following a corner.

5.25 Weierstrass E-Function

In order to resolve the two questions which have been left unanswered, namely, the ambiguity concerning the choice of principal value of thrust direction angle ψ and the optimum choice of mass flow rate regime, one may turn to a necessary condition for a *minimum* value of functional G. Such a condition is the requirement that the Weierstrass E-function be non-negative. For the problem treated here this condition is equivalent to requiring that the control variables ψ and β be chosen such as to maximize the expression

$$L \equiv \beta \left[\frac{c}{m} (\lambda_u \cos \psi + \lambda_v \sin \psi) - \lambda_m \right] \tag{5.19}$$

along the optimum path (see Appendix). This condition is related to the functional equation of Bellman's optimality principle[11] and equivalent to Pontryagin's maximum principle[12] (see also Chapter 7).

5.26 Optimum Thrust Direction

In order that L be maximum with respect to ψ

$$\frac{\partial L}{\partial \psi} = 0$$

$$\tag{5.20}$$

$$\frac{\partial^2 L}{\partial \psi^2} \leq 0$$

Conditions (5.20) immediately lead to Eq. (5.13) and the choice of the $+$ sign in Eqs. (5.14), thereby resolving the question of the optimum choice of thrust direction angle ψ. Consequently,

$$\lambda_u \cos \psi + \lambda_v \sin \psi = (\lambda_u{}^2 + \lambda_v{}^2)^{1/2} \tag{5.21}$$

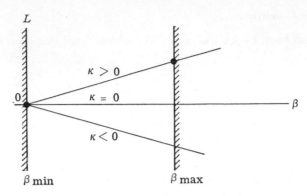

FIG. 1.   Weierstrass condition for mass flow rate.

Furthermore, it now follows from Eqs. (5.14) that ψ jumps by π radians whenever λ_u and λ_v pass through zero together.[13]

5.27 Optimum Mass Flow Rate—The Switching Function

With respect to mass flow rate β, Eq. (5.19) is now

$$L = \kappa\beta \tag{5.22}$$

that is, a linear function of β, where the slope

$$\kappa = \frac{c}{m}(\lambda_u{}^2 + \lambda_v{}^2)^{1/2} - \lambda_m \tag{5.23}$$

A plot of L as a function of β at any instant of time is shown in Fig. 1. It is clear that whenever

$$\kappa > 0, \qquad \beta = \beta_{\max}$$
$$\tag{5.24}$$
$$\kappa < 0, \qquad \beta = \beta_{\min}$$

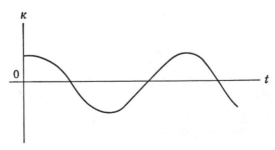

FIG. 2.   Mass flow rate switching function.

If κ merely passes through zero, no difficulty is encountered and κ may be considered as a switching function for the "bang-bang" control of mass flow rate. That is, if it can be shown that

$$\kappa \not\equiv 0 \tag{5.25}$$

a situation portrayed in Figs. 2 and 3, then the switching function κ can be computed from Eq. (5.23) with Eq. (5.9)$_7$ replaced by condition (5.24).

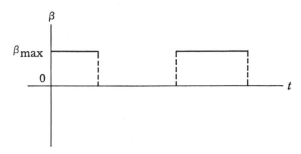

FIG. 3.   "Bang-bang" mass flow rate control.

However, if condition (5.25) cannot be ruled out,* then programmed intermediate mass flow rate may occur and the Weierstrass E-function gives no clue to the optimum choice of mass flow rate regime (see Fig. 1). However, there exists an important class of problems for which condition (5.25) and hence "bang-bang" control has been demonstrated.[10,14]

5.28 "Bang-Bang" Control of Mass Flow Rate

If the accelerations due to the external forces are linear functions of the position coordinates, i.e.,

$$X = X_0 + X_1 x + X_2 y$$
$$\tag{5.26}$$
$$Y = Y_0 + Y_1 x + Y_2 y$$

where the coefficients X_0, Y_0, X_1, $\cdots$, Y_2 are independent of position coordinates x and y, then Eqs. (5.9)$_{1-4}$ become

$$\ddot{\lambda}_u - \lambda_u X_1 - \lambda_v Y_1 = 0$$
$$\tag{5.27}$$
$$\ddot{\lambda}_v - \lambda_u X_2 - \lambda_v Y_2 = 0$$

Equations (5.27) are two second-order differential equations in the thrust

---

* For example, when aerodynamic forces are considered, condition (5.25) cannot be shown to hold in general.

direction numbers λ_u and λ_v which are now *decoupled* from the remaining Euler-Lagrange and constraint equations.

Furthermore, if condition (5.25) does not apply,

$$\dot{\kappa} = 0 \qquad (5.28)$$

in a finite time interval. Equation (5.28) together with Eqs. (5.9)$_5$ and (5.21) result in

$$\lambda_u \dot{\lambda}_u + \lambda_v \dot{\lambda}_v = 0 \qquad (5.29)$$

which is yet another equation involving only λ_u and λ_v.

Now it can be shown that the solution of Eqs. (5.27) does not satisfy Eq. (5.29), in general. The case of λ_u and λ_v identically equal to zero can be ruled out, since it corresponds to the vanishing of all multipliers.

Particular cases of interest are the following:

(1) Flight in a constant gravitational field, namely,

$$X = 0$$
$$\qquad (5.30)$$
$$Y = -g_0 = \text{constant}$$

For this case it has been shown[10] that one of two situations may arise:

(a) There are at most three mass flow rate regimes in any one optimum trajectory, i.e., the total trajectory is made up of no more than three parts, flown either at maximum or minimum (coast) thrust.

(b) There is no unique optimum solution.

(2) Flight in an approximately inverse-square radial field for which only first-order terms in the expansion of the gravitational acceleration are considered,[14] namely,

$$X = -\epsilon^2 x$$
$$\qquad (5.31)$$
$$Y = -g_0 + 2\epsilon^2 y$$

An example of such a problem is discussed in Section 5.6.

While it has not been possible to demonstrate the nonadmissibility of programmed intermediate mass flow rate for optimal flight in more general force fields, such behavior might nonetheless occur, if not in general, then perhaps in some regions of the field or under certain conditions.

In view of Eqs. (5.23) and (5.9)$_{1-5}$

$$\dot{\kappa} = -\frac{c}{m} (\lambda_x \lambda_u + \lambda_y \lambda_v) (\lambda_u{}^2 + \lambda_v{}^2)^{-1/2} \qquad (5.32)$$

so that $\dot{\kappa}$ is discontinuous—changes sign—whenever λ_u and λ_v pass through zero simultaneously, i.e., when ψ experiences a discontinuous jump. Figure

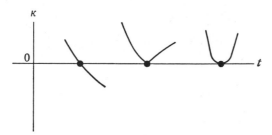

FIG. 4. Zeros of the switching function.

4 shows the possible ways in which κ may pass through zero. Consequently, an intermediate mass flow rate regime, $\kappa \equiv 0$, can only be entered continuously. Since the time derivatives of κ are continuous through the third derivative, it is required that

$$\kappa = \dot{\kappa} = \ddot{\kappa} = \dddot{\kappa} = 0 \tag{5.33}$$

before entering an intermediate mass flow rate regime. These conditions may be of help in ruling out the occurrence of such regimes.

5.29 Unbounded Mass Flow Rate

If no upper bound is placed on the mass flow rate, that is,

$$\beta_{\max} = \infty \tag{5.34}$$

and condition (5.25), i.e., "bang-bang" control, is assured, then periods of maximum mass flow rate go to zero. In other words, maximum thrust regimes are replaced by impulses. The behavior of the switching function for this case is shown in Fig. 5.

Thus, either

$$\kappa = \dot{\kappa} = 0 \tag{5.35a}$$

or

$$\kappa = 0 \tag{5.35b}$$

$$\lambda_u = \lambda_v = 0$$

Both of these conditions, (5.35a) and (5.35b), are embodied in[15]

$$\lambda_u \dot{\lambda}_u + \lambda_v \dot{\lambda}_v = 0 \tag{5.36}$$

which must be satisfied at every *interior* point of the trajectory, where an impulse is called for.

5.210 Intermediate Mass Flow Rate Program

If the occurrence of regimes of intermediate mass flow rate cannot be ruled out, the question of composing the total optimum trajectory remains

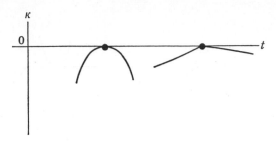

FIG. 5.   Switching function for impulsive thrust.

unanswered. Some results pertaining to such programmed mass flow rate regimes can be deduced, however. While not necessarily useful in the general case, nonetheless, such results may be of service in eliminating the possibility of the existence of such regimes. Thus, if

$$\kappa = 0 \tag{5.37}$$

in a nonzero interval, then Eq. (5.29) holds. Integration of Eq. (5.29) yields

$$\lambda \cdot \lambda = \text{const} \tag{5.38}$$

where λ is a vector with components λ_u and λ_v, i.e., in the direction of the thrust. In terms of vector λ, Eqs. $(5.9)_{1-4}$ then lead to

$$\dot{\lambda} \cdot \dot{\lambda} + \nabla(\mathbf{F} \cdot \lambda) \cdot \lambda = 0 \tag{5.39}$$

where, for the case of planar flight, $\mathbf{F}$ is the external force acceleration with components X and Y. A necessary condition for the existence of a programmed regime of intermediate mass flow rate is then

$$\nabla(\mathbf{F} \cdot \lambda) \cdot \lambda \leq 0 \tag{5.40}$$

For an inverse-square radial field,

$$\mathbf{F} = \nabla\phi, \qquad \phi \sim \frac{1}{r} \tag{5.41}$$

where r is the distance from the attracting center. For this case Ineq. (5.40) becomes[7]

$$\cos^2\theta \leq \tfrac{1}{3} \tag{5.42}$$

where θ is the angle between the thrust and the local vertical.

5.3 Propulsive Power Limited Systems

If the propulsive power rather than the mass flow rate imposes the prime limitation on the system, e.g., as in the case of electric propulsion systems, then constraints (5.6) and (5.7) are replaced by

$$\alpha_{\min} \leq \alpha \leq \alpha_{\max} \tag{5.43}$$

where

$$\alpha = \beta c^2 = 2P \tag{5.44}$$

and $\alpha_{\max}$ is specified. In general, $\alpha_{\min} = 0$ to allow for unpowered flight.

Since the thrust magnitude in energy-separate systems can be varied by adjusting the mass flow rate β as well as the exhaust speed c, there are now three control variables. It is convenient to choose as control variables ψ, α, and c.

5.31 First Variation

In order that functional G possess an extremum, subject to constraints (5.5) and (5.43), where Ineq. (5.43) is again imbedded by introducing a real variable γ, the first variation of the constrained functional must vanish. The resulting Euler-Lagrange equations are

$$\dot{\lambda}_u + \lambda_x = 0$$

$$\dot{\lambda}_v + \lambda_y = 0$$

$$\dot{\lambda}_x + \lambda_u \frac{\partial X}{\partial x} + \lambda_v \frac{\partial Y}{\partial x} = 0$$

$$\dot{\lambda}_y + \lambda_u \frac{\partial X}{\partial y} + \lambda_v \frac{\partial Y}{\partial y} = 0$$

$$\dot{\lambda}_m - \frac{\alpha}{cm^2} (\lambda_u \cos \psi + \lambda_v \sin \psi) = 0$$

$$\frac{\alpha}{mc} (\lambda_u \sin \psi - \lambda_v \cos \psi) = 0 \tag{5.45}$$

$$\frac{\alpha}{mc^2} (\lambda_u \cos \psi + \lambda_v \sin \psi) - 2\lambda_m \frac{\alpha}{c^3} = 0 \ ^*$$

$$\frac{1}{mc} (\lambda_u \cos \psi + \lambda_v \sin \psi) - \frac{1}{c^2} \lambda_m + \lambda_\gamma (2\alpha - \alpha_{\max} - \alpha_{\min}) = 0$$

$$\lambda_\gamma \gamma = 0$$

---

* This equation, corresponding to a *stationary* maximum of L, Eq. (5.47), with respect to c, is valid provided $\lambda_m > 0$. No such stationary extremum of L exists if $\lambda_m \leq 0$; in that case β should be used as control in place of c and must be assigned an upper bound.

In writing the constraint equations and the resulting Euler-Lagrange equations, it is assumed that the exhaust speed does not vanish and has at most a finite number of infinities.

In addition to Eqs. (5.45) there is the general transversality condition, Eq. (5.10), as in Section 5.21. Furthermore, the remarks of Section 5.21 concerning the integration of the constraint and Euler-Lagrange equations apply here.

5.32 Thrust Direction Program

The thrust direction angle is again given by Eq. (5.13). The question regarding the optimum choice of principal value is resolved as in Section 5.26.

5.33 Propulsive Power Program

As in Section 5.23 the inequality constraint, this time on α, and the corresponding Euler-Lagrange equation, Eq. (5.45)$_9$, require that

$$\gamma \neq 0, \quad \lambda_\gamma = 0 \quad \text{and} \quad \alpha_{\min} < \alpha < \alpha_{\max}$$

$$\left. \begin{array}{l} \gamma = 0, \quad \lambda_\gamma \neq 0 \\[2mm] \gamma = 0, \quad \lambda_\gamma = 0 \end{array} \right\} \quad \text{and} \quad \alpha = \alpha_{\min} \quad \text{or} \quad \alpha = \alpha_{\max}$$

(5.46)

Hence, there arises again the problem of composing the total optimum trajectory; in other words, how to arrive at the optimum choice among the three possible power regimes. To resolve this problem one may again turn to the Weierstrass E-function. Before doing so, it should be noted that possible discontinuities in the control variables may result in corners of the extremal arc. The corner conditions here are the same as those of Section 5.24, namely, Eqs. (5.17) and (5.18).

5.34 Weierstrass E-Function

The requirement that the Weierstrass E-function be nonnegative for a minimum of G leads to the condition that

$$L \equiv \alpha \left[\frac{1}{mc} \left(\lambda_u \cos \psi + \lambda_v \sin \psi \right) - \frac{1}{c^2} \lambda_m \right] \tag{5.47}$$

be maximum with respect to the control variables ψ, c, and α.

With respect to thrust direction angle ψ this condition yields Eq. (5.45)$_6$, hence Eqs. (5.14) with the $+$ sign, and Eq. (5.21). With respect to exhaust speed c, the maximality of expression (5.47) results in the corresponding Euler-Lagrange equation, Eq. (5.45)$_7$. For the bounded control variable α,

$$\frac{\partial L}{\partial \alpha} = \frac{1}{mc} (\lambda_u^2 + \lambda_v^2)^{1/2} - \frac{1}{c^2} \lambda_m \tag{5.48}$$

However, from Eq. (5.45)$_7$

$$\frac{1}{c^2} \lambda_m = \frac{1}{2mc} (\lambda_u^2 + \lambda_v^2)^{1/2} \tag{5.49}$$

Consequently,

$$\frac{\partial L}{\partial \alpha} = \frac{1}{2mc} (\lambda_u^2 + \lambda_v^2)^{1/2} \geq 0 \tag{5.50}$$

If the equality sign in expression (5.50) applies in a nonzero interval,

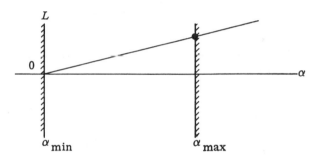

FIG. 6. Weierstrass condition for propulsive power.

$\lambda_u = \lambda_v \equiv 0$ and hence λ_x and λ_y vanish.* Consequently, Fig. 6 portrays the situation at every instant and the optimum power program is

$$\alpha = \alpha_{\max} \tag{5.51}$$

that is, operation at maximum propulsive power throughout the entire trajectory.

For the case of minimizing fuel consumption and with the assumption that unpowered flight does not occur, this result may be deduced directly.[16]

For some problems the results deduced thus far suffice. Among these is the problem of transfer in minimum time between given terminal positions and velocities, and with prescribed mass ratio.[17] Another group of problems amenable to solution by means of the results found here, including maximum speed increase with specified flight time and mass ratio, may be found in a recently published paper,[18] where, however, operation at maximum power was assumed *a priori*.

---

* In that case the payoff is insensitive to changes in velocity and position, and the entire trajectory is unpowered.

In general, there is no assurance that reasonable solutions can be obtained without placing further restrictions on the control variables. In particular, it is not clear that limiting only the propulsive power will prevent the demand for unbounded thrust.[17] Consequently, it may be necessary to impose bounds on the exhaust speed c or on the acceleration produced by the thrust. Only the latter will be considered here.

5.4 Thrust Acceleration Limited Systems

Another possible limitation on the propulsion system may be a bound on the acceleration due to thrust

$$a = \frac{c\beta}{m} \tag{5.52}$$

The problem considered now is that of minimizing G for the case of a power limited rocket operating at constant propulsive power P and with bounded thrust acceleration a.

It is convenient to introduce a new variable

$$\mu = \frac{2P}{m} \tag{5.53}$$

and to write the equations of motion in the form

$$\dot{u} = X + a \cos \psi$$

$$\dot{v} = Y + a \sin \psi$$

$$\dot{x} = u$$

$$\dot{y} = v$$

$$\dot{\mu} = a^2 \tag{5.54}$$

with

$$a_{\min} \leq a \leq a_{\max} \tag{5.55}$$

or equivalently

$$(a - a_{\min})(a_{\max} - a) = \gamma^2 \tag{5.56}$$

where $a_{\max}$ is given and $a_{\min} = 0$ to allow for flight at zero thrust. If the solution requires coasting flight, i.e., zero thrust acceleration in a nonzero interval, it may be necessary to impose inequality constraints on c or β, or to replace the condition of operation at constant power by inequality constraints on α and c. Indeed, if

$$\beta = 0 \quad \text{and} \quad c\beta = 0 \tag{5.57}$$

but

$$c^2\beta = \text{const} \neq 0 \tag{5.58}$$

then

$$c = \infty \tag{5.59}$$

Such behavior has been found in the solution of some problems.[17] However, it occurred only at isolated points of the flight interval and hence did not give rise to mathematical difficulties, although it is certainly not achievable in practice. It will be seen later that such behavior can occur indeed only at isolated instants.

5.41 First Variation

In order that functional G possess an extremum subject to constraints (5.54) and (5.56), the following Euler-Lagrange equations must be satisfied:

$$\dot{\lambda}_u + \lambda_x = 0$$

$$\dot{\lambda}_v + \lambda_y = 0$$

$$\dot{\lambda}_x + \lambda_u \frac{\partial X}{\partial x} + \lambda_v \frac{\partial Y}{\partial x} = 0$$

$$\dot{\lambda}_y + \lambda_u \frac{\partial X}{\partial y} + \lambda_v \frac{\partial Y}{\partial y} = 0 \tag{5.60}$$

$$\dot{\lambda}_\mu = 0$$

$$a(\lambda_u \sin \psi - \lambda_v \cos \psi) = 0$$

$$\lambda_u \cos \psi + \lambda_v \sin \psi + 2\lambda_\mu a + \lambda_\gamma(2a - a_{max} - a_{min}) = 0$$

$$\lambda_\gamma \gamma = 0$$

where now ψ and a are the control variables.

Furthermore, the general transversality condition is

$$dG + [\lambda_u \, du + \lambda_v \, dv + \lambda_x \, dx + \lambda_y \, dy + \lambda_\mu \, d\mu - C \, dt]_{t_i}^{t_f} = 0 \tag{5.61}$$

where

$$C = \lambda_u \dot{u} + \lambda_v \dot{v} + \lambda_x \dot{x} + \lambda_y \dot{y} + \lambda_\mu \dot{\mu} \tag{5.62}$$

Here, too, there apply the remarks of Section 5.21 concerning the integration of the equations of motion and the Euler-Lagrange equations. Once a solution is obtained for the state variables u, v, x, y, μ, and for the control variables ψ and a, as functions of time t, the mass m and hence the mass flow rate β can be determined from Eq. (5.53); the exhaust speed c is then found by means of Eq. (5.52).

5.42 Thrust Direction Program

The thrust direction angle is again given by Eq. (5.13) and the principal value of ψ is to be chosen as in Section 5.26.

5.43 Thrust Acceleration Program

As in the preceding sections, the Euler-Lagrange equation associated with the inequality constraint, Eq. (5.60)$_8$, results in the possibility of three thrust acceleration regimes, namely,

$$\gamma \neq 0, \quad \lambda_\gamma = 0 \quad \text{and} \quad a_{\min} < a < a_{\max}$$

$$\left.\begin{array}{l} \gamma = 0, \quad \lambda_\gamma \neq 0 \\ \\ \gamma = 0, \quad \lambda_\gamma = 0 \end{array}\right\} \quad \text{and} \quad a = a_{\min} \quad \text{or} \quad a = a_{\max} \qquad (5.63)$$

Again, there is the problem of choosing the optimum thrust acceleration regime and of composing the total optimum trajectory. The Weierstrass E-function may be used here, too, to resolve this question. Furthermore, at corners of the extremal arc, arising from discontinuities of the control variables ψ and a, there again apply corner conditions analogous to those of Section 5.24.

5.44 Weierstrass E-Function

The requirement that the Weierstrass E-function be nonnegative for a minimum of G results in the condition that

$$L \equiv a(\lambda_u \cos \psi + \lambda_v \sin \psi + \lambda_\mu a) \qquad (5.64)$$

be maximum with respect to control variables ψ and a.

With respect to thrust direction angle ψ this condition yields Eq. (5.60)$_6$, and hence again Eqs. (5.14) with the $+$ sign, and Eq. (5.21). With respect to the bounded control variable a,

$$\frac{\partial L}{\partial a} = (\lambda_u{}^2 + \lambda_v{}^2)^{1/2} + \lambda_\mu a \qquad (5.65)$$

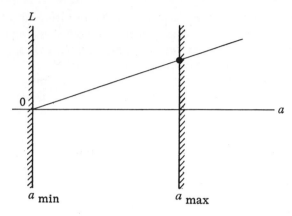

FIG. 7. Weierstrass condition for thrust acceleration, operation at constant power, mass ratio unspecified.

One must now distinguish among three possibilities depending on the multiplier λ_μ. First of all, in view of Eq. (5.60)$_5$

$$\lambda_\mu = \text{const} \tag{5.66}$$

If the mass ratio is unspecified, i.e., μ is unspecified at either terminal of the trajectory, then Eq. (5.61) together with Eq. (5.66) yields

$$\lambda_\mu = 0 \tag{5.67}$$

Hence,

$$\frac{\partial L}{\partial a} > 0 \tag{5.68}$$

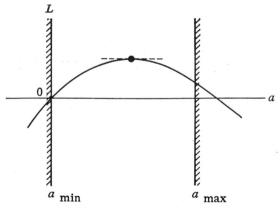

FIG. 8. Weierstrass condition for thrust acceleration, operation at constant power, negative λ_μ.

since the simultaneous vanishing of λ_u and λ_v, resulting in all multipliers being zero, may be ruled out. The situation embodied in Ineq. (5.68) and shown in Fig. 7 leads to the conclusion that maximum thrust acceleration is optimum, whenever the mass ratio is unspecified.

This case demonstrates clearly the need for adjoining an inequality constraint on thrust acceleration a. If constraint (5.55) is not imposed, i.e.,

$$\lambda_\gamma = 0 \tag{5.69}$$

and one proceeds formally, then Eqs. (5.60)$_7$ and (5.67) lead to

$$\lambda_u \cos \psi + \lambda_v \sin \psi = 0 \tag{5.70}$$

Together with Eq. (5.60)$_6$ this then results in

$$\sin^2 \psi + \cos^2 \psi = 0 \tag{5.71}$$

which is impossible, of course.

If

$$\lambda_\mu < 0 \tag{5.72}$$

and it is, for example, if fuel consumption is to be minimized, Fig. 8 shows L as a function of a. Thus, as long as constraint (5.55) is not violated, when

$$\frac{\partial L}{\partial a} = 0 \tag{5.73}$$

the optimum thrust acceleration program is given by condition (5.63)$_1$, with the optimum value of a determined by Eq. (5.73), which is simply Eq. (5.60)$_7$ with

$$\lambda_\gamma = 0 \tag{5.74}$$

Since the multipliers λ_u, λ_v, and λ_μ are continuous by virtue of the corner conditions, the thrust acceleration a must also be continuous to satisfy the maximality of L, Eq. (5.64). If the maximum value of L given by Eq. (5.73) occurs for a value of $a > a_{max}$, constraint (5.55) is violated (Fig. 9). In that case, the maximum permissible value of L is at

$$a = a_{max} \tag{5.75}$$

which is then the optimum value of a. The multiplier λ_γ is given by Eq. (5.60)$_7$

$$\lambda_\gamma = \frac{(\lambda_u{}^2 + \lambda_v{}^2)^{1/2} + 2\lambda_\mu\, a_{max}}{a_{min} - a_{max}} \neq 0 \tag{5.76}$$

When Eq. (5.74) is again satisfied, i.e., the maximum value of L occurs

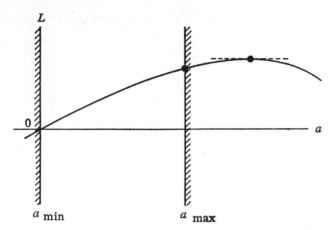

FIG. 9. Weierstrass condition for thrust acceleration, operation at constant power, negative λ_μ, optimum condition: $a = a_{\max}$.

within the permitted region, programmed intermediate thrust acceleration, Eq. (5.73), is once more optimum.

If the maximum value of L corresponds to the lower bound of a, i.e.,

$$a = a_{\min} = 0 \tag{5.77}$$

Fig. 10 portrays the situation. This situation can take place only if

$$\lambda_u = \lambda_v = 0 \tag{5.78}$$

However, this can occur at isolated instants only, lest all multipliers vanish

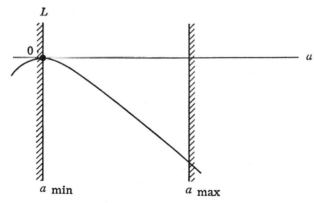

FIG. 10. Weierstrass condition for thrust acceleration, operation at constant power, negative λ_μ, optimum condition: $a = a_{\min}$.

in a nonzero interval. Condition (5.77) can arise and corresponds to isolated infinities of exhaust speed c.[17]

In the unlikely event that

$$\lambda_\mu > 0 \tag{5.79}$$

Fig. 11 shows L as a function of a. Consequently, the maximum permissible value of L occurs for

$$a = a_{max} \tag{5.80}$$

In conclusion then, if

$$\lambda_\mu \geq 0, \qquad a = a_{max}$$

$$\tag{5.81}$$

$$\lambda_\mu < 0, \qquad a_{min} \leq a \leq a_{max}$$

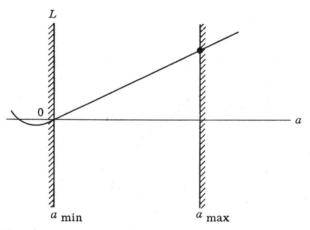

Fɪɢ. 11.   Weierstrass condition for thrust acceleration, operation at constant power, positive λ_μ.

5.5 Conclusions

An analysis of optimum rocket trajectories—optimum in the sense of leading to the minimum value of a functional which is a function of the initial and final values of the state variables—has been presented. In particular, applications to systems limited with respect to mass flow rate, propulsive power, and thrust acceleration, but operating at constant power, have been examined. The following main conclusions have been reached:

(1) With respect to the control variables the Weierstrass E-function condition, in the form of a maximality condition on a function of the control

variables, renders the optimum program for the control variables. This condition is applicable for both bounded and unbounded control variables. In the case of bounded control variables the inequality constraints must be properly adjoined to the set of constraint equations (equations of motion). No difficulties arise unless the control variables enter linearly into the constraint equations.

(2) No unresolved questions remain concerning the optimum programming of the *thrust direction*.

(3) For *mass flow rate limited* systems the optimum mass flow rate program is of the "bang-bang" type, provided the external force accelerations are at most linear functions of the position coordinates. In the case of other force fields it has not been possible to rule out programmed intermediate mass flow rate or to provide a criterion for the selection of the optimum mass flow rate regime.

(4) For *propulsive power limited* systems it has been shown that operation at maximum permissible power is optimum.

(5) For *thrust acceleration limited* systems operating at constant power, either maximum or programmed acceleration may be optimum, depending on the functional to be minimized and on the end conditions.

5.6 Example

In order to demonstrate the theory presented in this chapter the optimum trajectory of a mass flow rate limited rocket will be considered. In particular, it will be required to find the optimum thrust program—direction and mass flow rate—which results in minimum fuel consumption for a vehicle transferring a prescribed payload from a given position on a circular orbit about the Earth to a prescribed impact point on the earth.* The following simplifying assumptions are made:

(1) Flight takes place in vacuum, i.e., aerodynamic forces are neglected vis-a-vis thrust and weight.

(2) The earth is spherically symmetrical and nonrotating relative to the inertial coordinate system with respect to which the rocket's motion is described (Fig. 12).

(3) Range and altitude of the rocket are "small" compared with the

---

* This example is based on a more general problem treated in a Martin Company Technical Memorandum.[14] The numerical calculations were carried out on an analog computer by J. W. Tyndall and G. W. Haynes of the Martin Company, Denver, Colorado.

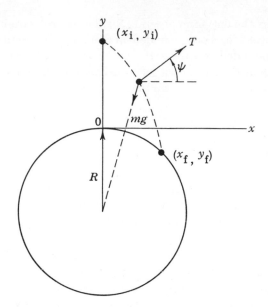

Fig. 12.   Coordinate system for out-of-orbit transfer (Section 5.6, example).

earth's radius; hence, only first-order terms in the expansion of the gravitational acceleration will be considered.

The equations of motion and constraint are Eqs. (5.5)–(5.7). The external force accelerations are given by Eqs. (5.31). The prescribed end conditions are

$$
t = t_i = 0 \begin{cases} x = 0 \\ y = y_i \\ u = u_i \\ v = 0 \end{cases}, \quad t = t_f \text{ (unspecified)} \begin{cases} x = x_f \\ y = y_f \\ m = m_f \end{cases} \quad (5.82)
$$

The problem is to minimize the initial mass

$$
G = m_i \tag{5.83}
$$

subject to the constraints and end conditions stated above.

5.61 First Variation

The pertinent Euler-Lagrange equations are Eqs. (5.9) and the transversality condition is given by Eq. (5.10). Furthermore, since the flight time is unspecified, the first integral, Eq. (5.11), is equal to zero. Also, since initial mass is to be minimized and final velocity is not given, Eq. (5.10) yields

$$t = t_i = 0 \{ \lambda_m = 1, \qquad t = t_f \begin{cases} \lambda_u = 0 \\ \\ \lambda_v = 0 \end{cases} \tag{5.84}$$

Consequently, the mixed end-value nature of the problem requires basically a five-parameter iteration.

5.62 Thrust Direction Program

In view of Eqs. $(5.9)_{1-4}$ and (5.84), and the discussion of Sections 5.22 and 5.26, the thrust direction is given by

$$\sin \psi = \frac{\lambda_v}{\sqrt{\lambda_u^2 + \lambda_v^2}}$$

$$\cos \psi = \frac{\lambda_u}{\sqrt{\lambda_u^2 + \lambda_v^2}} \tag{5.85}$$

where

$$\lambda_u = \frac{\lambda_{xf}}{\epsilon} \sin \left[\epsilon (t_f - t) \right]$$

$$\lambda_v = \frac{\lambda_{yf}}{\epsilon\sqrt{2}} \sinh \left[\epsilon\sqrt{2} (t_f - t) \right] \tag{5.86}$$

5.63 Mass Flow Rate Program

Since the external force accelerations are linear functions of the position components, the mass flow rate control is of the "bang-bang" kind, Section 5.28. The switching criterion is expressed by conditions (5.24) and the switching function is given by Eq. (5.23).

5.64 Outline of Solution

While it is clear that the initial portion of the trajectory must be powered, and hence must be flown at maximum thrust, in order to initiate the transfer, it is not *a priori* obvious whether or not the final portion is powered. If the integration is started at $t = t_f$, this information is required. From the

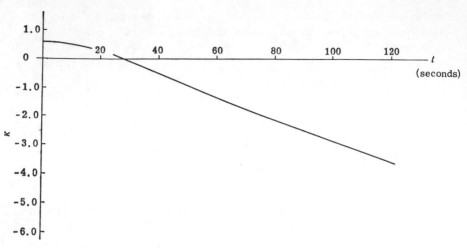

FIG. 13.   Mass flow rate switching function (Section 5.6, example).

definition of the switching function, Eq. (5.23), and end conditions (5.84),

$$\kappa_f = -\lambda_{mf} \tag{5.87}$$

However, it can be shown[19,20] that

$$\lambda_{mf} = \frac{\partial m_i}{\partial m_f} \tag{5.88}$$

and it is to be expected that

$$\frac{\partial m_i}{\partial m_f} > 0 \tag{5.89}$$

so that

$$\kappa_f < 0 \tag{5.90}$$

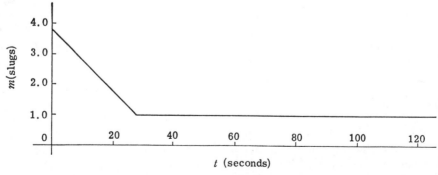

FIG. 14.   Mass as a function of time (Section 5.6, example).

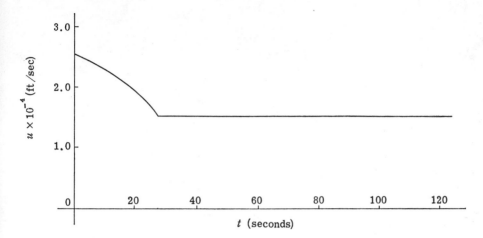

FIG. 15.   Horizontal velocity component as a function of time (Section 5.6, example).

that is, the final portion of the trajectory is unpowered. In effect, it is more advantageous to begin the integration at $t = 0$. Then the five-parameter iteration and the requirement to match

$$C_f = 0 \qquad (5.91)$$

since t_f is unspecified, can be reduced to a three-parameter iteration without the need to match Eq. (5.91). Equations $(5.9)_{1-4}$ can be inte-

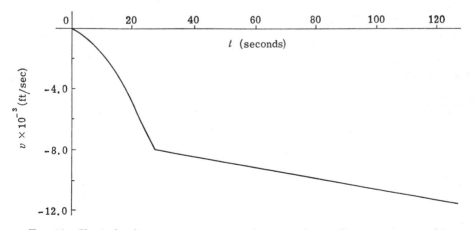

FIG. 16.   Vertical velocity component as a function of time (Section 5.6, example).

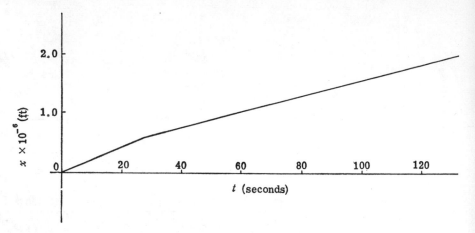

FIG. 17.   Horizontal position as a function of time (Section 5.6, example).

grated to yield

$$\lambda_{ui} = \frac{\lambda_{xf}}{\epsilon} \sin \epsilon t_f$$

$$\lambda_{vi} = \frac{\lambda_{yf}}{\epsilon\sqrt{2}} \sinh \epsilon\sqrt{2}t_f$$

$$\lambda_{xi} = \lambda_{xf} \cos \epsilon t_f \qquad (5.92)$$

$$\lambda_{yi} = \lambda_{yf} \cosh \epsilon\sqrt{2}t_f$$

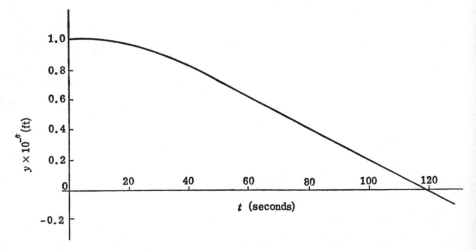

FIG. 18.   Vertical position as a function of time (Section 5.6, example).

Furthermore, upon substituting Eqs. (5.5) into

$$C_i = 0 \tag{5.93}$$

one can solve for

$$m_i = c\beta_{max}(\lambda_{ui}^2 + \lambda_{vi}^2)^{1/2}[-\beta_{max} + \lambda_{vi}(g_0 - 2\epsilon^2 y_i) - \lambda_{xi}u_i]^{-1} \tag{5.94}$$

and also assure the satisfaction of Eq. (5.91). Also in view of Eqs. (5.86), two of the terminal conditions, namely,

$$\lambda_{uf} = \lambda_{vf} = 0 \tag{5.95}$$

are automatically met. Hence, by assuming the values of the three variables t_f, λ_{xf}, and λ_{yf}, one has the initial values of λ_u, λ_v, λ_x, λ_y, and m from Eqs. (5.92) and (5.94). With these the integration proceeds from $t = 0$ to $t = t_f$, where the specified values of x, y, and m must be matched.

5.65 Numerical Results

An integration program was carried out using the following values:

$$\beta_{max} = 0.1 \text{ slug/sec}$$

$$c = 10^4 \text{ ft/sec}$$

$$g_0 = 32.0 \text{ ft/sec}^2$$

$$\epsilon = 1.26 \times 10^{-3} \text{ 1/sec}$$

$$x_i = 0 \text{ ft}$$

$$y_i = 10^6 \text{ ft}$$

$$u_i = 2.459 \times 10^4 \text{ ft/sec}$$

$$v_i = 0$$

$$x_f = 2 \times 10^6 \text{ ft}$$

$$y_f = -0.1003 \times 1^6 \text{ ft}$$

$$m_f = 1.0 \text{ slug}$$

The results are shown in Figs. 13–19.

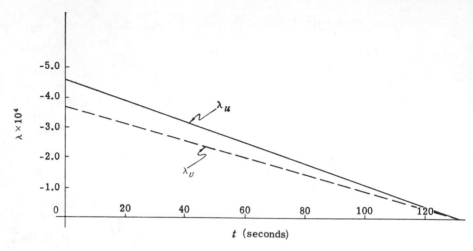

FIG. 19.   Thrust direction numbers as functions of time (Section 5.6, example).

Nomenclature

C Defined by Eqs. (5.11) or (5.62)

F External force acceleration

G Functional to be minimized

L Defined by Eqs. (5.19), (5.47), or (5.64)

P Propulsive power, $\frac{1}{2}\beta c^2$

R Earth's radius

T Thrust magnitude

X, Y Components of external force acceleration

a Thrust acceleration, T/m

c Effective exhaust speed

g_0 Acceleration of gravity at sea level

m Rocket mass

q_j State variable

r Distance from attracting center

t Time

u, v Rocket velocity components

x, y Rocket position coordinates

α $2P$

β Mass flow rate

γ Real variable

ϵ $\sqrt{g_0/R}$

κ Switching function, defined by Eq. (5.23)

5. Bounded Control

λ_q Lagrange multiplier associated with state variable q
λ Vector with components λ_u, λ_v
μ $2P/m$
θ Angle between thrust and local vertical
ψ Thrust direction angle

Subscripts

i   Initial value
f   Final value
max   Maximum value
min   Minimum value
$-$ Preceding corner
$+$ Following corner
$\cdot$ Dot denotes differentiation with respect to time

Appendix

It is desired to determine the state variables $y_j(x)$ and control variables $u_k(x)$ such that the function

$$G = G(x_i, x_f, y_1(x_i) \cdots y_m(x_i), y_1(x_f) \cdots y_m(x_f))$$

take on a minimum value subject to the differential equation side conditions

$$\phi_j = y_j' - f_j(x, y_1 \cdots y_m, u_1 \cdots u_n), \qquad j = 1, 2, \cdots, m$$

and at most $2m + 1$ end conditions involving x and y_j, as well as inequality constraints on the control variables*

$$u_{l\ min} \leq u_l \leq u_{l\ max}, \qquad l = 1 \cdots r \leq n$$

which may be expressed as[4,20,21]

$$\psi_l = (u_l - u_{l\ min})(u_{l\ max} - u_l) - \eta_l^2 = 0, \qquad l = 1 \cdots$$

where the η_l are real variables.

---

* By the same technique it is possible to impose bounds on func
† Actually, the number of inequality constraints may exceed
pendent control variables. In that case, however, care must be
the constraints are met.

The following necessary conditions for the existence of a local minimum value of G may be obtained from a slight modification of the classical calculus of variations.[5,19-21] From the vanishing of the first variation there arise (1) the *Euler-Lagrange equations*

$$\frac{d}{dx}\frac{\partial F}{\partial y_j'} - \frac{\partial F}{\partial y_j} = 0, \qquad j = 1 \cdots m$$

$$\frac{\partial F}{\partial u_k} = 0, \qquad k = 1 \cdots n$$

$$\frac{\partial F}{\partial \eta_l} = 0, \qquad l = 1 \cdots r$$

where

$$F = \sum_{j=1}^{m} \lambda_{y_j}(x)\phi_j + \sum_{l=1}^{r} \lambda_{\eta_l}(x)\psi_l = 0$$

and the $\lambda(x)$ are undetermined multipliers; (2) the *general transversality condition*

$$dG + \left[\sum_{j=1}^{m} \frac{\partial F}{\partial y_j'} \, dy_j + \left(F - \sum_{j=1}^{m} y_j' \frac{\partial F}{\partial y_j'} \right) dx \right]_{x_i}^{x_t} = 0$$

where the dx and dy_j are differentials which are connected by the prescribed end conditions; and (3) the *Weierstrass-Erdmann corner conditions* which apply at corners of the extremal arc, i.e., wherever the y_j' are discontinuous,

$$\left[\frac{\partial F}{\partial y_j'} \right]_{-} = \left[\frac{\partial F}{\partial y_j'} \right]_{+}$$

$$\left[F - \sum_{j=1}^{m} y_j' \frac{\partial F}{\partial y_j'} \right]_{-} = \left[F - \sum_{j=1}^{m} y_j' \frac{\partial F}{\partial y_j'} \right]_{+}$$

If the independent variable x does not occur explicitly in the side conditions, there exists a *first integral*

$$F - \sum_{j=1}^{m} y_j' \frac{\partial F}{\partial y_j'} = \text{const}$$

rther necessary condition for the existence of a local minimum value of G, arising from a consideration of the strong variation, is the *Weierstrass excess function condition*

$$E \equiv F(x, y_1 \cdots y_m, Y_1' \cdots Y_m', U_1 \cdots U_n, \lambda_{y_1} \cdots \lambda_{y_m}, \lambda_{\eta_1} \cdots \lambda_{\eta_r})$$

$$- F(x, y_1 \cdots y_m, y_1' \cdots y_m', u_1 \cdots u_n, \lambda_{y_1} \cdots \lambda_{y_m}, \lambda_{\eta_1} \cdots \lambda_{\eta_r})$$

$$- \sum_{j=1}^{m} (Y_j' - y_j') \frac{\partial F}{\partial y_j'} \geq 0$$

where the Y_j' and U_k are nonoptimum but permissible values of the y_j' and u_k. For the class of side conditions considered, the above inequality reduces to

$$\sum_{j=1}^{m} \lambda_{y_j} f_j(x, y_1 \cdots y_m, u_1 \cdots u_n) \geq \sum_{j=1}^{m} \lambda_{y_j} f_j(x, y_1 \cdots y_m, U_1 \cdots U_n)$$

for all permissible values of the control variables u_k. This inequality is clearly equivalent to the requirement that

$$L \equiv \sum_{j=1}^{m} \lambda_{y_j} f_j(x, y_1 \cdots y_m, u_1 \cdots u_n)$$

be maximum with respect the control variables u_k satisfying the imposed inequality constraints. In this form the Weierstrass E-function condition is equivalent to *Pontryagin's maximum principle* (see Chapter 7).

REFERENCES

1. G. Leitmann, Extremal rocket trajectories in position and time dependent force fields, Am. Astronaut. Soc. 7th Ann. Meeting, Dallas, Preprint 61–30 (1961).
2. G. Leitmann, On the equation of rocket motion, *J. Brit. Interplanet. Soc.* **16,** 141 (1947).
3. R. T. Stancil and L. J. Kulakowsky, Rocket boost vehicle mission optimizations, Am. Rocket Soc. 15th Ann. Meeting, Washington, D. C., Preprint 1449–60 (1960).
4. F. A. Valentine, The problem of Lagrange with differential inequalities as added side conditions, Dissertation, Department of Mathematics, Univ. of Chicago, Chicago, Illinois, 1937.
5. G. A. Bliss, "Lectures on the Calculus of Variations." Univ. of Chicago Press, Chicago, 1946.
6. D. F. Lawden, Dynamic problems of interplanetary flight, *Aeronaut. Quart.* 6 (1955).
7. B. D. Fried, *in* "Space Technology" (H. S. Seifert, ed.), Chapter 4. V York, 1959.
8. A. Miele, General variational theory of the flight paths of rocket- missiles and satellite carriers, Purdue University Rept. No. 9th Intern. Astronaut. Congr., Amsterdam, 1958 (1959).

9. D. E. Okhotsimskii and T. M. Eneev, Some variation(al) problems connected with the launching of artificial satellites of the earth, *Uspekhi Fiz. Nauk* **63,** 5 (1957) [(English translation: *J. Brit. Interplanet. Soc.* **16,** 261 (1958)].

10. G. Leitmann, On a class of variational problems in rocket flight, Lockheed MSD Rept. No. LMSD-5067 (1958); *J. Aero/Space Sci.* **26,** 586 (1959).

11. S. E. Dreyfus, Dynamic programming and the calculus of variations, *J. Math. Anal. and Appl.* **1,** 228 (1960).

12. V. G. Boltyanskii, R. V. Gamkrelidze, and L. S. Pontryagin, The theory of optimal control processes. I. The maximum principle, *Izvest. Akad. Nauk S.S.S.R. Ser. Mat.* **24,** 3 (1960).

13. G. Leitmann, Comment on "On a class of variational problems in rocket flight," *J. Aero/Space Sci.* **27,** 153 (1960).

14. G. Leitmann, On a minimum fuel satellite transfer trajectory, Tech. Memo. No. 491/2-01-60 The Martin Company, Inc., Denver, Colorado (1960).

15. D. F. Lawden, Necessary conditons for optimal rocket trajectories, *Quart. J. Mech. Appl. Math.* **12,** 476 (1959).

16. J. H. Irving, *in* "Space Technology" (H. S. Seifert, ed.), Chapter 10. Wiley, New York, 1959.

17. G. Leitmann, Minimum transfer time for a power-limited rocket, Lockheed MSD Rept. No. LMSD–49769 (1960); *J. Appl. Mech.* **28,** 171 (1961).

18. C. R. Faulders, Optimum thrust programming of electrically powered rocket vehicles in a gravitational field, *ARS Journal* **30,** 954 (1960).

19. J. V. Breakwell, The optimization of trajectories, Rept. AL-2706, North American Aviation Company (1957); *J. Soc. Ind. Appl. Math.* **7,** 215 (1959).

20. G. Leitmann, An elementary derivation of the optimal control conditions, *Proc. 12th Intern. Astronaut. Congr., Washington, D. C., 1961.*

21. L. D. Berkovitz, Variational methods in problems of control and programming. *J. Math. Anal. and Appl.* **3,** 145 (1961).

—6—

Method of Gradients

HENRY J. KELLEY

Grumman Aircraft Engineering Corporation,
Bethpage, New York

6.0 Introduction

The method of gradients or "method of steepest descent," as it is sometimes called, is an elementary concept for the solution of minimum problems.
It dates back to Cauchy[1-3] and, in variational version, to Hadamard.[4,5]
A particularly clear and attractive exposition of the method was given by
Courant in a 1941 address to the American Mathematical Society.[5] In
recent years the computational appeal of the method has led to its adoption
in a variety of applications—multivariable minimum problems of ordinary
calculus,[3,6-9] solution of systems of algebraic equations,[10,11] integral equations,[12] and variational problems.[9,13]

The gradient method has been applied to variational problems of flight
path optimization by the present writer in the investigation of reference 14,
a main source of material for this chapter. A similar scheme has been developed independently by Bryson and his colleagues.[15]

We will first discuss some of the main features of the gradient method
in the context of ordinary minimum problems subject to constraints.
Although this class of problems is chosen primarily for simplicity of
explanation, it is one which is increasingly of interest per se in aeronautical and astronautical applications. We will then turn to variational
problems of flight performance, introducing Green's functions in the role
played by partial derivatives in ordinary minimum problems, and attempting to preserve an analogy between the two classes of problems in the
subsequent development. Some numerical results illustrating the computational successive approximation procedure in examples will then be
presented.

6.1 Gradient Technique in Ordinary Minimum Problems

6.11 The Continuous Descent Process

To present the basic idea of the gradient method we consider a function f
of several variables $x_1, \cdots, x_n$, defined on an open domain, which possesses
continuous partial derivatives with respect to these variables. Starting at
some point $x_i = \bar{x}_i,\ i = 1, \cdots, n$, we move a small distance ds defined in the
Euclidean sense

$$ds^2 = \sum_{i=1}^{n} dx_i^2 \tag{6.1}$$

Seeking to move toward a minimum of f, we consider directions in which the rate of change of f with respect to s

$$\frac{df}{ds} = \sum_{i=1}^{n} \frac{\partial f}{\partial x_i} \frac{dx_i}{ds} \tag{6.2}$$

is negative. In fact we may find the direction of "steepest descent" (most negative df/ds) among the directions which make (6.2) stationary subject to (6.1).

Proceeding formally, we write the constraint (6.1)

$$1 - \sum_{i=1}^{n} \left(\frac{dx_i}{ds}\right)^2 = 0 \tag{6.3}$$

in terms of direction cosines dx_i/ds and adjoin it to (6.2) by means of a Lagrange multiplier λ_0, forming

$$\sum_{i=1}^{n} \frac{\partial f}{\partial x_i} \frac{dx_i}{ds} + \lambda_0 \left[1 - \sum_{i=1}^{n} \left(\frac{dx_i}{ds}\right)^2 \right] \tag{6.4}$$

Equating partial derivatives taken with respect to the dx_i/ds to zero,

$$\frac{\partial f}{\partial x_i} + \lambda_0 \left(-2 \frac{dx_i}{ds}\right) = 0, \qquad i = 1, \cdots, n \tag{6.5}$$

we obtain

$$\frac{dx_i}{ds} = \frac{1}{2\lambda_0} \frac{\partial f}{\partial x_i}, \qquad i = 1, \cdots, n \tag{6.6}$$

From the constraint equation (6.3) the multiplier λ_0 is determined as

$$\lambda_0 = \pm \tfrac{1}{2} \left[\sum_{i=1}^{n} \left(\frac{\partial f}{\partial x_i}\right)^2 \right]^{1/2} \tag{6.7}$$

Provided the partial derivatives $\partial f/\partial x_i$ are not all zero, there are two distinct sets of direction numbers which make df/ds stationary, namely,

$$\frac{dx_i}{ds} = \pm \frac{\partial f}{\partial x_i} \left[\sum_{i=1}^{n} \left(\frac{\partial f}{\partial x_i}\right)^2 \right]^{-1/2}, \qquad i = 1, \cdots, n \tag{6.8}$$

Inspection of the expression for the directional derivative df/ds in the two cases

$$\frac{df}{ds} = \pm \left[\sum_{i=1}^{n} \left(\frac{\partial f}{\partial x_i}\right)^2 \right]^{1/2} \tag{6.9}$$

enables identification of the two stationary directions as those of steepest ascent and steepest descent.

A simple geometric interpretation of these formulas is possible if the various quantities are regarded in vector terms: the x_i as components of a vector $\mathbf{X}$, the direction cosines dx_i/ds as components of a unit vector $d\mathbf{X}/ds$, and the partial derivatives $\partial f/\partial x_i$ as components of a gradient vector. The derivative df/ds is then the dot product

$$\frac{df}{ds} = \operatorname{grad} f \cdot \frac{d\mathbf{X}}{ds} \tag{6.10}$$

and, with the direction of motion oriented along the gradient as per Eq. (6.8), the magnitude is equal to that of the gradient vector as given by Eq. (6.9). Thus, steepest ascent corresponds to motion in the gradient direction and steepest descent to that along the negative gradient.

We now introduce a time parameter σ and consider motion along the negative gradient direction as a continuous process. For motion in n-space at a velocity of magnitude V

$$\frac{ds}{d\sigma} = \left[\sum_{i=1}^{n} \left(\frac{dx_i}{d\sigma} \right)^2 \right]^{1/2} = V \tag{6.11}$$

The expressions for the velocity components $dx_i/d\sigma$ become

$$\frac{dx_i}{d\sigma} = -V \left[\sum_{i=1}^{n} \left(\frac{\partial f}{\partial x_i} \right)^2 \right]^{-1/2} \frac{\partial f}{\partial x_i}, \qquad i = 1, \cdots, n \tag{6.12}$$

as a consequence of (6.8). These expressions become particularly simple if the velocity magnitude is taken proportional to that of the gradient

$$V = k \left[\sum_{i=1}^{n} \left(\frac{\partial f}{\partial x_i} \right)^2 \right]^{1/2}, \qquad k > 0 \tag{6.13}$$

$$\frac{dx_i}{d\sigma} = -k \frac{\partial f}{\partial x_i}, \qquad i = 1, \cdots, n \tag{6.14}$$

so that motion in the negative gradient direction is assured by merely setting the time derivatives of the coordinates proportional to the partial derivatives of f.

It is clear that in this continuous process, wherein the point $\mathbf{X}$ moves according to the system of ordinary differential equations (6.14), the process will for $\sigma \to \infty$ approach a position for which $\operatorname{grad} f = 0$, if f is bounded below. The stationary value so approached will correspond to a minimum of f if the x_i remain finite in the limit; otherwise a lower bound is approached.

6.12 Stepwise Version

As an alternative to the continuous procedure described by Eqs. (6.14) we may proceed stepwise, correcting a set of approximations to the solution $\partial f/\partial x_i = 0$ by increments proportional to the negative of the gradient:

$$x_i^{(p+1)} = x_i^{(p)} - k\,\frac{\partial f}{\partial x_i}\,\Delta\sigma, \qquad i = 1,\,\cdots,\,n \qquad (6.15)$$

It is clear that in this stepwise process, the proportionality constant k may be absorbed in the step size $\Delta\sigma$; hence we take $k = 1$.

Since the determination of the partial derivatives $\partial f/\partial x_i$ may be expensive in terms of volume of numerical computations in case the number of variables n is large, it is desirable to exploit each calculation of local gradient direction to the utmost, taking $\Delta\sigma$ as large as possible. One procedure is to follow the local gradient direction until f reaches a minimum, i.e., evaluate Eqs. (6.15) and the function f for a number of step sizes, determining $\Delta\sigma$ for minimum f by some suitable one-dimensional search technique. A new gradient direction is then calculated and the procedure repeated.

In this way an n-dimensional minimum problem is reduced to a sequence of one-dimensional problems. The gradient method shares this feature with another computational technique to be described in later chapters.

The continuous and stepwise processes are contrasted in the sketch of Fig. 1 which depicts the two types of motion as they may occur in the

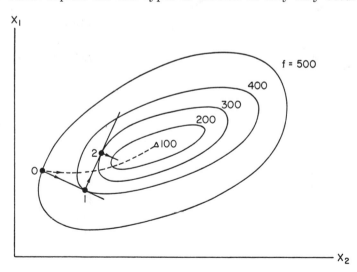

FIG. 1.   Continuous and stepwise descent processes.

vicinity of a minimum of a function of two variables $f(x_1, x_2)$. The gradient direction, as shown, is normal to a contour while the local minimum in the gradient direction is attained at a point of tangency to a contour. These characteristics are also common to higher dimensional cases.

It is apparent that the stepwise path is not independent of the coordinate system selected. If a transformation of coordinates could be found which maps the oval contours of Fig. 1 into circles, for example, the number of steps required to attain the minimum would be reduced to one. In the usual situation, of course, insufficient information is available *a priori* to permit a sophisticated choice of coordinates; otherwise the character of the surface would be known and gradient determination of minima unnecessary.

With typical engineering problems, however, one will often have some idea of the "practical range" of the variables x_i, and this will facilitate the introduction of normalized variables for gradient computations. Such a procedure is virtually a necessity where the variables have different dimensions and are numerically of different orders of magnitude. As a result of normalization some semblance of meaning may be attached to the concept of distance in the n-space in which the operations are performed.

6.13 Ordinary Minimum Problems with Constraints: Gradient Projection Technique

In many problems of practical interest, we may wish to determine a minimum of the function $f(x_1, \cdots, x_n)$ subject to subsidiary conditions relating the variables x_i. An important class of subsidiary conditions are *equations*

$$g_j(x_1, \cdots, x_n) = 0, \qquad j = 1, \cdots, m \tag{6.16}$$

numbering $m < n$, sometimes referred to in the literature as equality constraints.

If the functions g_j are given analytically, it may be possible to solve the set of Eqs. (6.16) for m of the variables x_i in terms of the others and, by their elimination from the function f, to reduce the problem to one without constraints. Such an approach will very often not be practicable in applications.

We may, however, consider a version of this procedure "in the small," i.e., in a neighborhood of the starting point $x_i = \bar{x}_i$. Retaining only first-order terms in a Taylor expansion

$$g_j(x_1, \cdots, x_n) \cong g_j(\bar{x}_1, \cdots, \bar{x}_n)$$

$$+ \sum_{i=1}^{n} \frac{\partial g_j}{\partial x_i} (\bar{x}_1, \cdots, \bar{x}_n)(x_i - \bar{x}_i), \qquad j = 1, \cdots, m \tag{6.17}$$

and assuming that Eqs. (6.16) are satisfied at the point $x_i = \bar{x}_i$, we obtain a system of linear equations in the increments $\Delta x_i = x_i - \bar{x}_i$ for the vanishing of the g_j to first order:

$$\sum_{i=1}^{n} \frac{\partial g_j}{\partial x_i} \Delta x_i = 0, \qquad j = 1, \cdots, m \qquad (6.18)$$

We may then attempt to solve this system for m of the increments Δx_i in terms of the remaining ones. This will be possible unless *all* of the $m \times m$ Jacobian determinants of the system vanish at the point $x_i = \bar{x}_i$. The procedure breaks down at such *singular points*.[16]

If solution is possible, the $n - m$ partial derivatives of f with respect to the $n - m$ remaining variables may be calculated by the chain rule of differentiation, and the gradient of f subject to the constraints thus determined. Geometrically, this is the projection of the free gradient vector upon the $n - m$ subspace determined by the intersection of the m hyperplanes (6.18). The terminology *gradient projection* for this scheme, as employed in the nonlinear programming literature[7,8] in connection with related problems involving inequality constraints, seems appropriate.

We may perform an analysis similar to that of Section 6.11 to determine the projected gradient direction. Again introducing direction cosines dx_i/ds, we seek stationary directions of df/ds as given by (6.2) subject to (6.3) and to

$$\frac{dg_j}{ds} = \sum_{i=1}^{n} \frac{\partial g_j}{\partial x_i} \frac{dx_i}{ds} = 0, \qquad j = 1, \cdots, m \qquad (6.19)$$

Introducing Lagrange multipliers λ_0 and λ_j, $j = 1, \cdots, m$, we form

$$\sum_{i=1}^{n} \frac{\partial f}{\partial x_i} \frac{dx_i}{ds} + \lambda_0 \left[1 - \sum_{i=1}^{n} \left(\frac{dx_i}{ds} \right)^2 \right] + \sum_{j=1}^{m} \lambda_j \sum_{i=1}^{n} \frac{\partial g_j}{\partial x_i} \frac{dx_i}{ds} \qquad (6.20)$$

Equating partial derivatives taken with respect to the dx_i/ds to zero, we obtain

$$\frac{\partial f}{\partial x_i} - 2\lambda_0 \frac{dx_i}{ds} + \sum_{j=1}^{m} \lambda_j \frac{\partial g_j}{\partial x_i} = 0, \qquad i = 1, \cdots, n \qquad (6.21)$$

$$2\lambda_0 = \left[\sum_{i=1}^{n} \left(\frac{\partial f}{\partial x_i} + \sum_{j=1}^{m} \lambda_j \frac{\partial g_j}{\partial x_i} \right)^2 \right]^{1/2} \qquad (6.22)$$

$$\frac{dx_i}{ds} = \frac{\left[\frac{\partial f}{\partial x_i} + \sum_{j=1}^{m} \lambda_j \frac{\partial g_j}{\partial x_i} \right]}{\left[\sum_{i=1}^{n} \left(\frac{\partial f}{\partial x_i} + \sum_{j=1}^{m} \lambda_j \frac{\partial g_j}{\partial x_i} \right)^2 \right]^{1/2}} \qquad (6.23)$$

Substituting this result into (6.19), we obtain relations determining the λ_j:

$$\sum_{j=1}^{m} \lambda_j \sum_{i=1}^{n} \frac{\partial g_j}{\partial x_i} \frac{\partial g_k}{\partial x_i} = - \sum_{i=1}^{n} \frac{\partial g_k}{\partial x_i} \frac{\partial f}{\partial x_i}, \qquad k = 1, \cdots, m \qquad (6.24)$$

This system of linear equations in the multipliers will have a solution provided that the $m \times m$ matrix whose elements are

$$a_{kj} = \sum_{i=1}^{n} \frac{\partial g_j}{\partial x_i} \frac{\partial g_k}{\partial x_i} \qquad (6.25)$$

is nonsingular. This statement is precisely the Gram determinant criterion for linear independence of the expressions (6.19) and it is equivalent to the earlier assertion concerning Jacobian determinants (see Courant and Hilbert,[17] p. 34). Fulfillment of this condition requires that the magnitudes of the vectors grad g_j be nonzero and that their directions be distinct from one another.

Mechanization of the gradient projection procedure thus requires numerical solution of the system of linear equations (6.24). The relations appropriate to a stepwise process analogous to that given by (6.15) are then

$$x_i^{(p+1)} = x_i^{(p)} - \left(\frac{\partial f}{\partial x_i} + \sum_{j=1}^{m} \lambda_j \frac{\partial g_j}{\partial x_i} \right) \Delta\sigma, \qquad i = 1, \cdots, n \qquad (6.26)$$

The gradient projection technique is an excellent one where the constraints (6.16) are linear in the x_i, or nearly so. There is a possibility of difficulty associated with ill-conditioning of the linear system (6.24) if the intersections of the hypersurfaces $g_j = 0$ are poorly defined, e.g., if two or more of the tangent hyperplanes are nearly parallel.

A considerable complication arises from significant nonlinearities in the constraints. For large step sizes $\Delta\sigma$, Eqs. (6.16), having been satisfied only in linearized version, may long since have been violated before minimum f is reached. A correction cycle designed to restore the constraints must then be introduced. Typically this will take the form of an iterative adjustment of the variables x_i. This feature of the gradient projection technique may entail a considerable increase in computation time.

6.14 Ordinary Minimum Problems with Constraints: An Approximation Technique

Another approach to the handling of constraints is provided by the idea of approximating a minimum problem subject to constraints by another problem without constraints. Thus, in lieu of the problem of the preceding section, we consider the problem of minimizing

$$f + \tfrac{1}{2} \sum_{j=1}^{m} K_j g_j^2 \qquad (6.27)$$

where the K_j are positive constants.

It is intuitively reasonable that the "penalty" terms of the second member of (6.27) will have the effect of making the constraint "violations" small in this problem, owing to the fact that these terms are nonnegative. For increasingly large positive K_j, it may be anticipated that the solution of this minimum problem will tend toward the desired solution of the minimum problem for f subject to the constraints (6.16). This idea is due to Courant.[5] It has been placed upon a rigorous basis in terms of an approximation theorem by Moser (see Courant[18]) for the case of a single constraint, and exploited in a particular class of variational problems involving multiple constraints by Rubin and Ungar.[19]

In the employment of this idea for computational purposes, numerically large values of the constants K_j are to be assigned. The choice of values must be decided on the basis of permissible approximations to the constraints. Thus "tolerances" may be set from physical considerations.

The penalty function technique is quite compatible with the successive approximation process provided by the gradient method. A plausible technique for computer operations is comparison of the constraint "violations" with preassigned "tolerances" at the end of each descent step, followed by appropriate adjustment of K_j values if necessary for the succeeding step.

Seeking a guide to the estimation and adjustment of the values of the K_j, we now examine the magnitudes of the "violations" g_j at a minimum of (6.27). We equate to zero the derivatives of (6.27) in the m-directions determined by the gradients of the g_j. The direction cosines of the gradient of g_k are

$$\frac{dx_i}{ds} = \frac{\partial g_k}{\partial x_i} \left[\sum_{l=1}^{n} \left(\frac{\partial g_k}{\partial x_l} \right)^2 \right]^{-1/2}, \qquad i = 1, \cdots, n \qquad (6.28)$$

and the derivative of (6.27) in this direction is assumed to vanish:

$$\frac{\left[\sum_{i=1}^{n} \left(\frac{\partial f}{\partial x_i} + \sum_{j=1}^{m} K_j g_j \frac{\partial g_j}{\partial x_i} \right) \frac{\partial g_k}{\partial x_i} \right]}{\left[\sum_{i=1}^{n} \left(\frac{\partial g_k}{\partial x_i} \right)^2 \right]^{1/2}} = 0, \qquad k = 1, \cdots, m \qquad (6.29)$$

We may regard this as a system of linear equations in the products $K_j g_j$:

$$\sum_{j=1}^{m} K_j g_j \sum_{i=1}^{n} \frac{\partial g_j}{\partial x_i} \frac{\partial g_k}{\partial x_i} = -\sum_{i=1}^{n} \frac{\partial g_k}{\partial x_i} \frac{\partial f}{\partial x_i}, \qquad k = 1, \cdots, m \qquad (6.30)$$

This system bears a strong resemblance to that governing the multipliers of the (converged) gradient projection process (6.24), the distinction being that the partial derivatives in the present case are evaluated at a minimum of (6.27) for which the constraint equations are satisfied only approximately.

The system (6.30) may be solved numerically under conditions mentioned previously in connection with determination of the multipliers. In the limit as $K_j \to \infty$, evidently

$$g_j \to \frac{\lambda_j}{K_j}, \qquad j = 1, \cdots, m \qquad (6.31)$$

and the "violations" are seen to vary inversely with the K_j values in the neighborhood of the solution.

This analysis suggests two plausible schemes for adjustment of the K_j values. The simplest is employment of the absolute value of "violation"/ "tolerance" ratio as a factor to increase or decrease the "current" K_j values at the end of each descent step. As an alternative, one may estimate the λ_j from (6.24) on the basis of "current" partial derivatives and compute

$$K_j = \left| \frac{\lambda_j \text{ (est.)}}{\epsilon_j} \right|$$

where ϵ_j is the "tolerance" set on the constraint $g_j = 0$. Preliminary indications from numerical experiments with analogous adjustment schemes in variational problems indicate that the second is preferable to the first in regard to speed of convergence.

The attractive feature of the "penalty function" scheme is that it avoids the need for iterative corrections to assure satisfaction of the constraint equations as the descent process continues. By the same token, the need for separate determination of a starting point $\bar{x}_i$ which satisfies the constraints is obviated. At the time of the present writing, there is insufficient computational experience with this method to permit comparison with other techniques in ordinary minimum problems; however, some experience with a similar technique in solution of variational problems will be reported in a later section.

6.15 Ordinary Minimum Problems with Constraints: Inequality Constraints

Constraints which take the form of inequalities

$$g_j(x_1, \cdots, x_n) \leq 0, \qquad j = 1, \cdots, m \tag{6.32}$$

are increasingly of interest in applications. Ordinary minimum problems featuring such constraints form the basis of nonlinear programming theory, for which the reader is referred to Rosen[7] and Wolfe.[8]

In employing the gradient projection idea for solution of such problems, one must first find a suitable starting point for which relations (6.32) are satisfied. If the starting point is an interior point [a point for which strict inequality signs apply in (6.32)], one then proceeds in the negative free gradient direction until a minimum of f is reached or until one of the g_j changes sign. When the threshold of a constraint is reached, one then employs gradient projection, regarding the constraint as an equality. The subsequent possibilities for motion subject to various degrees of constraint are numerous, and it is clear that extensive testing and provision for projecting upon various combinations of constraints will require quite a sophisticated computer program if several inequality constraints are to be dealt with simultaneously.

The "penalty function" notion may also be applied to minimum problems featuring inequality constraints. To the function f are added terms comprising a "penalty function" of the form

$$f + \tfrac{1}{2} \sum_{j=1}^{m} K_j g_j{}^2 H(g_j) \tag{6.33}$$

Here $H(g_j)$ is the Heaviside unit step function of argument g_j. With the K_j chosen as positive constants, the second member is nonnegative. Note that the partial derivatives of the second member are continuous if the partial derivatives of the functions g_j are continuous. This feature favors the retention of the square law form of penalty even though it is not required to make the second member nonnegative in the case of inequality constraints.

This scheme possesses an attractive simplicity when employed in conjunction with the gradient method in that computer logic is minimal. In gradient calculations, the influence of a particular inequality constraint is automatically nil if the constraint is satisfied and increasingly large as it is violated. As in the case of equality constraint "penalties," adjustment of the constants K_j should be performed systematically, after each local minimum is attained, on the basis of comparison between "violations" and preassigned "tolerances."

An analysis to determine the products $K_j g_j$ for adjustment purposes may be carried out in a manner similar to that of the preceding section. One will automatically lose a row and a column of the matrix of coefficients of the system analogous to (6.30) for each strict inequality satisfied at the point under examination, in that the partial derivatives

$$\frac{\partial}{\partial x_i} g_k^2 H(g_k), \qquad i = 1, \cdots, n$$

vanish at points for which $g_k < 0$.

6.2 Gradient Technique in Flight Path Optimization Problems

An earlier chapter has developed the classical "indirect" method of the calculus of variations which is based upon the reduction of variational problems to differential equations. Although many interesting results have been forthcoming from analytical solutions of the Euler-Lagrange differential equations governing optimal flight, the idealizing assumptions usually invoked limit their applicability in practical situations. Under more realistic assumptions, a numerical attack on these equations is required and in this approach a serious difficulty may arise in the satisfaction of two-point boundary conditions (see, for example, Mengel,[20] Irving and Blum,[21] and Faulders[22]). This difficulty becomes a limiting factor where the order of the differential equations governing the basic system is four or higher.

This situation has provided the motivation for attack on variational problems of flight performance by means of the gradient technique. An application of gradient method to fixed end-point variational problems was given by Stein.[13] The class of problems featuring differential equations as constraints is more complex, and our development will be heuristic in character. We will, in the following, assume whatever continuity and differentiability properties may be necessary to avoid difficulty.

6.21 Problem Formulation

For present purposes it will be assumed that the system of differential equations to be satisfied along the flight path is given in first-order form:

$$\dot{x}_m = g_m(x_1, \cdots, x_n, y, t), \qquad m = 1, \cdots, n \qquad (6.34)$$

These equations relate velocities and positions, forces and accelerations, mass and flow of propellants and coolants, and the like. The x_m are termed problem or "state" variables, and y the control variable. Differentiation with respect to the independent variable, time t, is denoted by a super-scribed dot.

An important class of problems is that in which the performance quantity to be minimized is expressed as a function of the final values of the variables x_m and t:

$$P = P(x_{1_f}, \cdots, x_{n_f}, t_f) \tag{6.35}$$

At a specified initial time t_0 as many as n boundary conditions on the x_m may be stipulated. Since an entire function $y(t)$ is at our disposal, we may reasonably consider problems in which numerous conditions are imposed upon the x_m at various subsequent t values. In the following we will restrict attention to conditions imposed at the terminal point of the flight path. Among the $n + 1$ quantities consisting of the n final values of the x_m plus the final time t_f, no more than n relations may be specified in order that the value of P not be predetermined.

This problem statement is essentially that employed in an earlier chapter in connection with the Mayer formulation of variational problems.

6.22 Neighboring Solutions and Green's Functions

We now assume that a solution of Eqs. (6.34) is available which does not minimize P. This solution is required to satisfy the specified initial conditions; it may or may not be required to also satisfy the specified conditions at the terminal point depending on the version of the gradient method to be adopted, as discussed in later sections. Denoting the solution by $x_m = \bar{x}_m(t)$, $y = \bar{y}(t)$, we examine behavior in the neighborhood of this solution by setting $x_m = \bar{x}_m + \delta x_m$, $y = \bar{y} + \delta y$ and linearizing:

$$\delta \dot{x}_m = \sum_{j=1}^{n} \frac{\partial g_m}{\partial x_j} \delta x_j + \frac{\partial g_m}{\partial y} \delta y, \qquad m = 1, \cdots, n \tag{6.36}$$

The partial derivatives of the g_m are evaluated along $x_m = \bar{x}_m$, $y = \bar{y}$ and are therefore known functions of the independent variable t. The functions δx_m and δy are the *variations* of x_m and y in the neighborhood of $\bar{x}_m, \bar{y}$. The motivation for study of the linearized system (6.36) is the alteration of the control function $y(t)$ by means of a gradient process such as to obtain a reduction in the function P whose minimum is sought.

A formal solution of Eqs. (6.36) may be written in the form:

$$\delta x_m = \sum_{p=1}^{n} \delta x_p(t_0) \xi_{mp}(t_0, t) + \int_{t_0}^{t} \mu_m(\tau, t) \, \delta y(\tau) \, d\tau, \qquad m = 1, \cdots, n$$

$$\tag{6.37}$$

where the first member represents solution of the homogeneous system of equations and the second a superposition of control variable effects. The functions μ_m are Green's functions or influence functions; $\mu_m(\tau, t)$ may be regarded as the solution for δx_m corresponding to a unit impulse (Dirac delta function) in control introduced at time τ.[23] The μ_m are related to the functions ξ_{mp} of the homogeneous system by

$$\mu_m(\tau, t) = \sum_{p=1}^{n} \xi_{mp}(\tau, t) \frac{\partial g_p}{\partial y}, \qquad m = 1, \cdots, n \qquad (6.38)$$

Since interest centers on final values of the x_m, we evaluate expressions (6.37) at $t = t_f$; however, to provide for determination of the effects of small variations in terminal time δt_f from the terminal time $t_f = \bar{t}_f$ of solution $\bar{x}_m$, $\bar{y}$, we include a first-order correction term:

$$\delta x_{m_f} = \sum_{p=1}^{n} \delta x_p(t_0) \xi_{mp}(t_0, \bar{t}_f) + \int_{t_0}^{\bar{t}_f} \mu_m(\tau, \bar{t}_f) \, \delta y(\tau) \, d\tau + \bar{g}_{m_f} \, \delta t_f$$

$$m = 1, \cdots, n \quad (6.39)$$

Here the symbol $\bar{g}_{m_f}$ denotes the derivative $\dot{x}_m(\bar{t}_f) = g_m[\bar{x}_1(\bar{t}_f), \cdots, \bar{x}_n(\bar{t}_f), \bar{y}(\bar{t}_f)]$ evaluated at the terminal point of the nonminimal solution.

6.23 The Adjoint System

Since computation of the functions $\mu_m(\tau, t)$ over a complete range of both arguments will be found unnecessary, only their evaluation at $t = \bar{t}_f$ being required for subsequent calculations, it is reasonable to seek a means for performing the special computation which avoids the labor of the more general one. The following development relates the functions $\mu_m(\tau, t)$ to solutions of an adjoint system of equations through an application of Green's theorem. The scheme is based on the work of Bliss[24] and Goodman and Lance.[25]

We rewrite Eqs. (6.36) employing a subscript notation suitable to our immediate purpose:

$$\delta \dot{x}_i = \sum_{j=1}^{n} \frac{\partial g_i}{\partial x_j} \delta x_j + \frac{\partial g_i}{\partial y} \delta y, \qquad i = 1, \cdots, n \qquad (6.40)$$

and write the system of equations adjoint to this system

$$\dot{\lambda}_i = -\sum_{j=1}^{n} \frac{\partial g_j}{\partial x_i} \lambda_j, \qquad i = 1, \cdots, n \qquad (6.41)$$

which by definition is the system obtained from the homogeneous system by transposing the matrix of coefficients and changing the sign.

The solutions of the two systems are related by

$$\frac{d}{dt} \sum_{i=1}^{n} \lambda_i \, \delta x_i = \sum_{i=1}^{n} \lambda_i \frac{\partial g_i}{\partial y} \, \delta y \qquad (6.42)$$

as may be verified directly by evaluating the derivative on the left:

$$\frac{d}{dt} \sum_{i=1}^{n} \lambda_i \, \delta x_i = \sum_{i=1}^{n} \dot{\lambda}_i \, \delta x_i + \sum_{i=1}^{n} \lambda_i \, \delta \dot{x}_i$$

$$= - \sum_{i=1}^{n} \sum_{j=1}^{n} \frac{\partial g_j}{\partial x_i} \lambda_j \, \delta x_i + \sum_{i=1}^{n} \sum_{j=1}^{n} \lambda_i \frac{\partial g_i}{\partial x_j} \, \delta x_j + \sum_{i=1}^{n} \lambda_i \frac{\partial g_i}{\partial y} \, \delta y$$

$$(6.43)$$

and noting the cancellation of terms arising by interchange of subscripts i and j in the double summations. After integration of both left and right members between definite limits t_0 and $\bar{t}_f$, we find

$$\sum_{i=1}^{n} \lambda_i(\bar{t}_f) \, \delta x_i(\bar{t}_f) - \sum_{i=1}^{n} \lambda_i(t_0) \, \delta x_i(t_0) = \int_{t_0}^{\bar{t}_f} \sum_{i=1}^{n} \lambda_i \frac{\partial g_i}{\partial y} \, \delta y \, dt \quad (6.44)$$

This is the one-dimensional form of Green's theorem.

We now consider numerical solution of the adjoint system with all boundary values specified at $t = \bar{t}_f$. To the special solutions corresponding to

$$\lambda_i(\bar{t}_f) = 0, \qquad i \neq m$$

$$\lambda_i(\bar{t}_f) = 1, \qquad i = m$$

$$(6.45)$$

we assign the symbols $\lambda_i^{(m)}(t)$. In this fashion n expressions for the values of the $\delta x_m(\bar{t}_f)$ are obtained from Eq. (6.44):

$$\delta x_m(\bar{t}_f) = \sum_{i=1}^{n} \lambda_i^{(m)}(t_0) \, \delta x_i(t_0) + \int_{t_0}^{\bar{t}_f} \sum_{i=1}^{n} \lambda_i^{(m)} \frac{\partial g_i}{\partial y} \, \delta y \, dt,$$

$$m = 1, \cdots, n \quad (6.46)$$

By comparison of Eqs. (6.39) and (6.46) we may now relate the functions ξ_{mp} to the unit adjoint solutions defined by Eq. (6.45) as

$$\xi_{mp}(t_0, \bar{t}_f) = \lambda_p^{(m)}(t_0), \qquad m = 1, \cdots, n$$

$$p = 1, \cdots, n$$

$$(6.47)$$

[Note that the dependence of the right-hand members upon $\bar{t}_f$ is implicit in the definition of (6.45).] The Green's functions μ_m may also be expressed in terms of unit adjoint solutions as

$$\mu_m(\tau, \bar{t}_f) = \sum_{p=1}^{n} \lambda_p^{(m)}(\tau) \frac{\partial g_p}{\partial y}(\tau), \qquad m = 1, \cdots, n \qquad (6.48)$$

In the preceding development the choice of symbols λ for the variables of the adjoint system is deliberate, for Eqs. (6.41) are precisely those governing the Lagrange multiplier functions of the "indirect" theory. We note the important distinction, however, that the coefficients of (6.41) employed in the "indirect" theory are evaluated along a minimal solution of Eqs. (6.34), whereas in gradient computations they correspond to nonminimal paths.

The close relationship between Green's functions or influence functions and the "error coefficients" of guidance theory has drawn attention to the usefulness of the adjoint system technique in guidance analysis.[26-28]

6.24 The Gradient in Function Space

Introducing, as before, a second independent variable σ, we seek analogous means of performing gradient computations. We first evaluate the slope of descent of the performance quantity P at a "point" in function space determined by the nonminimal solution $x_m = \bar{x}_m(t)$, $y = \bar{y}(t)$,

$$\frac{dP}{d\sigma} = \sum_{m=1}^{n} \frac{\partial P}{\partial x_{m_f}} \frac{dx_{m_f}}{d\sigma} + \frac{\partial P}{\partial t_f} \frac{dt_f}{d\sigma} \qquad (6.49)$$

If the σ derivatives of the initial and final values of the x_m, the final time t_f, and the function $y(t, \sigma)$ are taken and evaluated at $\sigma = \bar{\sigma}$, corresponding to the nonminimal solution, Eqs. (6.39) become

$$\frac{dx_{m_f}}{d\sigma} = \sum_{p=1}^{n} \frac{dx_{p_0}}{d\sigma} \xi_{mp}(\bar{t}_f) + \int_{t_0}^{\bar{t}_f} \mu_m \frac{\partial y}{\partial \sigma} d\tau + \bar{g}_{m_f} \frac{dt_f}{d\sigma}, \qquad m = 1, \cdots, n$$

$$(6.50)$$

and expression (6.49) may then be written in the following form:

$$\frac{dP}{d\sigma} = \sum_{p=1}^{n} \frac{dx_{p_0}}{d\sigma} \sum_{m=1}^{n} \frac{\partial P}{\partial x_{m_f}} \xi_{mp}(\bar{t}_f) + \frac{dt_f}{d\sigma} \left(\frac{\partial P}{\partial t_f} + \sum_{m=1}^{n} \frac{\partial P}{\partial x_{m_f}} \bar{g}_{m_f} \right)$$

$$+ \int_{t_0}^{\bar{t}_f} \left(\sum_{m=1}^{n} \frac{\partial P}{\partial x_{m_f}} \mu_m \right) \frac{\partial y}{\partial \sigma} d\tau \qquad (6.51)$$

In the type of problem presently under consideration, the performance quantity P depends implicitly upon a finite number of parameters, the initial values of the x_m and the final time t_f; it also depends upon the function $y(t)$. Hence the problem is of "mixed" type, having partly the character of an ordinary minimum problem and partly a variational character. We will momentarily assume that the initial x_m values and that of the final time t_f are fixed:

$$\frac{dx_{p_0}}{d\sigma} = 0, \qquad p = 1, \cdots, n$$

$$\frac{dt_f}{d\sigma} = 0 \tag{6.52}$$

in order to examine independently the variational aspect.

Under these circumstances the expression $dP/d\sigma$ takes the form of the integral

$$\frac{dP}{d\sigma} = \int_{t_0}^{\bar{t}_f} \left(\sum_{m=1}^{n} \frac{\partial P}{\partial x_{m_f}} \mu_m \right) \frac{\partial y}{\partial \sigma} \, d\tau \tag{6.53}$$

We wish to determine the "direction" $\partial y(\tau)/\partial \sigma$ of steepest descent in the function space $y(\tau)$. In a procedure analogous to the earlier treatment of ordinary minimum problems, we consider a differential distance ds in the function space $y(\tau)$, defined by

$$1 - \int_{t_0}^{\bar{t}_f} \left(\frac{\partial y}{\partial s} \right)^2 d\tau = 0 \tag{6.54}$$

and seek stationary values of

$$\frac{dP}{ds} = \int_{t_0}^{\bar{t}_f} \left(\sum_{m=1}^{n} \frac{\partial P}{\partial x_{m_f}} \mu_m \right) \frac{\partial y}{\partial s} \, d\tau \tag{6.55}$$

subject to (6.54) as a constraint.

We form

$$\frac{dP}{ds} + \Lambda_0 \left[1 - \int_{t_0}^{\bar{t}_f} \left(\frac{\partial y}{\partial s} \right)^2 d\tau \right] \tag{6.56}$$

and set the derivative of this expression with respect to $\partial y(\tau)/\partial s$ to zero for all τ, obtaining

$$2\Lambda_0 \frac{\partial y}{\partial s} = \sum_{m=1}^{n} \frac{\partial P}{\partial x_{m_f}} \mu_m \tag{6.57}$$

From (6.54) the multiplier Λ_0 is evaluated as

$$2\Lambda_0 = \pm\left[\int_{t_0}^{\bar{t}_f}\left(\sum_{m=1}^{n}\frac{\partial P}{\partial x_{m\,f}}\,\mu_m\right)^2 d\tau\right]^{1/2} \tag{6.58}$$

and

$$\frac{\partial y}{\partial s} = \frac{\pm\sum_{m=1}^{n}\dfrac{\partial P}{\partial x_{m\,f}}\,\mu_m}{\left[\displaystyle\int_{t_0}^{\bar{t}_f}\left(\sum_{m=1}^{n}\frac{\partial P}{\partial x_{m\,f}}\,\mu_m\right)^2 d\tau\right]^{1/2}} \tag{6.59}$$

Taking the "velocity" of motion in function space as

$$\frac{ds}{d\sigma} = k\left[\int_{t_0}^{\bar{t}_f}\left(\sum_{m=1}^{n}\frac{\partial P}{\partial x_{m\,f}}\,\mu_m\right)^2 d\tau\right]^{1/2} \tag{6.60}$$

we obtain

$$\frac{\partial y}{\partial \sigma} = \pm k\sum_{m=1}^{n}\frac{\partial P}{\partial x_{m\,f}}\,\mu_m \tag{6.61}$$

We thus identify

$$[P]_y = \sum_{m=1}^{n}\frac{\partial P}{\partial x_{m\,f}}\,\mu_m \tag{6.62}$$

as the "free" gradient direction and assure motion in the negative gradient direction by choosing the negative sign in (6.61). With $k = 1$

$$\frac{\partial y}{\partial \sigma} = -[P]_y \tag{6.63}$$

This development has been carried out by analogy with a characteristic property of a vector gradient, for a discussion of which the reader is referred to Courant[5] and to Courant and Hilbert[17] (pp. 222–224).

In this subsection the most convenient combination of boundary conditions has been assumed for simplicity of explanation, namely: t_0 and t_f fixed, x_{m_0} fixed for all m, $x_{m\,f}$ not appearing in the function P unspecified. The handling of other types of boundary conditions will be the subject of the next two subsections.

6.25 Boundary Conditions as Constraints

We consider boundary conditions of separated type, i.e., equations relating either initial values or final values. Terminal values, for example, may be variable on a surface typified by

$$\mathfrak{J}_j(x_{1f}, \cdots, x_{nf}, t_f) = 0 \tag{6.64}$$

and there may be a number of such relations specified $j = 1, \cdots, l < n + 1$ if the final time is variable and $l < n$ if it is fixed.

Linearized versions of such constraints are given by

$$\bar{\mathfrak{J}}_j + \delta\mathfrak{J}_j = \bar{\mathfrak{J}}_j + \sum_{m=1}^{n} \frac{\partial\mathfrak{J}_j}{\partial x_{mf}} \delta x_{mf} + \frac{\partial\mathfrak{J}_j}{\partial t_f} \delta t_f = 0, \qquad j = 1, \cdots, l \tag{6.65}$$

Similar constraints relating initial values x_{m_0} and t_0 may also be specified. For the present we confine attention to the case of fixed initial values and fixed final time t_f. Hence we assume

$$\frac{\partial\mathfrak{J}_j}{\partial t_f} = 0 \quad \text{and} \quad l < n \tag{6.66}$$

In an analysis similar to that given in the preceding section, we write the constraints (6.65) in the form

$$\frac{d\mathfrak{J}_j}{ds} = \int_{t_0}^{\bar{t}_f} \left(\sum_{m=1}^{n} \frac{\partial\mathfrak{J}_j}{\partial x_{mf}} \mu_m \right) \frac{\partial y}{\partial s} d\tau = 0 \tag{6.67}$$

and adjoin them to (6.56) by means of Lagrange multipliers $\Lambda_j, j = 1, \cdots, l$. The omission of zero-order terms in expressions (6.65) corresponds to an assumption that the solution $\bar{x}_m, \bar{y}$ satisfies the boundary conditions (6.64).

Leaving details of the derivation to the interested reader, we state the principal result for the "projected" gradient direction

$$[P]_y = \sum_{m=1}^{n} \frac{\partial P}{\partial x_{mf}} \mu_m + \sum_{j=1}^{l} \Lambda_j \sum_{m=1}^{n} \frac{\partial\mathfrak{J}_j}{\partial x_{mf}} \mu_m \tag{6.68}$$

$$\frac{\partial y}{\partial \sigma} = -[P]_y \tag{6.69}$$

The multipliers $\Lambda_j, j = 1, \cdots, l$ are determined by the system of linear equations

$$\sum_{j=1}^{l} \Lambda_j \int_{t_0}^{\bar{t}_f} \left(\sum_{m=1}^{n} \frac{\partial\mathfrak{J}_j}{\partial x_{mf}} \mu_m \right) \left(\sum_{m=1}^{n} \frac{\partial\mathfrak{J}_k}{\partial x_{mf}} \mu_m \right) d\tau$$

$$= -\int_{t_0}^{\bar{t}_f} \left(\sum_{m=1}^{n} \frac{\partial\mathfrak{J}_k}{\partial x_{mf}} \mu_m \right) \left(\sum_{m=1}^{n} \frac{\partial P}{\partial x_{mf}} \mu_m \right) d\tau, \qquad k = 1, \cdots, l \tag{6.70}$$

This system of equations will have a solution if the matrix of coefficients $A = (a_{kj})$

$$a_{kj} = \int_{t_0}^{\bar{t}_f} \left(\sum_{m=1}^{n} \frac{\partial \Im_j}{\partial x_{mf}} \mu_m \right) \left(\sum_{m=1}^{n} \frac{\partial \Im_k}{\partial x_{mf}} \mu_m \right) d\tau, \qquad j, k = 1, \cdots, l \qquad (6.71)$$

is nonsingular, and this will be the case if the matrix $B = (b_{kj})$

$$b_{kj} = \sum_{m=1}^{n} \frac{\partial \Im_j}{\partial x_{mf}} \frac{\partial \Im_k}{\partial x_{mf}}, \qquad j, k = 1, \cdots, l \qquad (6.72)$$

is nonsingular, i.e., if the boundary conditions are not locally redundant, and, further, if the matrix $C = (c_{mp})$

$$c_{mp} = \int_{t_0}^{\bar{t}_f} \mu_m \mu_p \, d\tau, \qquad m, p = 1, \cdots, n \qquad (6.73)$$

is of rank $r \geq l$.* A proof of this due to Norman Greenspan of Grumman's Research Department is given in Appendix A.

The technique for handling terminal constraints just discussed is essentially that employed by Bryson.[15] It may be termed "gradient projection" by analogy with the technique discussed earlier in connection with ordinary minimum problems. A somewhat related scheme employed by the present writer in the investigation of reference 14 is presented as follows.

If in lieu of introduction of the multipliers Λ_j, the control variable y is broken down as

$$y(t, \sigma) = \phi(t, \sigma) + \sum_{q=1}^{l} a_q(\sigma) f_q(t) \qquad (6.74)$$

then the l constants a_q may be employed for the purposes of satisfying the

---

* The latter test requires that at least l of the n functions μ_m be linearly independent (Courant and Hilbert,[17] pp. 61–62). Two circumstances where this requirement may be violated should be mentioned. The first concerns the case in which the system of differential equation subsidiary conditions (6.34) contains a holonomic condition, i. e., a differential equation obtainable by differentiation of a finite condition relating the variables x_m and t. In such a case the matrix of (6.73) may degenerate in rank for all values of the upper limit of the integrals (see Courant and Hilbert,[17] p. 221). More subtle cases of degeneracy may arise for special values of the upper limit corresponding to other *abnormality* phenomena and to the occurrence of *conjugate points*, as defined in connection with Jacobi's necessary condition.

constraints (6.67) which we rewrite in the form

$$\frac{d\Im_j}{d\sigma} = \int_{t_0}^{\bar{t}_f} \left(\sum_{m=1}^{n} \frac{\partial \Im_j}{\partial x_{mf}} \mu_m \right)\left(\frac{\partial \phi}{\partial \sigma} + \sum_{q=1}^{l} \frac{da_q}{d\sigma} f_q \right) d\tau = 0, \qquad j = 1, \cdots, l \quad (6.75)$$

These equations may be rearranged as

$$\sum_{q=1}^{l} \frac{da_q}{d\sigma} \sum_{m=1}^{n} \frac{\partial \Im_j}{\partial x_{mf}} \int_{t_0}^{\bar{t}_f} \mu_m f_q \, d\tau = -\sum_{m=1}^{n} \frac{\partial \Im_j}{\partial x_{mf}} \int_{t_0}^{\bar{t}_f} \mu_m \frac{\partial \phi}{\partial \sigma} \, d\tau, \qquad j = 1, \cdots, l$$

$$(6.76)$$

and regarded as a system of simultaneous equations in the $da_q/d\sigma$. This system will have a solution if the matrix $D = (d_{jq})$

$$d_{jq} = \sum_{m=1}^{n} \frac{\partial \Im_j}{\partial x_{mf}} \int_{t_0}^{\bar{t}_f} \mu_m f_q \, d\tau, \qquad j, q = 1, \cdots, l \qquad (6.77)$$

is nonsingular.

The $f_q(t)$ are arbitrary functions to be chosen so that requirements for the system to have a solution are met. The $da_q/d\sigma$ determined by simultaneous solution of (6.76) may then be substituted into

$$\frac{dP}{d\sigma} = \int_{t_0}^{\bar{t}_f} \left(\sum_{m=1}^{n} \frac{\partial P}{\partial x_{mf}} \mu_m \right)\left(\frac{\partial \phi}{\partial \sigma} + \sum_{q=1}^{l} \frac{da_q}{d\sigma} f_q \right) d\tau \qquad (6.78)$$

and the gradient $[P]_\phi$ determined as the collected coefficient of $\partial \phi/\partial \sigma$.

Both of the schemes so far described in this section suffer from "drift" of terminal values, for large steps in $\Delta\sigma$, as a result of the boundary linearizations. The terminal values must be restored in the course of the descent process, and, in the gradient projection case, this is accomplished by reinstatement of the zero-order terms in the linearized constraint expressions (6.65). In the case of the process just described, the coefficients a_q provide a natural choice of parameters by which the necessary adjustments may be performed. However, a difficulty in performing corrections may arise which is associated with the choice of the arbitrary functions f_q, as will be illustrated in an example.

The employment of a "penalty function" scheme has the advantage of "built-in" corrections. The constraints on terminal values will be satisfied only approximately, although within any desired tolerances. One seeks a minimum of

$$P' = P + \tfrac{1}{2} \sum_{j=1}^{l} K_j \Im_j^2 \qquad (6.79)$$

Just as in the ordinary minimum case, the products $K_j \Im_j$ will satisfy a system resembling that determining the multipliers Λ_j [Eq. (6.70)], namely,

$$\sum_{j=1}^{l} K_j \mathfrak{I}_j \int_{t_0}^{\bar{t}f} \left(\sum_{m=1}^{n} \frac{\partial \mathfrak{I}_j}{\partial x_{mf}} \mu_m \right) \left(\sum_{m=1}^{n} \frac{\partial \mathfrak{I}_k}{\partial x_{mf}} \mu_m \right) d\tau$$

$$= -\int_{t_0}^{\bar{t}f} \left(\sum_{m=1}^{n} \frac{\partial \mathfrak{I}_k}{\partial x_{mf}} \mu_m \right) \left(\sum_{m=1}^{n} \frac{\partial P}{\partial x_{mf}} \mu_m \right) d\tau, \qquad k = 1, \cdots, l \quad (6.80)$$

where the μ functions and the various partial derivatives are evaluated at a minimum of (6.79), for which the boundary constraints are satisfied only approximately. If the matrix whose coefficients are given by (6.71) is nonsingular, the errors in the terminal constraint equations (6.64) may be reduced to within desired tolerances by appropriate adjustment of the K_j as described in Section 6.14 in connection with ordinary minimum problems.

The expression for the gradient $[P']_y$ takes a form similar to (6.68), namely,

$$[P']_y = \sum_{m=1}^{n} \frac{\partial P}{\partial x_{mf}} \mu_m + \sum_{j=1}^{l} K_j \mathfrak{I}_j \sum_{m=1}^{n} \frac{\partial \mathfrak{I}_j}{\partial x_{mf}} \mu_m \quad (6.81)$$

From the vanishing of $[P']_y$ along the path approached in the limit of the descent process, we may estimate the effects of small changes in specified terminal values of the $\mathfrak{I}_j$. In fact, for an *arbitrary* small variation in the control variable $\delta y(\tau)$, we may obtain the relationship

$$\delta P = -\sum_{j=1}^{l} K_j \mathfrak{I}_j \, \delta \mathfrak{I}_j \quad (6.82)$$

by multiplication of (6.81) by δy and integration from t_0 to t_f. Thus the quantities $-K_j \mathfrak{I}_j$ play the role of trade-off slopes in penalty function computations as do the quantities $-\Lambda_j$ in the gradient projection case [see Eq. (6.68)]. This remarkable property of optimal paths which holds for small variations in their neighborhood has been noted by Cicala[29] in connection with the indirect theory.

6.26 Variable Terminal Time: Boundary Values as Parameters

The way in which the terminal value of the independent variable time, t_f, enters into problems of the type presently under discussion is such as to require special treatment if it is not fixed. If, in a particular application, one of the variables x_m behaves monotonically and has fixed initial and terminal values, then its adoption as independent variable provides a simple means of avoiding complication. Such a choice may very often not be available, and in these circumstances the matter is one to be left to the ingenuity of the individual investigator according to the application and the version of gradient scheme adopted. A particular scheme suited to the technique involving arbitrary functions discussed in the previous section will be illustrated later in an example. In this section we will present a treatment of t_f as a free parameter in connection with the use of a penalty function for handling terminal constraints. It is convenient to consider simultaneously a similar means of handling unspecified initial values.

In order to avoid undue complication in the expressions to follow, we will assume that the initial value of time, t_0, is fixed and that initial conditions on certain of the variables x_m are given as fixed values, the remainder being parameters free for optimization purposes. We proceed to determine the derivative with respect to σ of the performance function given by (6.79) as follows:

$$\frac{dP'}{d\sigma} = \sum_{m=1}^{n} \frac{\partial P}{\partial x_{mf}} \frac{dx_{mf}}{d\sigma} + \frac{\partial P}{\partial t_f} \frac{dt_f}{d\sigma} + \sum_{j=1}^{l} K_j \Im_j \left(\sum_{m=1}^{n} \frac{\partial \Im_j}{\partial x_{mf}} \frac{dx_{mf}}{d\sigma} + \frac{\partial \Im_j}{\partial t_f} \frac{dt_f}{d\sigma} \right) \quad (6.83)$$

Making use of the expressions (6.50), we expand this to the following:

$$\frac{dP'}{d\sigma} = \int_{t_0}^{\bar{t}_f} \left[\sum_{m=1}^{n} \left(\frac{\partial P}{\partial x_{mf}} + \sum_{j=1}^{l} K_j \Im_j \frac{\partial \Im_j}{\partial x_{mf}} \right) \mu_m \right] \frac{\partial y}{\partial \sigma} d\tau$$

$$+ \left[\sum_{m=1}^{n} \left(\frac{\partial P}{\partial x_{mf}} + \sum_{j=1}^{l} K_j \Im_j \frac{\partial \Im_j}{\partial x_{mf}} \right) \bar{g}_{mf} + \frac{\partial P}{\partial t_f} + \sum_{j=1}^{l} K_j \Im_j \frac{\partial \Im_j}{\partial t_f} \right] \frac{dt_f}{d\sigma}$$

$$+ \sum_{p=1}^{n} \left[\sum_{m=1}^{n} \left(\frac{\partial P}{\partial x_{mf}} + \sum_{j=1}^{l} K_j \Im_j \frac{\partial \Im_j}{\partial x_{mf}} \right) \xi_{mp}(\bar{t}_f) \right] \frac{dx_{p0}}{d\sigma} \quad (6.84)$$

(The summation over p is to be understood to range over only those initial values x_{p0} which are unspecified.)

We are now in a position to identify a "mixed" gradient direction on the basis of the coefficients of the various σ derivatives appearing in (6.84). We set

$$\frac{\partial y}{\partial \sigma} = -[P']_y = -\left[\sum_{m=1}^{n} \left(\frac{\partial P}{\partial x_{mf}} + \sum_{j=1}^{l} K_j \Im_j \frac{\partial \Im_j}{\partial x_{mf}} \right) \mu_m \right] \quad (6.85)$$

$$\frac{dt_f}{d\sigma} = -[P']_{tf} = -\left[\sum_{m=1}^{n} \left(\frac{\partial P}{\partial x_{mf}} + \sum_{j=1}^{l} K_j \Im_j \frac{\partial \Im_j}{\partial x_{mf}} \right) \bar{g}_{mf} \right.$$

$$\left. + \frac{\partial P}{\partial t_f} + \sum_{j=1}^{l} K_j \Im_j \frac{\partial \Im_j}{\partial t_f} \right] \quad (6.86)$$

$$\frac{dx_{p0}}{d\sigma} = -[P']_{x_{p0}} = -\left[\sum_{m=1}^{n} \left(\frac{\partial P}{\partial x_{mf}} + \sum_{j=1}^{l} K_j \Im_j \frac{\partial \Im_j}{\partial x_{mf}} \right) \xi_{mp}(\bar{t}_f) \right] \quad (6.87)$$

and, in the course of the descent process, we change the final time t_f and the free initial values x_{p_0}, along with the function y, linearly with increments in the descent parameter σ according to the slopes given by these expressions. In such a fashion we combine the features of variational problems and ordinary minimum problems in a single gradient optimization process.

A related scheme for determination of optimal t_f is employment of the vanishing of the expression (6.86) as run termination criterion. This may be viewed as a one-dimensional search for a minimum of P' versus t_f which may be performed simultaneously with numerical integration of trajectories.

We note again in passing that the quantities $\xi_{mp}(\bar{t}_f)$, the partial derivatives of the terminal x_m values with respect to initial x_m values are conveniently evaluated from unit solutions of the adjoint system of equations as previously discussed in Section 6.23.

6.27 Optimization with Respect to Configuration and System Parameters

In many practical engineering applications, optimal performance is sought not only in terms of flight path selection but also in terms of vehicle and system parameters. We have, for clarity, avoided complicating the preceding analytical work by such considerations. It is of interest to note, however, that such parameters may conveniently be handled as initial conditions by means of the following artifice which is due to Cicala.[29]

We characterize the parameters e_i as initial values of additional system variables x_i which are governed by the differential equations

$$\dot{x}_i = 0$$
$$i = n + 1, \cdots \qquad (6.88)$$
$$x_i(t_0) = e_i$$

Considering these equations as additional members of the basic system (6.34), we may obtain the partial derivatives of terminal x_m values with respect to the e_i in terms of unit solutions of the (now expanded) adjoint system as previously described. This offers a convenient means compatible with the computational scheme previously suggested for simultaneous treatment of variational and ordinary minimum problems.

6.28 Inequality Constraints

If to the problem statement of Section 6.21 one or more requirements in the form of inequality constraints on the variables x_m, y, and t are added,

$$Q_i(x_1, \cdots, x_n, y, t) \leq 0 \qquad (6.89)$$

the problem becomes of nonclassical type. If the control variable y appears in the expressions Q_i, certain techniques developed along the lines of the "indirect" variational method are applicable, namely, the techniques of Valentine[30] and Pontryagin,[31] discussed in other chapters. Relatively little theory is available, however, for treatment of cases in which the functions Q_i do not depend on the control variable y. Such cases are of great practical interest, e.g., in connection with air vehicle flight paths subject to a minimum altitude limit and to air speed/altitude envelope boundaries arising from structural and power plant limitations.

Examining first the situation where the control variable y appears in the Q_i, we assume that the inequalities are of the form

$$y_1 \leq y \leq y_2 \tag{6.90}$$

which is usually the case in applications. We now introduce a parameter $\beta(t, \sigma)$ as a new control variable by defining a function $y(\beta)$ as

$$y = y_1, \qquad\qquad\qquad \beta \leq 0 \tag{6.91}$$

$$y = y_1 + (y_2 - y_1)\beta, \qquad 0 \leq \beta \leq 1 \tag{6.92}$$

$$y = y_2, \qquad\qquad\qquad 1 \leq \beta \tag{6.93}$$

This is shown in the following sketch.

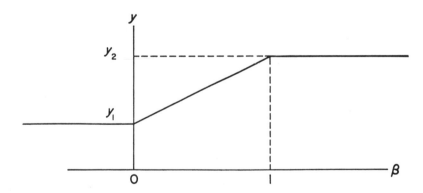

We may now apply the theory developed earlier in the absence of any constraint on the variable β. As a result of the transformation from $y(t, \sigma)$ to $\beta(t, \sigma)$ as control variable, the integrand typically arising in the integral expression for $dP/d\sigma$ becomes

$$[P]_y \frac{\partial y}{\partial \sigma} = [P]_y \frac{dy}{d\beta} \frac{\partial \beta}{\partial \sigma} \tag{6.94}$$

and motion in the negative gradient direction is determined by

$$\frac{\partial \beta}{\partial \sigma} = -[P]_v \frac{dy}{d\beta} \tag{6.95}$$

The derivative $dy/d\beta$ is given by the expression

$$\frac{dy}{d\beta} = (y_2 - y_1)[H(\beta) - H(\beta - 1)] \tag{6.96}$$

where H is the Heaviside unit step function $[H(\alpha) = 0$ for $\alpha < 0, H(\alpha) = 1$ for $\alpha > 0]$. The derivative is undefined at the points $\beta = 0$ and $\beta = 1$. These ambiguities may be removed conveniently by setting

$$\frac{dy}{d\beta} = (y_2 - y_1)H(-[P]_v), \qquad \beta = 0 \tag{6.97}$$

$$\frac{dy}{d\beta} = (y_2 - y_1)H([P]_v), \qquad \beta = 1 \tag{6.98}$$

which decides the question on whether or not the negative gradient direction leads into or out of the interval $0 \leq \beta \leq 1$.

In a continuous descent process, such a formulation will succeed in holding the control variable y in the desired region $y_1 \leq y \leq y_2$ and the parameter β will automatically remain in the region $0 \leq \beta \leq 1$. There will be difficulty, however, with a stepwise version, since the right-hand member of (6.95) is evaluated along the solution $x = \bar{x}(t), y = \bar{y}(t)$ and with finite step size $\Delta\sigma$, the control parameter β will not, in general, remain within limits. Consequently, it will be necessary before each calculation of $\partial \beta(t)/\partial \sigma$ to alter the function $\beta(t)$ obtained in the course of the preceding descent computations to conform to the inequality $0 \leq \beta \leq 1$; otherwise the right-hand member of (6.95) will vanish in all subsequent computations at points for which the inequality is violated.

Constraints $Q_i \leq 0$ which are independent of y may be handled approximately by construction of suitable penalty functions. If an additional variable x_i is introduced in connection with each constraint according to the equations

$$\dot{x}_i = \tfrac{1}{2}Q_i{}^2 H(Q_i)$$
$$\qquad\qquad i = n + 1, n + 2, \cdots, s \tag{6.99}$$
$$x_i(t_0) = 0$$

where H is the Heaviside unit step function, then the terminal values of these x_i will be

$$x_i(t_t) = \tfrac{1}{2}\int_{t_0}^{t_t} Q_i{}^2 H(Q_i) \, dt, \qquad i = n + 1, n + 2, \cdots, s \tag{6.100}$$

representing integral squares of the "violations" taken over those segments of the flight path which violate the constraints. Appropriate penalty terms proportional to these terminal values may then be added to Eq. (6.79), giving it the form

$$P' = P + \tfrac{1}{2} \sum_{j=1}^{l} K_j \mathfrak{I}_j^2 + \sum_{i=n+1}^{s} K_i x_i(t_f), \qquad l < n \qquad (6.101)$$

Evidently "tolerances" for comparison with the x_i terminal values and adjustment of constants K_i must be specified in similar terms. If ϵ_i is a specified error tolerance in the sense of an rms average over instantaneous values, then the appropriate "tolerance" for comparison with x_{if} is

$$E_i = \tfrac{1}{2} \int_{t_0}^{t_f} \epsilon_i^2 H(Q_i) \, dt \qquad (6.102)$$

The ratio $x_i(t_f)/E_i$ will then serve as a "violation"/"tolerance" index for adjustment of K_i in the course of the descent process.

6.29 Penalty Functions: Error Estimates

In connection with computer mechanization of the penalty function scheme, it is useful to have available a means for estimation of the error in the functional P in terms of the constraint "violations." Thus those "violations" which have a particularly strong effect on P may be noted and a more rational basis provided for the establishment of the "tolerances" discussed previously.

The increment in P due to small changes in terminal values of the x_m and t is given to first order as

$$\Delta P = \sum_{m=1}^{n} \frac{\partial P}{\partial x_{mf}} \, \delta x_{mf} + \frac{\partial P}{\partial t_f} \, \delta t_f$$

$$= \int_{t_0}^{t_f} \left(\sum_{m=1}^{n} \frac{\partial P}{\partial x_{mf}} \, \mu_m \right) \delta y \, d\tau + \left(\frac{\partial P}{\partial t_f} + \sum_{m=1}^{n} \frac{\partial P}{\partial x_{mf}} \, \bar{g}_{mf} \right) \delta t_f \qquad (6.103)$$

Assuming that a minimum of P' as given by (6.101) has been attained for certain fixed values of the penalty constants, we have the following equation for the vanishing of the gradient $[P']_y$:

$$[P']_y = \sum_{m=1}^{n} \frac{\partial P}{\partial x_{mf}} \, \mu_m + \sum_{j=1}^{l} K_j \mathfrak{I}_j \sum_{m=1}^{n} \frac{\partial \mathfrak{I}_j}{\partial x_{mf}} \, \mu_m + \sum_{i=n+1}^{s} K_i \mu_i = 0$$

$$(6.104)$$

From the condition t_f open,

$$[P']_{t_f} = \sum_{m=1}^{n} \left(\frac{\partial P}{\partial x_{mf}} + \sum_{j=1}^{l} K_j \mathfrak{I}_j \frac{\partial \mathfrak{I}_j}{\partial x_{mf}} \right) \bar{g}_{mf} + \sum_{i=n+1}^{s} K_i \bar{g}_{if} + \frac{\partial P}{\partial t_f}$$

$$+ \sum_{j=1}^{l} K_j \mathfrak{I}_j \frac{\partial \mathfrak{I}_j}{\partial t_f} = 0 \quad (6.105)$$

Making use of these expressions, we obtain for ΔP

$$\Delta P = - \int_{t_0}^{\bar{t}_f} \left(\sum_{j=1}^{l} K_j \mathfrak{I}_j \sum_{m=1}^{n} \frac{\partial \mathfrak{I}_j}{\partial x_{mf}} \mu_m + \sum_{i=n+1}^{s} K_i \mu_i \right) \delta y \, d\tau$$

$$- \left[\sum_{j=1}^{l} K_j \mathfrak{I}_j \frac{\partial \mathfrak{I}_j}{\partial t_f} + \sum_{m=1}^{n} \sum_{j=1}^{l} K_j \mathfrak{I}_j \frac{\partial \mathfrak{I}_j}{\partial x_{mf}} \bar{g}_{mf} + \sum_{i=n+1}^{s} K_i \bar{g}_{if} \right] \delta t_f$$

$$= - \sum_{j=1}^{l} K_j \mathfrak{I}_j \Delta \mathfrak{I}_j - \sum_{i=n+1}^{s} K_i \Delta x_{if} \qquad (6.106)$$

If we now consider corrections in control $\delta y(\tau)$ and in terminal time δt_f such as to produce increments

$$\Delta \mathfrak{I}_j = - \mathfrak{I}_j \qquad (6.107)$$

$$\Delta x_{if} = - x_{if} \qquad (6.108)$$

which will null the "violations," then the resulting increase in P may be estimated as

$$\Delta P = \sum_{j=1}^{l} K_j \mathfrak{I}_j^2 + 2 \sum_{i=n+1}^{s} K_i x_{if} \qquad (6.109)$$

where the factor of 2 in the second member is introduced to account approximately for the square-law behavior of the integrand in (6.100) near $Q_i = 0$.

The increment in P may be conveniently evaluated in terms of known terminal values. The contributions of the various components of ΔP provide a basis for the setting of "tolerances" and hence for the adjustment of the K_j and K_i. In terms of P and P' evaluated for finite K_j and K_i, a "best" estimate of the limiting value of P is

$$P + \Delta P = P + 2(P' - P) = 2P' - P \qquad (6.110)$$

as obtained from (6.101) and (6.109).

6.3 Solar Sailing Example

For the purpose of exploring the computational aspect of the gradient optimization technique, we have chosen a planar case of transfer between planetary orbits by means of the interesting solar sailing scheme. The potential capabilities of solar sail propulsion have been investigated in the papers of Garwin,[32] Cotter,[33] Tsu,[34] and London.[35] This problem has the simplicity appropriate to an exploration of method, yet sufficient complexity to render analytical solution quite difficult unless drastic simplifications are introduced.

6.31 System Equations

The equations of motion and kinematic relations are given in a notation nearly the same as that of Tsu.[34] With reference to the schematic of Fig. 2, these are as follows:

Radial acceleration

$$\dot{u} = g_1 = \frac{v^2}{R} - A_0 \left(\frac{R_0}{R}\right)^2 + \alpha \left(\frac{R_0}{R}\right)^2 |\cos^3 \theta| \qquad (6.111)$$

Circumferential acceleration

$$\dot{v} = g_2 = -\frac{uv}{R} - \alpha \left(\frac{R_0}{R}\right)^2 \sin \theta \cos^2 \theta \qquad (6.112)$$

Radial velocity

$$\dot{R} = g_3 = u \qquad (6.113)$$

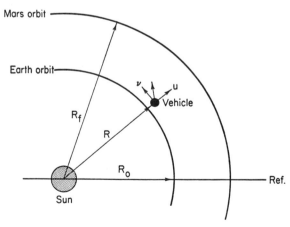

Fig. 2. Orbital transfer schematic.

Circumferential angular velocity

$$\dot{\psi} = \frac{v}{R} \tag{6.114}$$

Since the heliocentric angle ψ does not appear in the first three equations, nor will it appear in the statements of boundary conditions to be considered, Eq. (6.114) may be ignored for purposes of gradient optimization. This amounts to an assumption that terminal matching of the heliocentric angles of vehicle and "target" planet is accomplished by selection of launch time.

6.32 Boundary Values

Seeking minimum-time transfer, we identify the functional P as

$$P = t_f \tag{6.115}$$

The functions u, v, R are the variables x_m of the theoretical development, and the sail angle θ appears in the role of the control variable y.

As initial conditions we specify velocity components u, v, and radius R corresponding to motion in the earth's orbit approximated as a circle:

$$t_0 = 0 \tag{6.116}$$

$$u(0) = u_0 = u_E = 0 \tag{6.117}$$

$$v(0) = v_0 = v_E \tag{6.118}$$

$$R(0) = R_0 = R_E \tag{6.119}$$

We consider terminal conditions corresponding to arrival at the orbit of the planet Mars (also taken as a circle) with prescribed velocity components:

$$u(t_f) = u_f \tag{6.120}$$

$$v(t_f) = v_f \tag{6.121}$$

$$R(t_f) = R_f = R_M \tag{6.122}$$

6.33 Correction Functions

For fixed boundary values of u, v, and R, the equations corresponding to Eqs. (6.39) of the preceding theoretical development are

$$\delta u_{\mathrm{f}} = \int_0^{\bar{\imath}\mathrm{f}} \mu_1 \, \delta\theta \, d\tau + \bar{g}_{1\mathrm{f}} \, \delta t_{\mathrm{f}} = 0 \qquad (6.123)$$

$$\delta v_{\mathrm{f}} = \int_0^{\bar{\imath}\mathrm{f}} \mu_2 \, \delta\theta \, d\tau + \bar{g}_{2\mathrm{f}} \, \delta t_{\mathrm{f}} = 0 \qquad (6.124)$$

$$\delta R_{\mathrm{f}} = \int_0^{\bar{\imath}\mathrm{f}} \mu_3 \, \delta\theta \, d\tau + \bar{g}_{3\mathrm{f}} \, \delta t_{\mathrm{f}} = 0 \qquad (6.125)$$

In this case the number of functions f_q and coefficients a_q required is

$$r = n - 1 - s = 3 - 1 - 0 = 2 \qquad (6.126)$$

We select the functions f_q as

$$f_1(t) = t \qquad (6.127)$$

$$f_2(t) = t^2 \qquad (6.128)$$

and the control function $\theta(t)$ is broken down as

$$\theta = \phi + a_1 t + a_2 t^2 \qquad (6.129)$$

The system of equations (6.123)–(6.125) becomes

$$\left[\int_0^{\bar{\imath}\mathrm{f}} f_1(\tau)\mu_1 \, d\tau \right] \frac{da_1}{d\sigma} + \left[\int_0^{\bar{\imath}\mathrm{f}} f_2(\tau)\mu_1 \, d\tau \right] \frac{da_2}{d\sigma} + \bar{g}_{1\mathrm{f}} \frac{dt_{\mathrm{f}}}{d\sigma} = - \int_0^{\bar{\imath}\mathrm{f}} \mu_1 \frac{\partial\phi}{\partial\sigma} \, d\tau$$

$$(6.130)$$

$$\left[\int_0^{\bar{\imath}\mathrm{f}} f_1(\tau)\mu_2 \, d\tau \right] \frac{da_1}{d\sigma} + \left[\int_0^{\bar{\imath}\mathrm{f}} f_2(\tau)\mu_2 \, d\tau \right] \frac{da_2}{d\sigma} + \bar{g}_{2\mathrm{f}} \frac{dt_{\mathrm{f}}}{d\sigma} = - \int_0^{\bar{\imath}\mathrm{f}} \mu_2 \frac{\partial\phi}{\partial\sigma} \, d\tau$$

$$(6.131)$$

$$\left[\int_0^{\bar{\imath}\mathrm{f}} f_1(\tau)\mu_3 \, d\tau \right] \frac{da_1}{d\sigma} + \left[\int_0^{\bar{\imath}\mathrm{f}} f_2(\tau)\mu_3 \, d\tau \right] \frac{da_2}{d\sigma} + \bar{g}_{3\mathrm{f}} \frac{dt_{\mathrm{f}}}{d\sigma} = - \int_0^{\bar{\imath}\mathrm{f}} \mu_3 \frac{\partial\phi}{\partial\sigma} \, d\tau$$

$$(6.132)$$

This 3 × 3 case may conveniently be inverted analytically. There seems little point in listing the inverse elements here, however.

$$
\begin{bmatrix} \dfrac{da_1}{d\sigma} \\[2ex] \dfrac{da_2}{d\sigma} \\[2ex] \dfrac{dt_f}{d\sigma} \end{bmatrix} = - \begin{bmatrix} \\ C \\ \\ \end{bmatrix} \begin{bmatrix} \displaystyle\int_0^{\bar{t}_f} \mu_1 \dfrac{\partial\phi}{\partial\sigma}\, d\tau \\[2ex] \displaystyle\int_0^{\bar{t}_f} \mu_2 \dfrac{\partial\phi}{\partial\sigma}\, d\tau \\[2ex] \displaystyle\int_0^{\bar{t}_f} \mu_3 \dfrac{\partial\phi}{\partial\sigma}\, d\tau \end{bmatrix} \tag{6.133}
$$

The slope of descent $dt_f/d\sigma$ is given by

$$
\frac{dt_f}{d\sigma} = - \int_0^{\bar{t}_f} [C_{31}\mu_1 + C_{32}\mu_2 + C_{33}\mu_3]\frac{\partial\phi}{\partial\sigma}\, d\tau \tag{6.134}
$$

and the gradient of P by

$$
[P]_\phi = -[C_{31}\mu_1 + C_{32}\mu_2 + C_{33}\mu_3] \tag{6.135}
$$

Accordingly, we set

$$
\frac{\partial\phi}{\partial\sigma} = -[P]_\phi = C_{31}\mu_1 + C_{32}\mu_2 + C_{33}\mu_3 \tag{6.136}
$$

and proceed with stepwise descent.

A particularly suitable case for a first illustration of computational technique is the one in which terminal velocity components are unspecified—"free" boundary conditions. Here Eqs. (6.123) and (6.124) may be deleted and

$$
r = n - 1 - s = 3 - 1 - 2 = 0 \tag{6.137}
$$

so that no functions f_q are needed. Hence

$$
\theta = \phi \tag{6.138}
$$

and

$$
\frac{\partial\phi}{\partial\sigma} = \frac{\mu_3}{\bar{g}_{3f}} \tag{6.139}
$$

$$
\frac{dt_f}{d\sigma} = -\frac{1}{\bar{g}_{3f}^2}\int_0^{\bar{t}_f} \mu_3{}^2\, d\tau \tag{6.140}
$$

in this case.

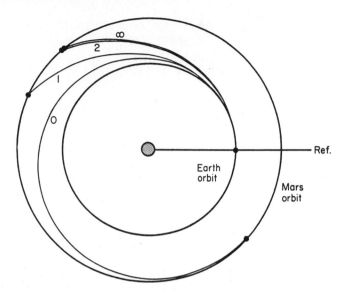

FIG. 3.   Successive approximations to optimal transfer path, terminal velocity components open.

Computations have employed numerical values of the various constants from Tsu's paper, with

$$\alpha = 0.1 \text{ cm/sec}^2 = 3.28 \times 10^{-3} \text{ ft/sec}^2 \qquad (6.141)$$

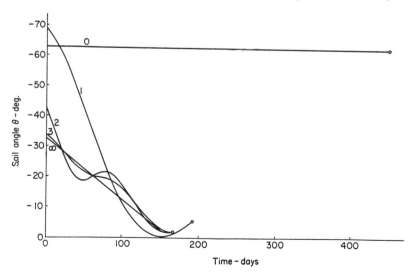

FIG. 4.   Successive approximations to optimal sail angle program, terminal velocity components open.

This value corresponds to about $10^{-4}g$ thrust acceleration developed by the sail when oriented broadside to the sun ($\theta = 0$) at earth's orbit radius, or about 17% of the sun's gravitational attraction.

6.34 Orbit Transfer Computations

Results of descent computations for the case of "open" terminal velocity components are shown in Figs. 3–5. The control program of the original

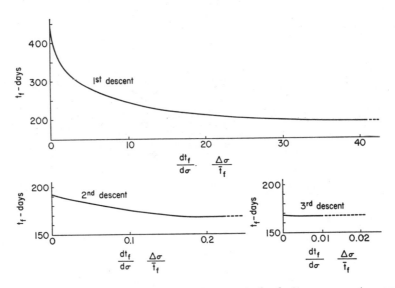

FIG. 5.   Descent curves—solar sail transfer, terminal velocity components open.

flight path (Figs. 3 and 4), chosen arbitrarily, was far from optimal in that the radial velocity component at crossing of Mars orbit was small. The greatest reduction in flight time—more than half of the original—is seen to be obtained in the course of the first descent (Fig. 5). In three descents minimum flight time has been attained for practical purposes, although small changes in the detailed structure of the control program are still in evidence.

Results for the case of terminal velocity components matched to the target planet

$$u_f = u_M,\ v_f = v_M \tag{6.142}$$

are presented in Figs. 6–9. The tendency of the terminal values to depart from the prescribed values is shown in Fig. 6. These were restored via an iterative correction process employing increments in the coefficients a_1

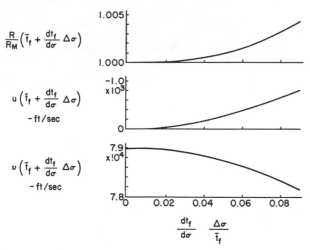

FIG. 6. Departure of terminal values, "matched" terminal velocity components.

and a_2 of Eq. (6.129). Typically, two or three iteration cycles were required to correct each point. Descent curves are shown in Fig. 7. The approach to the minimum-time solution is depicted in Figs. 8 and 9.

6.35 Convergence Considerations

The first attempt at computations for this "matched velocity" case employed functions f_q constant and linear with time. This met with near-

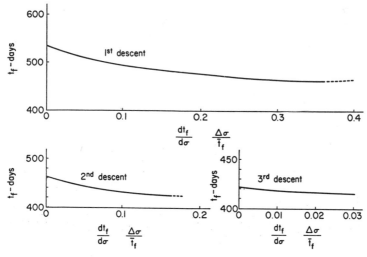

FIG. 7. Descent curves—solar sail transfer, "matched" terminal velocity components.

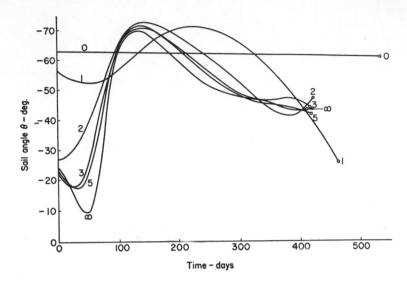

FIG. 8. Successive approximations to optimal sail angle program, "matched" terminal velocity components.

zero determinant difficulty, whereas the combination of linear and square-law corrections indicated above was successful in avoiding this difficulty.

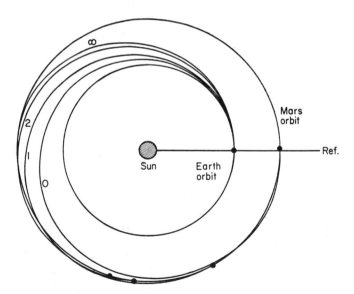

FIG. 9. Successive approximations to optimal transfer path, "matched" terminal velocity components.

A subsequent examination of the behavior of the determinant in question during the course of the descent process was instructive on the matter of choice of correction functions. Values of the determinant of the matrix on the left of Eqs. (6.130)–(6.132), which is required in calculation of the inverse matrix C of Eq. (6.133), were tabulated for the first few descent steps and for the converged trajectory as shown in Table I.

TABLE I

DETERMINANT BEHAVIOR

Descent no. i	$f_1 = 1$ Case: $f_2 = t$ Δ_i/Δ_∞	$f_1 = t$ Case: $f_2 = t^2$ Δ_i/Δ_∞
1	-2.383	3.983
2	-2.695	3.268
3	-0.770	1.527
4	-0.340	1.104
∞	1.000	1.000

A check showed that the numerical values of both determinants evaluated for the converged trajectory were large enough to permit terminal value adjustments without difficulty of ill-conditioning. Thus the convergence of a descent process which employs correction functions depends upon a choice of functions for which the determinant may not change sign. With the benefit of hindsight gained from this experiment, we observe that a choice of influence functions μ_m in the role of correction functions f_q appears attractive in that the determinant in question will be well behaved except in the special circumstances noted in the footnote of Section 6.25.

6.4 Low-Thrust Example

6.41 System Equations and Boundary Values

A second, closely related, example for which numerical computations have been performed concerns orbit transfer by means of low-thrust propulsion, e.g., ion rocket or plasma jet. In this case the penalty function technique for treatment of terminal constraints is adopted. The results of this section are due to Lindorfer and Moyer.[36]

The equations of motion and kinematic relations resemble those for the solar sail example, with differences appearing only in the expressions for thrust components:

Radial acceleration

$$\dot{u} = g_1 = \frac{v^2}{R} - A_0 \left(\frac{R_0}{R}\right)^2 + \frac{T}{m} \sin \theta \qquad (6.143)$$

Circumferential acceleration

$$\dot{v} = g_2 = -\frac{uv}{R} + \frac{T}{m} \cos \theta \qquad (6.144)$$

Radial velocity

$$\dot{R} = g_3 = u \qquad (6.145)$$

Circumferential angular velocity

$$\dot{\psi} = g_4 = \frac{v}{R} \qquad (6.146)$$

The thrust magnitude T has been taken as constant at a value corresponding to an initial thrust acceleration

$$\frac{T}{m_0 g} = 0.846 \times 10^{-4} \qquad (6.147)$$

and the mass has been assumed to decrease linearly with time

$$m = m_0 - Qt \qquad (6.148)$$

at a rate corresponding to

$$\frac{Q}{m_0} = 1.29 \times 10^{-3} \text{ per day} \qquad (6.149)$$

These estimates are taken from the paper of Edwards and Brown.[37] The thrust direction θ is measured from the circumferential direction in the above.

Boundary conditions considered in the computations are those for the "matched velocity" case of transfer from earth's orbit to the Martian orbit. These orbits are idealized as circular as in the example of the preceding section.

6.42 Orbit Transfer and Rendezvous Computations

The orbit transfer case, ψ_f open, was examined first. The convergence of the successive approximation process was fairly rapid. Although the number of descents required was larger than in the solar sail example of the preceding section, the absence of any need for correction of the "drift" exhibited in Fig. 6 resulted in an over-all reduction in computation time. Experimentation with penalty constant adjustment schemes indi-

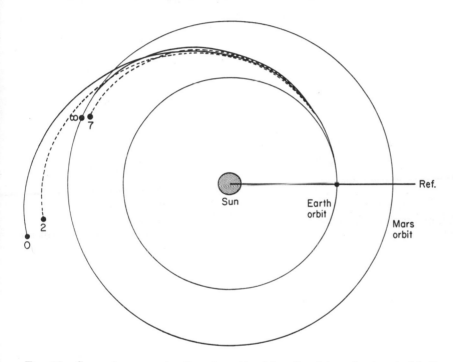

Fig. 10. Successive approximations to optimal low-thrust transfer, terminal helio-centric angle open.

cated that convergence is improved if the values of the penalty constants are initially taken small—"loose tolerances"—and the descent process allowed to proceed through a number of steps before the tolerances are "tightened." Thus in Figs. 10 and 11 the first 25 descent steps were performed with somewhat low values of the K_j and a minimum of P' approached. The K_j were then increased in proportion to the absolute value of error/tolerance ratio for each variable (radial velocity excepted, since this was employed as run termination variable) and the process continued as shown.

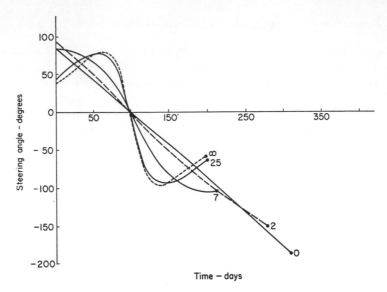

FIG. 11.   Successive approximations to optimal low-thrust direction program, terminal heliocentric angle open.

For the planetary rendezvous problem it is required that the heliocentric angle of the vehicle, ψ, match that of Mars at the terminal point. Figures 12 and 13 present results obtained for various assumed initial configurations of the vehicle(earth)-Mars system. Minimum transfer time is plotted

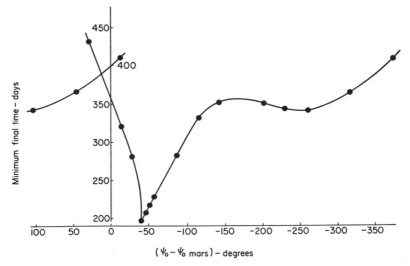

FIG. 12.   Minimum time for orbital rendezvous.

against the initial configuration angle in Fig. 12. The lowest point on this curve corresponds to the minimum time for the orbit transfer case (terminal angle open). On the basis of the few data points shown, the minimum appears to have a cusplike character.

This particular point also divides the solutions to the rendezvous problem into two operationally distinct classes. One class ($\psi_0 - \psi_{0\ Mars} > -46°$) consists of solutions in which the vehicle "waits" for Mars to overtake it. To accomplish this, the vehicle flies out past the Martian orbit, decreasing

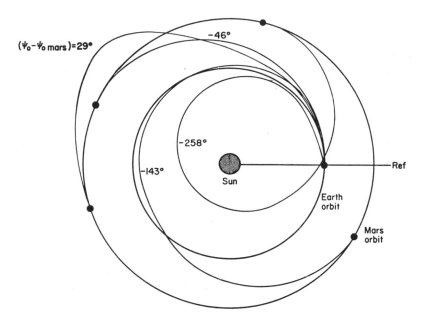

Fig. 13. Optimal transfer paths for rendezvous, various initial configurations.

circumferential velocity until it becomes lower than Martian circular velocity. As the relative heliocentric angle decreases, the vehicle's circumferential velocity is increased to match that of Mars.

The second class of solutions ($\psi_0 - \psi_{0\ Mars} < -46°$) is characterized by an initial inward motion toward the sun resulting in velocity build-up and final tangential approach to the Mars orbit from within.

The results of Fig. 12 indicate that transit time as a function of launch configuration of the planets exhibits a fairly sharp minimum, and that on a majority of "unfavorable" launch dates the technique of pursuit from behind permits faster transit than the "waiting" technique.

6.5 Remarks on the Relative Merits of Various
Computational Techniques

The reader may have correctly inferred that the present chapter amounts to a status report on research still underway rather than a definitive exposition of a standard technique. Indeed, the diversity of viewpoints in the various chapters of this volume serves to indicate the current general uncertainty regarding the applicability and relative merits of the numerous schemes in actual numerical computations. Accordingly, the remarks of the present section will be qualitative, provisional, and confined to the gradient and "indirect" methods with which the author has firsthand experience.

The writer has occasionally been asked to compare gradient methods with the classical "indirect" method (numerical solution of the Euler-Lagrange equations) in regard to speed and ease of computation. It is not easy to draw such a comparison since gradient methods have a "hammer-and-tongs" character while the numerical solution of the two-point boundary-value problem for the Euler equations is very much an art. In problems simple enough to yield to a survey of a one- or two-parameter family of Euler solutions, the classical approach is effective; yet there are few problems of practical interest which can be manipulated into so simple a form. Treatments of the more complicated problems reported in the literature have centered on determination of the mapping between initial and final values, either by mechanized iterative procedures or by extensive cross-plotting of boundary values. This sort of process may be complicated, depending on the particular application, by extremely high sensitivity to small changes in initial values and/or by encounter with near-singular matrices governing successive adjustments. Even the most successful procedures depend upon first obtaining a trial Euler solution whose terminal values lie somewhere in the vicinity of those specified; and the preliminary search for such a solution may consume much time and effort.

It seems possible and even likely that improved means for solution of the mapping problem will materialize. The state-of-the-art in nonlinear differential equations is perhaps not very encouraging, however, in regard to the early development of a powerful general scheme.

Another approach based upon the Euler equations and Newton's method should be mentioned. This is a proposed iterative technique due to Hestenes[38] designed to lead to an Euler solution which satisfies the specified boundary conditions. This idea has been pursued by Kalaba[39] whose theoretical studies have indicated favorable convergence properties within the limits of a convexity assumption. Computational experience with the method and examination of the practical implications of the convexity assumption are presently lacking.

Insofar as comparison between the various versions of the gradient method presented herein are concerned, the active competition appears to be between gradient projection and the penalty function scheme. The former requires an expensive error correction cycle which is unnecessary with the latter. On the other hand, the concentration of effort with the penalty function technique is overly heavy on reduction of errors in terminal values. If "tight" tolerances are employed, the process is oscillatory and convergence is slowed. The employment of "loose" tolerances in initial computations, with later tightening, appears to represent an effective compromise. The writer has considered, but not yet tried, the two versions in combination, i.e., in alternate cycles. This would relieve the need for corrections during the projection cycle and perhaps combine the good features of the two versions. In general, the computational experience with gradient methods has been sufficiently encouraging throughout the exploratory work reported herein to warrant future attack on comparatively large scale problems.

The writer and his colleagues have compared the gradient and Euler solutions for a limited number of cases in the problems described in the preceding sections. The motivation for this work happened to be a desire for an "exact" solution as a test extremal in some work on the second variation, rather than a comparison of technique. The first lesson from these experiments was that the control variable time history for a gradient solution converged within "engineering" accuracy (say 1% of minimum P) did not agree well over certain time intervals with an Euler solution. The disagreement was confined to those portions of the path over which the terminal values affecting P are relatively insensitive to control variations (see, for example, Fig. 14). From an engineering viewpoint this is unimportant if only the value of P is of main interest, as in flight performance work. It is inconvenient if a family of neighboring extremals are required, as, for example, in connection with a guidance study, for this requires that additional computations be performed to converge the control variable history to within the desired accuracy.

It has been speculated that an appropriate procedure for treatment of this situation is transition to a scheme for systematic numerical solution of the Euler equations, and this appears plausible on first consideration. One finds, however, that the appropriate linear combinations of adjoint solutions do *not* yield a good approximation to the multiplier functions of the indirect theory, and, in particular, the initial values of the multipliers may be sufficiently in error to cause difficulty in an iterative adjustment process.

In this connection, we will present in the following section a scheme intended to refine the control program of a near-minimal gradient solution

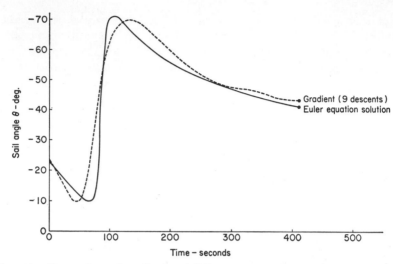

Fɪɢ. 14.   Comparison of gradient and Euler equation solutions for solar sail orbital transfer example.

into a close approximation to an Euler solution. Although this development may appear to be an afterthought, as is actually the case, an account seems worthwhile in the spirit of the present volume. While computational experience with this technique is extremely limited at the present writing, its potential as a primary computational scheme as well as a refinement scheme is perhaps of future interest.

6.6 A Successive Approximation Scheme Employing the Min Operation

While the method outlined in this section is not, properly speaking, a gradient method, it is a close relative both in concept and operation. We consider the problem of minimizing the function P' of terminal values given by (6.79), referring the reader to earlier discussions on the matter of penalty constant determination. Initial values of the x_i are presumed fixed. A nonminimal solution corresponding to $y = \bar{y}(t)$ is generated by numerical integration of the basic system (6.34). For run termination we may employ the criterion $dP'/dt_f = 0$, this feature being equally applicable to computations with the penalty function version of the gradient technique. At the time $t = \bar{t}_f$ so determined, the terminal conditions

$$\lambda_i(\bar{t}_f) = \frac{\partial P'}{\partial x_i} \tag{6.150}$$

are imposed upon the λ_i and a solution of the adjoint system (6.41) generated by numerical integration proceeding from $\bar{t}_f$ to t_0.

We designate this solution by $\lambda_i^*(t)$, and from (6.44) we then have that

$$\delta P' = \sum_{i=1}^n \frac{\partial P'}{\partial x_{if}} \, \delta x_i(\bar{t}_f) = \int_{t_0}^{\bar{t}_f} \sum_{i=1}^n \lambda_i^* \frac{\partial g_i}{\partial y} \, \delta y \, dt \qquad (6.151)$$

(Note that the term $(dP'/dt_f)\delta t_f$ missing from the $\delta P'$ expression vanishes by virtue of the run termination criterion chosen above.)

We now define a function $H^*(y, t)$ as

$$H^* = \sum_{i=1}^n \lambda_i^*(t) g_i(\bar{x}_1, \, \cdots, \, \bar{x}_n, \, y, \, t) \qquad (6.152)$$

where the functions $\bar{x}_i(t)$ correspond to the nonminimal solution $y = \bar{y}(t)$. We get then that

$$\delta P' = \int_{t_0}^{\bar{t}_f} \frac{\partial H^*}{\partial y} \, \delta y \, dt \qquad (6.153)$$

where the partial derivative $\partial H^*(y, t)/\partial y$ is evaluated at $y = \bar{y}(t)$. The argument to this point is essentially identical with that of Section 6.5, and if we were to specify steepest descent subject to a Euclidean metric,

$$ds = \int_{t_0}^{\bar{t}_f} \delta y^2 \, dt \qquad (6.154)$$

[cf. Eq. (6.54)] we would then have a gradient method, leading to

$$\delta y = k \frac{\partial H^*}{\partial y} \qquad (k < 0) \qquad (6.155)$$

A shortcoming of such a process is that over intervals in which $\partial H^*/\partial y$ is small in magnitude, the corresponding changes in y will be small. After several steps y may still be far from its optimal value over such "insensitive" intervals owing to this feature of the gradient process. This, of course, stems from the rather arbitrary imposition of the Euclidean distance measure.

We may choose an equally arbitrary alternative, dropping the distance constraint altogether and adding a term

$$\delta P' = \int_{t_0}^{\bar{t}_f} \left[\frac{\partial H^*}{\partial y} \, \delta y + \frac{1}{2} \frac{\partial^2 H^*}{\partial y^2} \, \delta y^2 \right] dt \qquad (6.156)$$

The only justification which can be offered for this alteration is that the term provides assurance that $\delta P'$ possesses a minimum for some finite δy, if indeed this is the case. By a formal process we obtain

$$\delta y = -\frac{\partial H^*/\partial y}{\partial^2 H^*/\partial y^2} \tag{6.157}$$

as the value of δy making $\delta P'$ stationary. The stationary value will yield a negative integrand only if $\partial^2 H^*/\partial y^2 > 0$. If $\partial^2 H^*/\partial y^2$ is zero or negative, the integrand is not bounded below and the minimum problem for $\delta P'$ ill-posed. Evidently this first attempt at modification, then, is a failure.

If, however, we add enough higher order terms to the integrand we will approach the operation

$$\min_{y} H^* \tag{6.158}$$

in the limit as the solution of the minimum problem for $\delta P'$, and this appears more promising since H^* can be expected to possess a minimum except in the unusual case where H^* does not depend upon y (a so-called abnormal case).

In adopting the control $y = y^*(t)$ generated by min H^* as our next approximation, we must risk the violation of our linearizing assumptions, for this may represent a large step process. For the purpose intended, the refinement of a near-minimal solution, this represents a calculated risk. However, being conservative, we may elect to replace the large step by an exploratory series of small ones, setting

$$y = \bar{y}(t) + \zeta[y^*(t) - \bar{y}(t)] \tag{6.159}$$

and evaluating P' versus ζ, a one-dimensional search analogous to that versus σ in gradient computations.

The reasoning leading up to the min H^* scheme for successive approximations is presented here as a matter of interest. The result might equally have been arrived at by analogy with the Pontryagin principle of the next chapter. (The difference between min H and Pontryagin's max H is one of sign convention between East and West.) Note that as the process converges the function H^* tends toward the function H, the generalized Hamiltonian.

In limited experience obtained with a single low-thrust example as of this writing, it appears that the method of this section converges to a solution which is a much better approximation to an Euler solution than normally obtainable with a gradient method as far as details of the control variable time history $y(t)$ are concerned, the improvement being in the "insensitive" regions discussed earlier. The speed of convergence of the method appears to make it competitive with the gradient/penalty function scheme, although insufficient evidence exists as yet to support any firm conclusion.

Some recent publications relating to the material of this chapter are listed as references 40–49.

ACKNOWLEDGMENTS

The writer is pleased to acknowledge the contributions of William P. O'Dwyer and H. Gardner Moyer of Grumman's Computation Facility in handling the computational phase of these studies on the IBM 704, and of Mrs. Agnes Zevens in checking and preparing the numerical results for publication.

Portions of the material of this chapter were generated in connection with USAF Contracts AF 29(600)–2671 and AF 29(600)–2733 monitored by AFOSR Directorate of Research Analysis, Holloman Air Force Base, New Mexico, and NASA Contract NAS 8–1549 with the Aeroballistics Division of the Marshall Space Flight Center, Huntsville, Alabama.

Appendix A

The rank of the matrix A whose elements are given by Eq. (6.71) may be examined by recourse to factorization as follows:

$$A = \beta C \beta'$$

where the prime indicates the transpose matrix. The elements of β are

$$\beta_{jm} = \frac{\partial \mathfrak{I}_j}{\partial x_{mf}}, \qquad \begin{array}{l} m = 1, \cdots, n \\ j = 1, \cdots, l \end{array}$$

and the elements of C are given by Eq. (6.73).

We denote the ranks of β and C as s and r, respectively, and observe that the three-way product above must have rank l for A to be nonsingular. Since the rank of this product may not exceed the rank of the premultiplicative matrix β, we have that

$$l \leq s = R(\beta)$$

(see reference 50, Chapter 3). Further, since the rank of β may not exceed the number of rows,

$$R(\beta) = s \leq l$$

and it follows that

$$R(\beta) = s = l$$

Since the rank of the product may not exceed the rank of the post-multiplicative matrix, we have that

$$R(\beta C\beta') = l \leq R(C\beta')$$

and since the rank of a matrix may not exceed the number of columns,

$$R(C\beta') \leq l$$

from which we conclude

$$R(C\beta') = l$$

Similar considerations establish that

$$R(C\beta') = l \leq r = R(C)$$

The rank of the product

$$B = \beta\beta'$$

may be deduced from the special case in which C is the identity matrix

$$R(\beta\beta') = R(A)$$

The results of interest in the text may thus be summarized as

$$l = R(A) \leq R(C) = r$$

and

$$l = R(A) = R(B)$$

REFERENCES

1. A. L. Cauchy, Méthode générale pour la résolution systèmes d'équations simultanées, *Compt. rend. acad. sci.* **25,** 536–538 (1847).
2. K. Levenberg, A method for the solution of certain non-linear problems in least squares, *Quart. Appl. Math.* **2,** 164–168 (1944).
3. H. B. Curry, The method of steepest descent for non-linear minimization problems, *Quart. Appl. Math.* **2,** 258–261 (1944).
4. J. Hadamard, Mémoire sur le problèm d'analyse relatif à l'équilibre des plaques élastiques encastrées, *Mém. prés. acad. sci. France* [2] **33,** No. 4 (1908).
5. R. Courant, Variational methods for the solution of problems of equilibrium and vibrations, *Bull. Am. Math. Soc.* **49,** 1–23 (1943).
6. G. E. P. Box and K. B. Wilson, On the experimental attainment of optimum conditions, *J. Roy. Statist. Soc. Ser. B* **13,** 1–45 (1951).
7. J. B. Rosen, The gradient projection method for nonlinear programming. Part I. Linear constraints, *J. Soc. Ind. Appl. Math.* **8,** 181–217 (1960).
8. P. Wolfe, The present status of nonlinear programming, RAND-University of California Symposium on Mathematical Optimization Techniques, Santa Monica, California, October 18–20, 1960.

9. C. B. Tompkins, Methods of steep descent, *in* "Modern Mathematics for the Engineer" (E. F. Beckenbach, ed.), Chapter 18. McGraw-Hill, New York, 1956.

10. M. R. Hestenes and E. Stiefel, Method of conjugate gradients for solving linear systems, *J. Research Natl. Bur. Standards* **49,** 409–436 (1952).

11. A. I. Forsythe and G. E. Forsythe, Punched-card experiments with accelerated gradient methods for linear equations, *Natl. Bur. Standards Appl. Math. Ser.* **39,** 55–69, (1954).

12. C. Müller, A new method for solving Fredholm integral equations, Rept. No. BR-15, New York University Institute of Mathematical Sciences, Division of Electromagnetic Research (1955).

13. M. L. Stein, On methods for obtaining solutions of fixed end-point problems in the calculus of variations, *J. Research Natl. Bur. Standards,* **50,** 277–297 (1953).

14. H. J. Kelley, Gradient theory of optimal flight paths, presented at Am. Rocket Soc. Semi-Annual Meeting, Los Angeles, California, May 9–12, 1960; *ARS Journal* **30,** 947–954 (1960).

15. A. E. Bryson, F. J. Carroll, K. Mikami, and W. F. Denham, Determination of the lift or drag program that minimizes re-entry heating with acceleration or range constraints using a steepest descent computation procedure, presented at IAS 29th Annual Meeting, New York, New York, January 23–25, 1961.

16. R. Courant, "Differential and Integral Calculus," Vol. II, Chapter 3. Interscience, New York, 1936.

17. R. Courant and D. Hilbert, "Methods of Mathematical Physics," first English ed. Interscience, New York, 1953.

18. R. Courant, Calculus of variations and supplementary notes and exercises," 1945–1946. Revised and amended by J. Moser, New York University Institute of Mathematical Sciences, New York (mimeographed lecture notes), 1956–1957.

19. H. Rubin and P. Ungar, Motion under a strong constraining force, *Communs. Pure Appl. Math.* **10,** 65–87 (1957).

20. A. S. Mengel, Optimum trajectories, *Proc. Project Cyclone Symposium 1 on REAC Techniques,* Reeves Instrument Corp. and USN Special Devices Center, New York, March 15–16, 1951.

21. J. H. Irving and E. K. Blum, Comparative performance of ballistic and low-thrust vehicles for flight to Mars, *in* "Vistas in Astronautics," Vol. II, pp. 191–218. Pergamon, New York, 1959.

22. C. R. Faulders, Low-thrust steering program for minimum time transfer between planetary orbits, SAE National Aeronautic Meeting, Los Angeles, California, September 29–October 4, 1958.

23. B. Friedman, "Principles and Techniques of Applied Mathematics." Wiley, New York, 1956.

24. G. A. Bliss, "Mathematics for Exterior Ballistics." Wiley, New York, 1944.

25. T. R. Goodman and G. N. Lance, The numerical integration of two-point boundary value problems, *Math. Tables and Other Aids to Computation* **10,** 82–86 (1956).

26. W. Kizner, Perturbation theory and Green's functions, Section Rept. No. 12-152, Jet Propulsion Laboratory, California Institute of Technology, Pasadena, California (October 21, 1957).

27. C. G. Pfeiffer, Guidance for space missions, External Publ. No. 656, Jet Propulsion Laboratory, Pasadena, California (June 23, 1959).

28. J. C. Dunn, Green's functions for space trajectory perturbation analysis, *J. Astronaut Sci.* **8,** 95–103 (1961).

29. P. Cicala, "An Engineering Approach to the Calculus of Variations," Levrotto-Bella, Torino, 1957.

30. F. A. Valentine, The problem of Lagrange with differential inequalities as added side conditions, Dissertation, Department of Mathematics, University of Chicago, Chicago, Illinois, 1937.

31. L. I. Rozonoer, L. S. Pontryagin principle in the theory of optimum systems, *Avtomat. i Telemekh.* **20** (1959). English Translation: *Automation Remote Control U.S.S.R.* **21**, 1288–1302, 1405–1421, 1517–1532 (1960).

32. R. L. Garwin, Solar sailing—a practical method of propulsion within the solar system, *Jet Propulsion* **28**, 188–190 (1958).

33. T. P. Cotter, Solar sailing, Sandis Research Colloquium, April, 1959, Albuquerque, New Mexico.

34. T. C. Tsu, Interplanetary travel by solar sail, *ARS Journal* **29**, 422–427 (1959).

35. H. S. London, Some exact solutions of the equations of motion of a solar sail with constant sail setting, *ARS Journal* **30**, 198–200 (1960).

36. W. Lindorfer and H. G. Moyer, An application of a low-thrust trajectory optimization scheme to planar Earth-Mars transfer, *ARS Journal* **32**, 260–262 (1962).

37. R. N. Edwards and H. Brown, Ion rockets for small satellites, Am. Rocket Soc. Controllable Satellites Conference, Massachusetts Institute of Technology, Cambridge, Massachusetts, April 30–May 1, 1959.

38. M. R. Hestenes, Numerical methods of obtaining solutions of fixed end-point problems in the calculus of variations, RAND Rept. No. RM 102, The RAND Corporation, Santa Monica, California (August, 1949).

39. R. Kalaba, On nonlinear differential equations, the maximum operation, and monotone convergence, *J. Math. and Mech.* **8**, 519–584 (1959).

40. H. J. Kelley, R. E. Kopp, and H. G. Moyer, Successive approximation techniques for trajectory optimization, presented at the IAS Vehicle Systems Optimization Symposium, Garden City, New York, November 28–29, 1961.

41. Y.-C. Ho, A successive approximation technique for optimal control systems subject to input constraints, presented at the 1961 Joint Automatic Control Conference, Boulder, Colorado, June 28–30, 1961.

42. Y.-C. Ho, A computational procedure for optimal control problems with state variable inequality constraints, Rept. No. P–2402, the RAND Corp., Santa Monica, California, September 1961 (to be published in *J. Math. Anal. and Appl.*).

43. A. E. Bryson and W. F. Denham, A steepest ascent method for solving optimum programming problems, Am. Soc. Mech. Eng. Conf. on Applied Mechanics, Chicago, Illinois, June 1961 (to be published in *J. Appl. Mech.*).

44. C. Saltzer and C. W. Fetheroff, A direct variational method for the calculation of optimum thrust programs for power-limited interplanetary flight, *Astronaut. Acta* **7**, 8–20 (1961).

45. T. Butler and A. V. Martin, On a method of Courant for minimizing functionals (to be published).

46. S. Dreyfus, Variational problems with inequality constraints, Rept. No. P-2357, the RAND Corp., Santa Monica, California (to be published in *J. Math. Anal. and Appl.*).

47. S. Dreyfus, Numerical Solution of variational problems, Rept. No. P-2374, the RAND Corp., Santa Monica, California (to be published in *J. Math. Anal. and Appl.*).

48. I. M. Gel'fand and M. L. Tsetlin, The organized search principle in systems with automatic stabilization, *Doklady Akad. Nauk S.S.S.R.* **137**(2), 295–298 (1961).

49. N. S. Bromberg, Maximization and minimization of complicated multivariable functions, *Communication and Electronics* **58**, 725–730 (1962).

50. S. Perlis, "Theory of Matrices." Addison-Wesley, Reading, Massachusetts, 1952.

—7—

Pontryagin Maximum Principle

RICHARD E. KOPP

Grumman Aircraft Engineering Corporation,
Bethpage, New York

7.0 Introduction

Recently the work of the Soviet mathematician, Pontryagin, in the study of optimum systems has come to light through the translation of several Soviet papers.[1-7]* In this chapter the maximum principle will first be developed in a manner similar to that of Rozonoér and then compared with better-known approaches to the solution of variational problems. Bass suggested the use of adjoint systems for optimization techniques with bounded control variables in 1956.[20] It will be seen that the auxiliary p variables in Pontryagin's approach are the adjoint system variables, and that this principle can be derived from an extension of the properties of adjoint systems.

In comparison with the calculus of variations using the methods of Bliss,[21] we find that the differential equations describing the auxiliary p variables are the same as the Euler equations corresponding to the state variables. Further, we see an equivalence between the Euler equations for the control variables and the maximum principle applied to the Pontryagin H-function. An extension of Weierstrass' and Cicala's[22] work gives the maximum principle directly. Finally, a development of the maximum principle is made using Bellman's[23] dynamic programming technique.

The Pontryagin maximum principle affords a very elegant method of handling variational problems with constraints of boundedness applied to the control variables. From a computational aspect, however, it appears debatable as to whether any substantial advantages are gained.

7.1 An Introduction to the Pontryagin Maximum Principle

7.11 Problem Formulation

We formulate the optimization problem in terms of a Mayer variational problem[21]; that is, given the system of differential equations

$$\dot{x}_i = f_i(x_1 \cdots x_j \cdots x_n, u_1 \cdots u_k \cdots u_r, t), \qquad x_i(0) = x_i^0, \qquad i = 1 \cdots n \quad (7.1)$$

maximize (minimize)

$$S = \sum_{i=1}^{n} c_i x_i(t_f) \quad (7.2)$$

with respect to the control variables $u_k(t)$. The x_j are designated as state variables. Constraints on the control variables are expressed as:

$$\mathbf{u}(t) \in U \quad (7.3)$$

where U is the admissible class of control functions in r space. The quantity $\mathbf{u}(t)$ is the vector control function with components $u_k(t)$.

---

* Additional translations have been made available to the author since the writing of this chapter.[8-19]

Additional state variables may be added to Eqs. (7.1) to include non-linear and integral relationships in the payoff function S. For example, if the integral-square value of one of the state variables x_s is to be maximized (minimized), then we define a new state variable x_{n+1} as

$$x_{n+1} = \int_{t_0}^{t_f} x_s^2 \, dt \tag{7.4}$$

or

$$\dot{x}_{n+1} = x_s^2, \qquad x_{n+1}(0) = 0 \tag{7.5}$$

The payoff function S under these conditions is

$$S = x_{n+1}(t_f) \tag{7.6}$$

We will assume in the development which follows that Eqs. (7.1) include any additional state variables required to specify the payoff function.

7.12 Maximum Principle for Fixed Time with Free Right End Conditions

We will first derive the Pontryagin maximum principle with final time fixed and assume complete freedom of the final values of the state variables. Succeeding sections will indicate how the results are modified to include transversality conditions and constraints on the final values of the state variables as well as the condition when final time is open.

Let us define an auxiliary variable $p_i(t)$ such that

$$\dot{p}_i = -\sum_{j=1}^{n} p_j \frac{\partial f_j}{\partial x_i}, \qquad p_i(t_f) = -c_i, \qquad i = 1 \cdots n \tag{7.7}$$

Motivation for defining $p_i(t)$ in this manner will become apparent in later sections of this chapter.

We will first assume that an optimum control vector $\bar{\mathbf{u}}(t)$ has been found which maximizes (minimizes) the payoff function S. If a variation $\Delta\mathbf{u}(t)$ from the optimum control vector $\bar{\mathbf{u}}(t)$ is considered, the resulting total variation from the optimum state vector $\bar{\mathbf{x}}(t)$ is designated as $\Delta\mathbf{x}(t)$.

From Eqs. (7.1),

$$\sum_{i=1}^{n} p_i \, \Delta\dot{x}_i = \sum_{i=1}^{n} p_i [\, f_i(\bar{\mathbf{x}} + \Delta\mathbf{x}, \, \bar{\mathbf{u}} + \Delta\mathbf{u}, \, t) - f_i(\bar{\mathbf{x}}, \, \bar{\mathbf{u}}, \, t) \,] \tag{7.8}$$

If both sides of Eq. (7.8) are multiplied by dt and integrated between the limits t_0 and t_f, we obtain

$$\int_{t_0}^{t_f} \sum_{i=1}^{n} p_i \, \Delta\dot{x}_i \, dt = \int_{t_0}^{t_f} \sum_{i=1}^{n} p_i [\, f_i(\bar{\mathbf{x}} + \Delta\mathbf{x}, \, \bar{\mathbf{u}} + \Delta\mathbf{u}, \, t) - f_i(\bar{\mathbf{x}}, \, \bar{\mathbf{u}}, \, t) \,] \, dt$$

$$\tag{7.9}$$

Another expression for the left-hand member of Eq. (7.9) may be obtained by considering the derivative of $\sum p_i \Delta x_i$:

$$\frac{d}{dt} \sum_{i=1}^{n} p_i \Delta x_i = \sum_{i=1}^{n} \dot{p}_i \Delta x_i + \sum_{i=1}^{n} p_i \Delta \dot{x}_i \qquad (7.10)$$

Both left- and right-hand members of Eq. (7.10) are multiplied by dt and integrated as before between the limits t_0 and t_f giving

$$\int_{t_0}^{t_f} \sum_{i=1}^{n} p_i \Delta \dot{x}_i \, dt = \sum_{i=1}^{n} p_i \Delta x_i \Big|_{t_0}^{t_f} - \int_{t_0}^{t_f} \sum_{i=1}^{n} \dot{p}_i \Delta x_i \, dt \qquad (7.11)$$

By combining Eqs. (7.9) and (7.11), we obtain the following expression:

$$\sum_{i=1}^{n} p_i \Delta x_i \Big|_{t_0}^{t_f} = \int_{t_0}^{t_f} \sum_{i=1}^{n} \dot{p}_i \Delta x_i \, dt$$

$$+ \int_{t_0}^{t_f} \sum_{i=1}^{n} p_i [f_i(\bar{\mathbf{x}} + \Delta \mathbf{x}, \bar{\mathbf{u}} + \Delta \mathbf{u}, t) - f_i(\bar{\mathbf{x}}, \bar{\mathbf{u}}, t)] \, dt \qquad (7.12)$$

The left-hand member of Eq. (7.12) will now be examined. Since the initial conditions have been assumed specified for the state vector, $\Delta x_i(t_0)$ is equal to zero. The final values of the auxiliary variables $p_i(t_f)$ were chosen to be $-c_i$; therefore,

$$\sum_{i=1}^{n} p_i \Delta x_i \Big|_{t_0}^{t_f} = -\Delta S \qquad (7.13)$$

where ΔS is the total variation in the payoff function S. The right-hand member of Eq. (7.12) is evaluated by separating the variations in f_i due to the variation in control variables from those due to the variation in state variables. The variation in f_i due to the latter is expanded in a Taylor series with a remainder term giving

$$f_i(\bar{\mathbf{x}} + \Delta \mathbf{x}, \bar{\mathbf{u}} + \Delta \mathbf{u}, t) - f_i(\bar{\mathbf{x}}, \bar{\mathbf{u}}, t) = f_i(\bar{\mathbf{x}}, \bar{\mathbf{u}} + \Delta \mathbf{u}, t) - f_i(\bar{\mathbf{x}}, \bar{\mathbf{u}}, t)$$

$$+ \sum_{j=1}^{n} \frac{\partial f_i(\bar{\mathbf{x}}, \bar{\mathbf{u}} + \Delta \mathbf{u}, t)}{\partial x_j} \Delta x_j + \frac{1}{2} \sum_{\substack{j=1 \\ s=1}}^{n} \frac{\partial^2 f_i(\bar{\mathbf{x}} + \xi \Delta \mathbf{x}, \bar{\mathbf{u}} + \Delta \mathbf{u}, t)}{\partial x_j \, \partial x_s} \Delta x_j \Delta x_s$$

$$(7.14)$$

where $0 \leq \xi \leq 1$. It is tacitly assumed that the first and second partial derivatives of f_i with respect to the state variables exist. From Eqs. (7.7) and (7.12)–(7.14) we obtain an expression for the total variation in the payoff function:

$$\Delta S = - \int_{t_0}^{t_f} \sum_{i=1}^{n} p_i [f_i(\bar{x}, \bar{u} + \Delta u, t) - f_i(\bar{x}, \bar{u}, t)] \, dt$$

$$- \int_{t_0}^{t_f} \sum_{\substack{i=1 \\ j=1}}^{n} p_i \left\{ \frac{\partial}{\partial x_j} [f_i(\bar{x}, \bar{u} + \Delta u, t) - f_i(\bar{x}, \bar{u}, t)] \right\} \Delta x_j \, dt$$

$$- \frac{1}{2} \int_{t_0}^{t_f} \sum_{\substack{i=1 \\ j=1 \\ s=1}}^{n} p_i \frac{\partial^2 f_i(\bar{x} + \xi \, \Delta x, \bar{u} + \Delta u, t)}{\partial x_j \partial x_s} \Delta x_j \, \Delta x_s \, dt \qquad (7.15)$$

First let us consider the special case of a linear system in which the control variables are separable in f_i. In this case

$$f_i = \sum_{j=1}^{n} a_{ij}(t) x_j + \varphi(u, t) \qquad (7.16)$$

The last two members on the right-hand side of Eq. (7.15) vanish and ΔS becomes

$$\Delta S = - \int_{t_0}^{t_f} [H(\bar{x}, \bar{u} + \Delta u, t) - H(\bar{x}, \bar{u}, t)] \, dt \qquad (7.17)$$

where

$$H = \sum_{i=1}^{n} p_i f_i \qquad (7.18)$$

A sufficient condition for a maximum (minimum) of the payoff function S is that $\Delta S < 0$ ($\Delta S > 0$). From Eq. (7.17) it is seen that a sufficient condition for $\Delta S < 0$ is that

$$H(\bar{x}, \bar{u} + \Delta u, t) - H(\bar{x}, \bar{u}, t) > 0 \qquad (7.19)$$

for all t, $t_0 \leq t \leq t_f$. To obtain a necessary condition for a maximum (minimum) of S, a special variation in the control vector is chosen. We will assume a variation Δu_k in only one component of the control vector $\bar{u}$. For this variation, Δu_k is zero everywhere except in the interval $t_1, t_2 (t_2 > t_1)$. This interval is assumed completely adjustable in the interval t_0, t_f. Let us examine the consequence of reversing the inequality in Eq. (7.19):

$$H(\bar{x}, \bar{u} + \Delta u, t) - H(\bar{x}, \bar{u}, t) < 0 \qquad (7.20)$$

for some interval between t_0 and t_f. If the interval t_1, t_2 is chosen to include the interval over which Ineq. (7.20) is satisfied, then $\Delta S > 0$. A similar argument may be presented for all the control variables. Therefore a necessary condition for a maximum of S is as follows:

$$H(\bar{\mathbf{x}}, \bar{\mathbf{u}} + \Delta\mathbf{u}, t) - H(\bar{\mathbf{x}}, \bar{\mathbf{u}}, t) \geq 0 \tag{7.21}$$

for all t, $t_0 \leq t \leq t_f$. An analogous development may be made for a minimum of S.

To deal with nonlinear systems we must evaluate the additional terms in Eq. (7.15). It is assumed that f_i, $\partial f_i/\partial x_j$, $\partial^2 f_i/\partial x_j \partial x_s$, and u_k are bounded functions. From these assumptions it can be shown that

$$|\Delta x_i| \leq M\tau \tag{7.22}$$

where M is a positive bounded constant and τ is the increment of time $t_2 - t_1$. The control vector $\bar{\mathbf{u}}(t)$ is again varied in the special manner discussed for the linear case. By making τ small enough it can be argued that Ineq. (7.21) remains as a necessary condition for a maximum of S. Therefore, the necessary condition for a maximum (minimum) of the payoff function S is that H be minimized (maximized) with respect to the control vector at all times. An interesting interpretation of this is that the control vector $\bar{\mathbf{u}}(t)$ is adjusted such that the dot product of the state velocity vector $\dot{\bar{\mathbf{x}}}(t)$ with the auxiliary vector $\bar{\mathbf{p}}$ is a minimum for a maximum of S, and a maximum for a minimum of S.

7.13 Maximum Principle with Constraints Imposed on the Right End State Variables

The effect of constraining the right end state variables is seen[*] by using unknown constants in a role similar to that of the Lagrangian multipliers in an ordinary minimum problem. Let us assume that the constraining conditions can be specified as

$$F_\alpha[\mathbf{x}(t_f)] = 0, \qquad \alpha = 1 \cdots l \tag{7.23}$$

where $l < n$. We now define the function to be maximized (minimized) as

$$S = \sum_{i=1}^{n} c_i x_i(t_f) + \sum_{\alpha=1}^{l} \lambda_\alpha F_\alpha[\mathbf{x}(t_f)] \tag{7.24}$$

where λ_α are unknown multiplier constants. If it is assumed that F_α is twice differentiable with respect to the $x_i(t_f)$, ΔS becomes

$$\Delta S = \sum_{i=1}^{n} c_i \, \Delta x_i(t_f) + \sum_{\alpha=1}^{l} \sum_{i=1}^{n} \lambda_\alpha \frac{\partial F_\alpha}{\partial x_i(t_f)} \Delta x_i(t_f)$$

$$+ \tfrac{1}{2} \sum_{\alpha=1}^{l} \sum_{\substack{i=1 \\ =1}}^{n} \lambda_\alpha \frac{\partial^2 F_\alpha[\mathbf{x}(t_f) + \xi \, \Delta\mathbf{x}(t_f)]}{\partial x_i(t_f)\partial x_j(t_f)} \Delta x_i(t_f) \, \Delta x_j(t_f) \tag{7.25}$$

---

[*] For a rigorous proof of the Maximum Principle with constraints on the right end state variables, see Ref. 6.

where $0 \leq \xi \leq 1$. Boundary conditions on the auxiliary variables are now specified as

$$p_i(t_f) = -\left[c_i + \sum_{\alpha=1}^{l} \lambda_\alpha \frac{\partial F_\alpha}{\partial x_i(t_f)}\right], \qquad i = 1 \cdots n \qquad (7.26)$$

The last member of Eq. (7.25) approaches zero for the special control vector variation discussed in Section 7.12. With the addition of the constraints, l more unknowns λ_α, $\alpha = 1 \cdots l$, have been added. The l additional equations necessary to determine a solution of the system of Eqs. (7.1), (7.7), and (7.26) are given by Eqs. (7.23).

7.14 Maximum Principle with Fixed Right End Conditions

A special case of constrained right end conditions arises when some of the final values of the state variables are fixed. Let us assume that m of the final state variables are fixed with no other constraining conditions imposed on the remaining state variables $(m < n)$. Equations (7.23) become

$$F_\alpha[\mathbf{x}(t_f)] = x_i(t_f) - x_i{}^f = 0, \qquad \alpha, i = 1 \cdots m \qquad (7.27)$$

If we substitute Eqs. (7.27) into Eqs. (7.26), the boundary conditions on $p_i(t_f)$ become

$$p_i(t_f) = -[c_i + \lambda_i], \qquad i = 1 \cdots m \qquad (7.28)$$

and

$$p_i(t_f) = -c_i, \qquad i = m + 1 \cdots n \qquad (7.29)$$

Since m of the state variables are fixed at t_f, they will not appear in the payoff function S, and hence the c_i in Eqs. (7.28) are zero. Thus the final values of the auxiliary variables associated with the free right end state variables are equal to $-c_i$, while the final values of the auxiliary variables associated with the fixed right end state variables are left open.

A combination of fixed right end state variables and other constraining conditions are handled in a straightforward manner. In addition to Eqs. (7.27) q additional constraints may be added $(q < n - m - 1)$:

$$F_\alpha[\mathbf{x}(t_f)] = 0, \qquad \alpha = 1 \cdots q \qquad (7.30)$$

7.15 Maximum Principle with Final Time Open

In the previous development we have assumed the final time t_f fixed. To consider the case in which final time is unspecified, let us assume that the optimum state vector $\bar{\mathbf{x}}(t)$ and the optimum control vector $\bar{\mathbf{u}}(t)$ have been found. Further, let us assume that final time t_f is equal to $\bar{T}$. We may now consider the same problem as a fixed time problem with final time fixed at $\bar{T}$. If the final time appears in the payoff function, an additional state variable x_{n+1} is introduced such that

$$\dot{x}_{n+1} = 1, \qquad x_{n+1}(0) = 0 \tag{7.31}$$

The final value of x_{n+1} replaces t_f in the payoff function.

Since one additional degree of freedom has been added to the system, an additional equation is required. This additional equation is as follows:

$$H(t_f) = \sum_{i=1}^{n+1} p_i \dot{x}_i \big|_{t_f} = 0 \tag{7.32}$$

To show this we consider the change in the payoff function due to a change in final time t_f:

$$\Delta S = \sum_{i=1}^{n+1} \frac{\partial S}{\partial x_i(t_f)} \Delta x_i(t_f) = \sum_{i=1}^{n+1} \frac{\partial S}{\partial x_i(t_f)} \dot{x}_i \, \delta t \bigg|_{t_f} \tag{7.33}$$

From Eqs. (7.24) and (7.33) we arrive at the relationship

$$\Delta S = \sum_{i=1}^{n+1} \left[c_i + \sum_{\alpha=1}^{l} \lambda_\alpha \frac{\partial F_\alpha}{\partial x_i(t_f)} \right] \dot{x}_i \, \delta t \bigg|_{t_f} = - \sum_{i=1}^{n+1} p_i \dot{x}_i \, \delta t \bigg|_{t_f} \tag{7.34}$$

Since ΔS must be less than or equal to zero for a maximum of S, and since δt may be positive or negative, ΔS must equal zero; thus we are led to Eq. (7.32).

7.2 The Adjoint System and the Pontryagin Maximum Principle

7.21 The Adjoint System and Stationary Solutions

In the previous development of the Pontryagin maximum principle, little if any motivation was given. We will now try to provide motivation for the development of the maximum principle by examining the properties of adjoint systems.[24,25] The effect of a first-order perturbation δu_k in the control vector in the neighborhood of a stationary solution is considered for unbounded control. From Eqs. (7.1) we obtain by linearization, a system satisfied by the state variable increments:

$$\delta \dot{x}_i = \sum_{j=1}^{n} \frac{\partial \bar{f}_i}{\partial x_j} \delta x_j + \sum_{k=1}^{r} \frac{\partial \bar{f}_i}{\partial u_k} \delta u_k, \qquad \delta x_i(0) = 0 \tag{7.35}$$

where the bar over the partial derivatives denotes that they are evaluated on the stationary path.

The adjoint system of equations by definition is obtained by deletion of control terms and transposition of elements with change of sign:

$$p_i = -\sum_{j=1}^{n} p_i \frac{\partial \bar{f}_i}{\partial x_i} \tag{7.36}$$

The solutions of the two systems are related by

$$\frac{d}{dt} \sum_{i=1}^{n} p_i \, \delta x_i = \sum_{i=1}^{n} \sum_{k=1}^{r} p_i \frac{\partial \bar{f}_i}{\partial u_k} \delta u_k \tag{7.37}$$

Multiplying both sides of Eq. (7.37) by dt and integrating between t_0 and t_f, we obtain the following:

$$\sum_{i=1}^{n} p_i \, \delta x_i \bigg|_{t_0}^{t_f} = \int_{t_0}^{t_f} \sum_{i=1}^{n} \sum_{k=1}^{r} p_i \frac{\partial \bar{f}_i}{\partial u_k} \delta u_k \, dt \tag{7.38}$$

For stationary paths, the first variation in the payoff function S vanishes:

$$\delta S = \sum_{i=1}^{n} c_i \, \delta x_i(t_f) = 0 \tag{7.39}$$

If we impose boundary conditions in connection with Eq. (7.38) such that $p_i(t_f) = -c_i$, Eq. (7.39) can be satisfied for arbitrary variations in the control vector only if

$$\sum_{i=1}^{n} p_i \frac{\partial \bar{f}_i}{\partial u_k} = \frac{\partial H}{\partial u_k} = 0 \tag{7.40}$$

Equation (7.40) is the same equation, in a weaker sense (search for stationary solutions rather than maxima or minima), obtained by using the Pontryagin maximum principle for the case of unbounded control variables.

7.22 A Derivation of the Maximum Principle from the Adjoint System

Through a similar development we will now derive the Pontryagin maximum principle for local maxima and minima with bounded control variables. A total variation about the optimum path is considered and the time derivative of $\sum p_i \, \Delta x_i$ examined as follows:

$$\frac{d}{dt} \sum_{i=1}^{n} p_i \, \Delta x_i = \sum_{i=1}^{n} \dot{p}_i \, \Delta x_i + \sum_{i=1}^{n} p_i \, \Delta \dot{x}_i \tag{7.41}$$

The total variation $\Delta \dot{x}_i$ is evaluated from Eqs. (7.1) and substituted in Eq. (7.41). By multiplying Eq. (7.41) by dt and integrating each member between the limits t_0 and t_f, we obtain Eq. (7.12). The remainder of the development is identical to that discussed in Section 7.1. We now see that the variables we referred to in Section 7.1 as auxiliary variables are actually the adjoint variables. A motivation for the development of the maximum principle is provided by an extension of the properties of adjoint systems.

7.3 The Calculus of Variations and the Pontryagin Maximum Principle

7.31 The Calculus of Variations and Stationary Solutions

A comparison of the methods of the calculus of variations and of the maximum principle proves interesting. Again we consider the problem of determining the stationary solutions of the system described by Eqs. (7.1) with unbounded control variables for fixed time. First-order variations are taken about an assumed stationary path where

$$u_k = \bar{u}_k + \epsilon \eta_k{}^u(t)$$

$$x_i = \bar{x}_i + \epsilon \eta_i{}^x(t) \tag{7.42}$$

$$\dot{x}_i = \dot{\bar{x}}_i + \epsilon \dot{\eta}_i{}^x(t)$$

where $\eta_k{}^u(t)$ and $\eta_i{}^x(t)$ are arbitrary functions of time satisfying $\eta_i{}^x(t_0) = 0$. The payoff function S is defined again by Eq. (7.2) written in the form

$$S = \int_{t_0}^{t_f} \sum_{i=1}^{n} c_i \dot{x}_i \, dt + \sum_{i=1}^{n} c_i x_i(t_0) \tag{7.43}$$

We use Lagrange multipliers $\lambda(t)$ to adjoin the constraints imposed by Eqs. (7.1) giving the following:

$$S' = \int_{t_0}^{t_f} \left[\sum_{i=1}^{n} c_i \dot{x}_i + \sum_{i=1}^{n} \lambda_i (\dot{x}_i - f_i) \right] dt + \sum_{i=1}^{n} c_i x_i(t_0) \tag{7.44}$$

Stationary values of S' are determined by the vanishing of the partial derivative of S' with respect to ϵ:

$$\frac{\partial S'}{\partial \epsilon} = \int_{t_0}^{t_f} \left[\sum_{i=1}^{n} (c_i + \lambda_i) \dot{\eta}_i{}^x - \sum_{\substack{i=1 \\ j=1}}^{n} \lambda_i \frac{\partial \bar{f}_i}{\partial x_j} \eta_i{}^x \right] dt$$

$$- \int_{t_0}^{t_f} \left[\sum_{i=1}^{n} \sum_{k=1}^{r} \lambda_i \frac{\partial \bar{f}_i}{\partial u_k} \eta_k{}^u \right] dt = 0 \tag{7.45}$$

Integrating the first member of the right-hand side of Eq. (7.45) by parts yields the following:

$$\sum_{i=1}^{n} (c_i + \lambda_i)\eta_i^x \bigg|_{t_0}^{t_f} = \int_{t_0}^{t_f} \left[\sum_{i=1}^{n} \lambda_i + \sum_{\substack{i=1 \\ j=1}}^{n} \lambda_j \frac{\partial \bar{f}_i}{\partial x_i}\right] \eta_i^x \, dt$$

$$+ \int_{t_0}^{t_f} \sum_{i=1}^{n} \sum_{k=1}^{r} \lambda_i \frac{\partial \bar{f}_i}{\partial u_k} \eta_k^u \, dt \quad (7.46)$$

Since Eq. (7.46) must be satisfied for arbitrary η_i^x and η_k^u, the following equations must be satisfied:

$$\lambda_i = -\sum_{j=1}^{n} \lambda_j \frac{\partial \bar{f}_j}{\partial x_i}, \qquad \lambda_i(t_f) = -c_i, \qquad i = 1 \cdots n \quad (7.47)$$

and

$$\sum_{i=1}^{n} \lambda_i \frac{\partial \bar{f}_i}{\partial u_k} = 0, \qquad k = 1 \cdots r \quad (7.48)$$

Equations (7.47) are identical to Eqs. (7.7) with p_i replaced by λ_i while Eqs. (7.48) are the same equations, in a weaker sense, obtained by using the maximum principle for unbounded control variables.

7.32 The Derivation of the Maximum Principle Using the Calculus of Variations Techniques

We will now derive the maximum principle by extending the concepts of the calculus of variations. A variation from the optimum path is considered where

$$u_k = \bar{u}_k + \Delta u_k$$
$$x_i = \bar{x}_i + \Delta x_i \quad (7.49)$$
$$\dot{x}_i = \dot{\bar{x}}_i + \Delta \dot{x}_i$$

The payoff function S' is again defined as in Eq. (7.44) with λ_i replaced by p_i:

$$S' = \int_{t_0}^{t_f} \left[\sum_{i=1}^{n} c_i \dot{x}_i + \sum_{i=1}^{n} p_i(\dot{x}_i - f_i)\right] dt + \sum_{i=1}^{n} c_i x_i(t_0) \quad (7.50)$$

We find the total variation in the payoff function:

$$\Delta S' = \int_{t_0}^{t_f} \sum_{i=1}^{n} (c_i + p_i) \, \Delta \dot{x}_i \, dt$$

$$- \int_{t_0}^{t_f} \sum_{i=1}^{n} p_i [f_i(\bar{x} + \Delta x, \bar{u} + \Delta u, t) - f_i(\bar{x}, \bar{u}, t)] \, dt \quad (7.51)$$

If the second member of the right-hand side of Eq. (7.51) is expanded as before and an integration by parts performed, we obtain

$$\Delta S' = \sum_{i=1}^{n} (c_i + p_i)\, \Delta x_i \bigg|_{t_0}^{t_f} - \int_{t_0}^{t_f} \left[\sum_{i=1}^{n} \dot{p}_i + \sum_{\substack{i=1 \\ j=1}}^{n} p_i \frac{\partial \bar{f}_j}{\partial x_i} \right] \Delta x_i\, dt$$

$$- \int_{t_0}^{t_f} \sum_{\substack{i=1 \\ j=1}}^{n} p_i \left[\frac{\partial f_i(\bar{\mathbf{x}},\, \bar{\mathbf{u}} + \Delta \mathbf{u},\, t)}{\partial x_j} - \frac{\partial f_i(\bar{\mathbf{x}},\, \bar{\mathbf{u}},\, t)}{\partial x_j} \right] \Delta x_j\, dt$$

$$- \tfrac{1}{2} \int_{t_0}^{t_f} \sum_{\substack{i=1 \\ j=1 \\ s=1}}^{n} p_i \frac{\partial^2 f_i(\bar{\mathbf{x}} + \xi\, \Delta \mathbf{x},\, \bar{\mathbf{u}} + \Delta \mathbf{u},\, t)}{\partial x_j\, \partial x_s}\, \Delta x_s\, \Delta x_j\, dt$$

$$- \int_{t_0}^{t_f} \sum_{i=1}^{n} p_i [\, f_i(\bar{\mathbf{x}},\, \bar{\mathbf{u}} + \Delta \mathbf{u},\, t) - f_i(\bar{\mathbf{x}},\, \bar{\mathbf{u}},\, t) \,]\, dt \qquad (7.52)$$

where $0 \le \xi \le 1$. Keeping in mind that for the special variation in $\bar{\mathbf{u}}$ discussed previously, $|\Delta x_i| \le M \Delta \tau$, a necessary condition for a maximum ($\Delta S \le 0$) for arbitrary variations in Δx_i is as follows:

$$\dot{p}_i = -\sum_{j=1}^{n} p_j \frac{\partial \bar{f}_j}{\partial x_i}, \qquad p_i(t_f) = -c_i \qquad (7.53)$$

and

$$\sum_{i=1}^{n} p_i [\, f_i(\bar{\mathbf{x}},\, \bar{\mathbf{u}} + \Delta \mathbf{u},\, t) - f_i(\bar{\mathbf{x}},\, \bar{\mathbf{u}},\, t) \,] \ge 0 \qquad (7.54)$$

for all t, $t_0 \le t \le t_f$. Equation (7.54) is the Pontryagin maximum condition with p_i as defined in Eqs. (7.52). In this development it was tacitly assumed that the multiplier rule applies for total variations.

7.33 The Weierstrass Excess Function and Cicala's Index Value

We will show how an extension of Weierstrass' work leads to the Pontryagin maximum principle.* Let us consider the system described by Eqs. (7.1) for unbounded control variables. Further, let the payoff function S be a differentiable function of the final values of the state variables only.

---

* It has recently been brought to the attention of the author that Boltyanskii *et al.*[6] discuss this point for unbounded control variables and arrive at conclusions which contradict those presented here.

Using the variational techniques as employed by Bliss[21] and Breakwell,[26] we obtain from the vanishing of the first variation the following:

$$\dot{\lambda}_i = -\sum_{j=1}^{n} \lambda_j \frac{\partial f_j}{\partial x_i}, \qquad i = 1 \cdots n$$

$$\lambda_i \Big|_{t_f} = -\frac{\partial S}{\partial x_i}\Big|_{t_f}, \qquad \begin{array}{l}\text{natural boundary conditions} \\ \text{for open terminal values}\end{array} \qquad (7.55)$$

$$\sum_{i=1}^{n} \lambda_i \frac{\partial f_i}{\partial u_k} = 0, \qquad k = 1 \cdots r$$

The boundary conditions of the first variation provide the explicit relationships for the final values of the λ's associated with the free state variables. For paths neighboring the extremal path

$$\sum_{i=1}^{n} \lambda_i \, \delta x_i \Big|_{t_0}^{t_f} = \sum_{i=1}^{n} \lambda_i \, \Delta x_i \Big|_{t_0}^{t_f} - \sum_{i=1}^{n} \lambda_i \dot{x}_i \, \delta t \Big|_{t_0}^{t_f} = 0 \qquad (7.56)$$

where Δx_i are the variations in the state variables due to explicit variations δx_i as well as variations δt in time. The constancy of $\sum \lambda_i \, \delta x_i$ can be shown by differentiation and Eqs. (7.55).

FIG. 1.   Development of the Weierstrass excess function.

A development, similar to that presented by Cicala,[22] of Weierstrass' excess function follows. In Fig. 1 is shown a segment ab of an extremal path. Let us assume that at a the control vector $\mathbf{u}$ is varied from its optimum value $\bar{\mathbf{u}}$ for a period of time δt_0 resulting in arc ac. It is further assumed that δt_0 is small enough such that path cb can be considered a neighboring path to the extremal path ab. We designate the total time over path acb as $t_f - t_0 + \delta t_f$ and the time over path ac as δt_0.

Applying Eq. (7.56) to path cb, we obtain

$$\sum_{i=1}^{n} \lambda_i \, \Delta x_i \Big|_{b} - \sum_{i=1}^{n} \lambda_i \, \Delta x_i \Big|_{a} - \sum_{i=1}^{n} \lambda_i \dot{x}_i \Big|_{b} \, \delta t_f + \sum_{i=1}^{n} \lambda_i \dot{x}_i \Big|_{a} \, \delta t_0 = 0 \qquad (7.57)$$

where $\dot{x}_i$ is evaluated on extremal path ab. The change ΔS in the payoff function for path acb is

$$\Delta S = \sum_{i=1}^{n} \frac{\partial S}{\partial x_i} \Delta x_i \Big|_b = -\sum_{i=1}^{n} \lambda_i \Delta x_i \Big|_b \qquad (7.58)$$

The boundary terms for the first variation also provide the relationship

$$\sum_{i=1}^{n} \lambda_i \dot{x}_i \, \delta t_f \Big|_b = 0 \qquad (7.59)$$

From Eqs. (7.58) and (7.59) and the evaluation of $\Delta x_i \big|_a$,

$$\Delta x_i \big|_a = \dot{x}_i \big|_a \, \delta t_0 \qquad (7.60)$$

we obtain by substituting in Eq. (7.57)

$$\Delta S = \sum_{i=1}^{n} \lambda_i (\dot{\bar{x}}_i - \dot{x}_i) \Big|_a \, \delta t_0 = E \, \delta t_0 \qquad (7.61)$$

Weierstrass gave the name excess function to E. Since arc ab was an arbitrary arc of an extremal path, a necessary condition for a maximum of S is that $E \leq 0$ in all regions of the optimum path. It is observed that the comparison of $\dot{x}_i$ and $\dot{\bar{x}}_i$ in Eq. (7.61) is made with respect to the control variables only. With this observation we see that $-E$ is the ΔH in the Pontryagin maximum principle:

$$E = -[H(\bar{\mathbf{x}}, \bar{\mathbf{u}} + \Delta\mathbf{u}, t) - H(\bar{\mathbf{x}}, \bar{\mathbf{u}}, t)] \qquad (7.62)$$

To include constraints of boundedness of the control variables

$$u_{1k} \leq u_k \leq u_{2k}, \qquad k = 1 \cdots r \qquad (7.63)$$

the technique of Valentine[27] may be used. The additional equations

$$\gamma_k{}^2 = (u_{2k} - u_k)(u_k - u_{1k}), \qquad k = 1 \cdots r \qquad (7.64)$$

are added to Eqs. (7.1) describing the system. With this addition, r more Euler equations are obtained:

$$\lambda_{\gamma k} \gamma_k = 0, \qquad k = 1 \cdots r \qquad (7.65)$$

Also, Eqs. (7.55)$_3$ become

$$\sum_{i=1}^{n} \lambda_i \frac{\partial f_i}{\partial u_k} + \lambda_{\gamma k}(u_{2k} + u_{1k} - 2u_k) = 0, \qquad k = 1 \cdots r \qquad (7.66)$$

and the equality sign in Eq. (7.56) is replaced with an inequality condition which enables us to draw the same conclusions for the case of bounded control variables as we did for the case of unbounded control variables. Of course Eqs. (7.64)–(7.66) must be satisfied.

Cicala made use of the Weierstrass device in a scheme which he called "index value." Let us consider the example

$$\dot{x}_1 = u, \qquad \dot{x}_2 = f(x_1, u, t)$$

$$\gamma^2 = (u_2 - u)(u - u_1) \tag{7.67}$$

$$S = x_2(t_f) - x_2(t_0)$$

The Euler equations yield

$$\dot{\lambda}_1 = -\lambda_2 \frac{\partial f}{\partial x_1}, \qquad \lambda_2 = -1, \qquad \gamma \lambda_3 = 0$$

$$\tag{7.68}$$

$$\lambda_1 = \frac{\partial f}{\partial u} - \lambda_3(u_1 + u_2 - 2u)$$

First we will consider the situation when $u_1 < u < u_2$. From Eqs. (7.68),

$$\lambda_3 = 0, \qquad \lambda_1 - \frac{\partial f}{\partial u} \tag{7.69}$$

The Weierstrass E-function is

$$E = f - \bar{f} - \lambda_1(u - \bar{u}) \tag{7.70}$$

where $\bar{f}$ is f evaluated at $\bar{u}$. For a minimum of S, $E \geq 0$. In Fig. 2a is shown

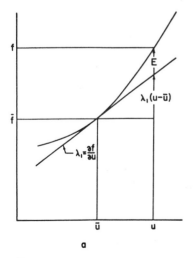
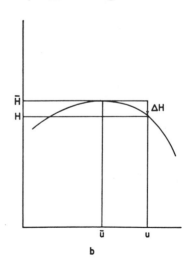

FIG. 2. Geometric interpretation of Cicala's index value for unbounded control variables.

a geometrical interpretation of the E-function. To satisfy the condition of Weierstrass the f curve must lie entirely above the tangent line of slope λ_1. The equivalent situation for the Pontryagin H-function is shown in Fig. 2b. The maximum principle states that $\Delta H \leq 0$.

When the control variable u is on the boundary u_1 or u_2, $\gamma = 0$ and

$$\lambda_1 = \frac{\partial f}{\partial u} - \lambda_3(u_2 - u_1), \quad \text{when} \quad u = u_1$$

$$(7.71)$$

$$\lambda_1 = \frac{\partial f}{\partial u} + \lambda_3(u_2 - u_1), \quad \text{when} \quad u = u_2$$

In Fig. 3a is shown the case where $u = u_1$. To have $E > 0$,

$$\lambda_1 < \frac{\partial f}{\partial u} \qquad (7.72)$$

from which we conclude that $\lambda_3 > 0$. A comparison is again made in Fig. 3b

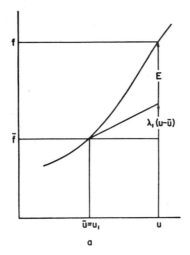
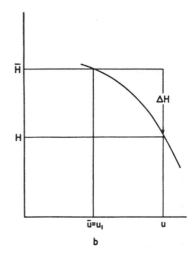

Fɪɢ. 3.   Geometric interpretation of Cicala's index value for bounded control variables.

to the Pontryagin H-function. A similar development arises when $u = u_2$, giving

$$\lambda_1 > \frac{\partial f}{\partial u} \qquad (7.73)$$

Cicala suggests that λ_1 acts like a pointer on a dial indicating the different cases that can occur:

$$\lambda_1 < \frac{\partial f}{\partial u}, \qquad u = u_1$$

$$\lambda_1 = \frac{\partial f}{\partial u}, \qquad u_1 < u < u_2 \qquad (7.74)$$

$$\lambda_1 > \frac{\partial f}{\partial u}, \qquad u = u_2$$

Many examples utilizing the index value are illustrated in Cicala's booklet.[22]

7.4 Dynamic Programming and the Pontryagin Maximum Principle

7.41 A Derivation of the Maximum Principle by Dynamic Programming

An interesting development of the maximum principle occurs using the techniques exploited by Bellman.[23]

We formulate the problem as in Section 7.11 with final time fixed and free right end conditions. The optimum payoff function is designated $\bar{S}$, and is implicitly a function of the initial state vector $\mathbf{x}(t_0)$ and t_0:

$$\bar{S} = \bar{S}[\mathbf{x}(t_0), t_0] = \max \sum_{i=1}^{n} c_i x_i(t_f) \qquad (7.75)$$

The optimum control vector $\bar{\mathbf{u}}(t)$ and state vector $\bar{\mathbf{x}}(t)$ are also functions of $\mathbf{x}(t_0)$ and t_0. After a lapse of time Δt we designate the optimum control and state vectors as $\bar{\mathbf{u}}'$ and $\bar{\mathbf{x}}'$, and the control and state vectors for any other path as $\mathbf{u}'$ and $\mathbf{x}'$ (see Fig. 4).

Since $\bar{S}[\mathbf{x}(t_0), t_0]$ is determined by the end condition of the optimum path,

$$\bar{S}[\mathbf{x}(t_0), t_0] = \bar{S}[\bar{\mathbf{x}}', t'] \qquad (7.76)$$

For any other path to $\mathbf{x}'$, t', we will let the remainder of the path from t' to t_f be optimum. The payoff function for this path is designated as $\bar{S}[\mathbf{x}', t']$. Therefore, from Eq. (7.76) we have

$$\bar{S}[\mathbf{x}(t_0), t_0] = \max_{u \,\epsilon\, U} \bar{S}[\mathbf{x}', t'] \qquad t_0 \le t \le t' \qquad (7.77)$$

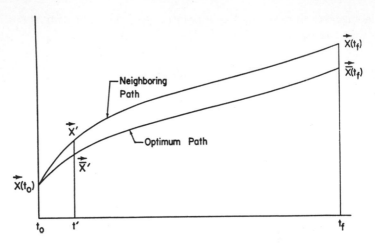

Fig. 4. Development of Pontryagin maximum principle by dynamic programming. (Arrows over letters in figure are equivalent to boldface letters in text.)

The payoff function $\bar{S}[\mathbf{x}', t']$ is expanded in a Taylor series neglecting second- and higher order terms:

$$\bar{S}[\mathbf{x}', t'] = \bar{S}[\mathbf{x}(t_0), t_0] + \frac{\partial \bar{S}}{\partial t_0} \Delta t + \sum_{i=1}^{n} \frac{\partial S}{\partial x_i} \Delta x_i \qquad (7.78)$$

The partial derivatives are tacitly assumed to exist and evaluated at $\mathbf{x}(t_0)$, t_0. Substituting Eq. (7.78) in Eq. (7.77), we obtain

$$\bar{S}[\mathbf{x}(t_0), t_0] = \max_{u \,\epsilon\, U} \left[\bar{S}[\mathbf{x}(t_0), t_0] + \frac{\partial \bar{S}}{\partial t_0} \Delta t + \sum_{i=1}^{n} \frac{\partial \bar{S}}{\partial x_i} \dot{x}_i(t_0) \, \Delta t \right]$$

$$t_0 \leq t \leq t_0 + \Delta t \quad (7.79)$$

where

$$\Delta x_i = \dot{x}_i(t_0) \, \Delta t \qquad (7.80)$$

If we examine the right-hand side of Eq. (7.79) we see that the only term which is a function of $\mathbf{u}$ is $\dot{x}_i(t_0)$. Therefore in the limit, as Δt approaches zero,

$$\frac{\partial \bar{S}}{\partial t_0} = -\max_{u \,\epsilon\, U} \sum_{i=1}^{n} \frac{\partial \bar{S}}{\partial x_i} \dot{x}_i(t_0) \qquad (7.81)$$

Since t_0 could occur at any time t, $t_0 \leq t \leq t_f$, the subscripts in Eq. (7.81) can be dropped, giving

$$\frac{\partial \bar{S}}{\partial t} = -\max_{u \,\epsilon\, U} \sum_{i=1}^{n} \frac{\partial \bar{S}}{\partial x_i} \dot{x}_i(t) \qquad (7.82)$$

with boundary conditions

$$\bar{S}[\bar{\mathbf{x}}, t_f] = \sum_{i=1}^{n} c_i x_i(t_f) \tag{7.83}$$

Along the optimum trajectory the payoff function remains constant,

$$\frac{d}{dt} \bar{S}(\bar{\mathbf{x}}, t) = 0 \tag{7.84}$$

When the derivative is evaluated we obtain the equation

$$\frac{\partial \bar{S}}{\partial t} = -\sum_{i=1}^{n} \frac{\partial \bar{S}}{\partial x_i} \dot{x}_i \tag{7.85}$$

Equation (7.85) could also be obtained directly from Eq. (7.82) by performing the max operation indicated. The auxiliary variables p_i are defined as

$$p_i = -\frac{\partial \bar{S}}{\partial x_i}, \qquad p_i(t_f) = -c_i \tag{7.86}$$

From Eqs. (7.85) and (7.86) we obtain

$$\dot{p}_i = -\sum_{j=1}^{n} p_j \frac{\partial \bar{f}_j}{\partial x_i}, \qquad p_i(t_f) = -c_i \tag{7.87}$$

The maximum principle is obtained from Eq. (7.82)

$$\max_{u \,\epsilon\, U} \sum_{i=1}^{n} - p_i \dot{x}_i(t) = \min_{u \,\epsilon\, U} H(\mathbf{x}, \mathbf{u}, t) \tag{7.88}$$

The optimum trajectory may be found using dynamic programming techniques from Eqs. (7.1), (7.82), and (7.83). This, in general, requires a numerical stepwise decision process. To obtain the optimum trajectory via the Pontryagin maximum principle requires the solution of Eqs. (7.1), (7.87), and (7.88). These nonlinear differential equations, subject to two-point boundary conditions, may be solved using numerical iteration techniques. The advantage of the dynamic programming approach is that it affords a systematic numerical scheme of solution. However, for systems with more than a few degrees of freedom, the computational requirements become excessive for presently available computing equipment. An advantage of the Pontryagin principle, as well as other variational techniques, is that many characteristics of the optimum path may be determined without solving the entire problem.

7.5 Examples

7.51 Systems Separable and Linear in the Control Variables

We will now show how the maximum principle may be applied to specific examples. The first example discussed will be the case in which the control variables are separable and occur linearly in the system. From Eqs. (7.1),

$$\dot{x}_i = f_i(\mathbf{x}, t) + \sum_{k=1}^{r} a_{ik} u_k, \qquad x_i(0) = x_i^0, \qquad i = 1 \cdots n \quad (7.89)$$

Constraints on the control variables are designated by

$$|u_k| \leq m_k \qquad (7.90)$$

where m_k is a positive constant. The H-function for this system is

$$H = \sum_{i=1}^{n} p_i f_i(\mathbf{x}, t) + \sum_{i=1}^{n} \sum_{k=1}^{r} p_i a_{ik} u_k \qquad (7.91)$$

From the application of the maximum principle, a necessary condition for a minimum of the payoff function S is

$$u_k = m_k \operatorname{sgn} \sum_{i=1}^{n} p_i a_{ik}, \qquad k = 1 \cdots r \qquad (7.92)$$

Equations (7.92) indicate that full control is always used except in the ambiguous case where $\sum p_i a_{ik} = 0$. For this situation the payoff function is said to be insensitive to the particular control variable u_k. Of course it must be kept in mind that in addition to Eqs. (7.92), the differential constraints on x_i and p_i must be satisfied along with the prescribed boundary conditions.

7.52 Second-Order Linear Control System with Complex Stable Roots

In this example we will show how the maximum principle is applied to a specific control problem. Let us assume that we wish to determine the control variable u as a function of the state variables x_1 and x_2, such that the system will reach an equilibrium state in a minimum time. The differential equations describing the system are as follows:

$$\dot{x}_1 = x_2, \qquad x_1(0) = x_1^0, \qquad x_1(t_f) = 0$$

$$\dot{x}_2 = -ax_2 - bx_1 + u, \qquad x_2(0) = x_2^0, \qquad x_2(t_f) = 0 \qquad (7.93)$$

$$\dot{x}_3 = 1, \qquad x_3(0) = 0$$

$$a > 0, \qquad a^2 - 4b^2 < 0$$

with constraints on the control variable

$$|u| \leq M \tag{7.94}$$

The payoff function S is

$$S = x_3(t_f) \tag{7.95}$$

We obtain the H-function from Eq. (7.18) giving the following:

$$H = p_1 x_2 + p_2(-ax_2 - bx_1 + u) + p_3 \tag{7.96}$$

where

$$\dot{p}_1 = bp_2$$

$$\dot{p}_2 = ap_2 - p_1 \tag{7.97}$$

$$\dot{p}_3 = 0, \qquad p_3(t_f) = -1$$

By applying the maximum principle to Eq. (7.96) we obtain

$$u = M \text{ sgn } p_2 \tag{7.98}$$

The auxiliary variable p_2 is determined by Eqs. (7.97);

$$p_2 = Ae^{\alpha t} \sin (\omega t + \varphi) \tag{7.99}$$

$$\alpha = a/2, \qquad \omega = \tfrac{1}{2}\sqrt{4b^2 - a}$$

where A and φ are functions of the boundary conditions. We may conclude from Eq. (7.99) that the switching sequence is periodic with the exception of the first and last switchings.

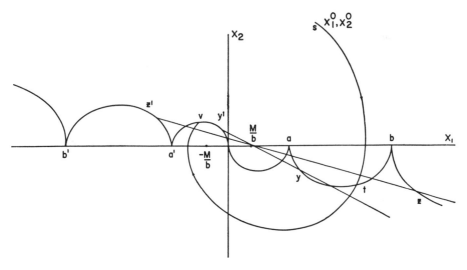

FIG. 5. Switching boundary for second-order linear system with complex stable roots.

From the conclusion concerning the periodicity of the switching sequence, the switching boundary in the x_1, x_2 plane may be constructed geometrically as shown in Fig. 5. If the system is to reach an equilibrium state, it is necessary that the final trajectory include a portion of the arc oa' or oa, since these are the only trajectories that pass through the equilibrium point o. The arcs oa' and oa are obtained from Eqs. (7.93). Let us assume that the final arc is $y'o$. With this assumption we conclude from Eqs. (7.98) and (7.99) that the previous switching must have occurred one-half a period sooner, or somewhere on the line $y'pm$. From Eqs. (7.93) we also conclude that the length of the line yp must be $e^{\alpha\pi/\omega}$ times the length of the line $y'p$. The point y on the switching boundary is therefore determined. If we allow the point y' to move on the arc oa', the portion of the switching boundary ab is generated. This procedure may be continued to determine the complete boundary. A typical optimum trajectory $stvo$ is illustrated. The control variable u is $-M$ on arc st, $+M$ on arc tv, and $-M$ on arc vo.

7.53 Problem in Rocket Flight

The example to be discussed now has been analyzed in detail by Leitmann[28] using the variational techniques of Bliss[21] and Valentine.[27]* The purpose of discussing the problem here is to give a further comparison between the Pontryagin maximum principle and the calculus of variations. The problem is that of determining the direction and magnitude of the bounded thrust of a rocket vehicle, traveling in a constant gravitational field, such that a function of the final values of the state variables is minimized or maximized. Vehicle dynamics have been neglected.

The differential equations describing the system are

$$\dot{x}_1 = \dot{p} = \frac{c\beta}{m}\cos\psi, \qquad x_1(0) = x_1^0$$

$$\dot{x}_2 = \dot{q} = \frac{c\beta}{m}\sin\psi - g, \qquad x_2(0) = x_2^0$$

$$\dot{x}_3 = \dot{x} = p, \qquad x_3(0) = x_3^0 \qquad (7.100)$$

$$\dot{x}_4 = \dot{y} = q, \qquad x_4(0) = x_4^0$$

$$\dot{x}_5 = \dot{m} = -\beta, \qquad x_5(0) = x_5^0$$

$$\dot{x}_6 = 1, \qquad x_6(0) = 0$$

---

* See also Chapter 5.

The notation is the same as that used by Leitmann, with state variables p, q, x, y, m and two control variables β and ψ. To include the possibility of time appearing in the payoff function, the additional variable x_6 is added. The mass flow rate β is bounded by

$$\beta_1 \leq \beta \leq \beta_u \qquad (7.101)$$

From Eq. (7.18)

$$H = p_1 \frac{c\beta}{m} \cos \psi + p_2 \left(\frac{c\beta}{m} \sin \psi - g\right) + p_3 p + p_4 q - p_5 \beta + p_6 \qquad (7.102)$$

The differential equations defining the auxiliary variables are

$$\dot{p}_1 = -p_3, \qquad \dot{p}_2 = -p_4, \qquad \dot{p}_3 = 0, \qquad \dot{p}_4 = 0$$

$$\dot{p}_5 = p_1 \frac{c\beta}{m^2} \cos \psi + p_2 \frac{c\beta}{m^2} \sin \psi, \qquad \dot{p}_6 = 0 \qquad (7.103)$$

It is to be noted that the first five equations of Eqs. (7.103) are identical with the first five equations in Eqs. (7.7) of Leitmann's paper.[28] (The Euler-Lagrange equations with respect to the state variables are identical with those obtained from the Pontryagin maximum principle for the auxiliary variables.)

Let us assume that the payoff function S is a linear function of the final values of the state variables. If this is not the case, additional variables can be defined to include nonlinear and integral relationships. To minimize S, an application of the maximum principle gives for the β control variable the following:

$$\beta = \beta_u \quad \text{when} \quad k > 0$$

$$\beta = \beta_1 \quad \text{when} \quad k < 0 \qquad (7.104)$$

where

$$k = \frac{c}{m} (p_1 \cos \psi + p_2 \sin \psi) - p_5 \qquad (7.105)$$

and

$$\tan \psi = \frac{p_2}{p_1}$$

$$(7.106)$$

$$p_1 \cos \psi + p_2 \sin \psi \geq 0$$

for ψ, the thrust direction. These are the same relationships obtained by Leitmann when the Weierstrass and Clebsch conditions were applied.

An examination of $\dot{k}$,

$$\dot{k} = -\frac{c}{m} (p_3 \cos \psi + p_4 \sin \psi) \qquad (7.107)$$

indicates that there are at most two zeros of $\dot{k}$. This leads to the conclusion that there are no more than three subarcs to the optimum path. If $\dot{k} = 0$ over some period of time, the payoff function S does not depend on β during this time; the payoff function is said to be insensitive to β during this time and the solution is not unique. Leitmann covers several specific examples in his paper.

Acknowledgments

The writer wishes to acknowledge the contributions of George Clark and Mrs. Agnes Zevens of the Grumman Research Department for their assistance in proofreading and preparing this chapter for publication.

Portions of this material were prepared in connection with contract Nonr 3384(00) under the cognizance of the Information Systems Branch of the Office of Naval Research.

References

1. A. A. Feldbaum, Synthesis of optimum systems with the aid of the phase space, *Avtomat. i Telemekh.* **16,** 129–149 (1955).
2. L. S. Pontryagin, Some mathematical problems arising in connexion with the theory of optimal systems of automatic control, *Proc. Acad. Sci.,* U.S.S.R. **11,** 107–117 (1957).
3. R. V. Gamkrelidze, On the general theory of optimal processes, *Doklady Akad. Nauk S.S.S.R.* **123,** 223–226 (1958).
4. L. S. Pontryagin, Optimal control processes, *Uspekhi Mat. Nauk* **14,** 3–20 (1959).
5. L. I. Rozonoer, L. S. Pontryagin maximum principle in the theory of optimum systems, *Avtomat. i Telemekh.* **20** (1959). [English translation: *Automation Remote Control* 1288–1302, 1405–1421, 1517–1532 (1960)].
6. V. G. Boltyanskii, R. V. Gamkrelidze, and L. S. Pontryagin, The theory of optimal processes. I. Maximum principle, *Izvest. Akad. Nauk S.S.S.R. Ser. Mat.* **24,** 3–43 (1960). Translated by L. W. Neustadt, *Trans. Am. Math. Soc.* **17,** 341–382 (1961).
7. L. S. Pontryagin, "Optimal Processes of Regulation," *Proc. Intern. Math. Conf., Edinburgh, 1958,* pp. 182–202 (1960).
8. V. G. Boltyanskii, R. V. Gamkrelidze, and L. S. Pontryagin, Theory of optimal processes, *Doklady Akad. Nauk S.S.S.R.* **110,** 7–10 (1956).
9. N. N. Krasovskii, On one particular problem of optimum regulation, *Priklad. Mat. i Mekh.* **21** (Inst. Mekh. Akad. Nauk Soyuza S.S.R.), (1957).
10. R. V. Gamkrelidze, On the theory of optimal processes in linear systems, *Doklady Akad. Nauk S.S.S.R.* **116,** 9–11 (1957).
11. V. G. Boltyanskii, The maximum principle in the theory of optimal processes, *Doklady Akad. Nauk S.S.S.R.* **119,** 1070–1073 (1958).

12. R. V. Gamkrelidze, The theory of time optimal processes in linear systems, *Izvest. Akad. Nauk S.S.S.R. Ser. Mat.* **2,** 449–474 (1958).
13. A. D. Aleksandrov, Investigations of the maximum principle, *Izvest. Vysshikh Ucheb. Zavedenĭ Mat.* No. 5, 6, 126–157 (1958).
14. L. I. Rozonoer, On conditions sufficient for optimum, *Doklady Akad. Nauk S.S.S.R.* **127,** 520–523 (1959).
15. N. N. Krasovskii, To the theory of optimal regulation, *Appl. Mat. and Mech.* (Dept. of Tech. Sci. of the Acad. of Sci. of U.S.S.R.), **23** (1959).
16. E. A. Rozenman, Optimal control systems with two forcing functions, *Automat. i Telemekh.* **20,** 1345–1349 (1959).
17. R. V. Gamkrelidze, Optimal processes with bounded phase coordinates, *Izvest. Akad. Nauk S.S.S.R. Ser. Mat.* **24,** 315–356 (1960).
18. F. M. Kirillova, The problem of the existence of optimal trajectories of nonlinear systems, *Izvest. Vysshikh Ucheb. Zavedenĭ Mat.* No. 2, 41–53 (1961).
19. Y. F. Mishchenko and L. S. Pontryagin, Concerning one statistical problem of optimal control, *Izvest. Akad. Nauk S.S.S.R. Ser. Mat.* **25,** 477–498 (1961).
20. R. W. Bass, "Equivalent Linearization, Nonlinear Circuit Synthesis and the Stabilization and Optimization of Control Systems," *Proc. Symposium on Nonlinear Circuit Anal.* **6,** 163–198 (1957).
21. G. A. Bliss, "Lectures on the Calculus of Variations." Univ. Chicago Press, Chicago, Illinois, 1946.
22. P. Cicala, "An Engineering Approach to the Calculus of Variations." Levrotto and Bella, Torino, 1957.
23. R. Bellman, "Dynamic Programming." Princeton Univ. Press, Princeton, New Jersey, 1957.
24. G. A. Bliss, "Mathematics for Exterior Ballistics." Wiley, New York, 1944.
25. H. S. Tsien, "Engineering Cybernetics." McGraw-Hill, New York, 1954.
26. J. V. Breakwell, The optimization of trajectories, *J. Soc. Ind. Appl. Math.* **7,** 215–246 (1959).
27. F. A.-Valentine, The problem of Lagrange with differential inequalities as added side conditions, Dissertation, Department of Mathematics, University of Chicago, Chicago, Illinois, 1937.
28. G. Leitmann, On a class of variational problems in rocket flight, *J. Aero/Space Sci.* **26,** 586–591 (1959).

On the Determination of Optimal Trajectories Via Dynamic Programming

RICHARD BELLMAN

The RAND Corporation, Santa Monica, California

8.1 Introduction

There is little difficulty in formulating various problems arising in the study of optimal trajectories as questions within the calculus of variations. Standard variational techniques then transform the original problems into those of solving nonlinear differential equations subject to two-point boundary conditions. In many cases, the presence of constraints on the possible motions introduces a combination of equations and inequalities.

Even in the simpler cases where constraints are not present, the two-point aspect introduces complications which often render a computational solution extremely difficult to achieve, even when equipped with the biggest and fastest of modern computers.

In this chapter we wish to discuss the application of the theory of dynamic programming to the numerical solution of problems in the calculus of variations. Our aim is to describe a systematic approach to these problems which will permit routine solutions with the aid of digital computers.

8.2 Dynamic Programming

The basic step is the recognition of the fact that the calculus of variations is a particular example of a multistage decision process of continuous type. The reader interested in the fundamentals of the theory of dynamic programming, an alternate term for the theory of multistage decision processes, may refer to Bellman[1,2] or Bellman and Dreyfus.[3] In what follows we shall assume that the reader is familiar with the basic ideas of the theory.

8.3 One-Dimensional Problems

Let us begin our discussion with the problem of minimizing the functional

$$J(u) = \int_0^T g(u, u') \, dt \tag{8.1}$$

over all functions $u(t)$ defined over the interval $[0, T]$ and satisfying the initial condition $u(0) = c$.

Writing

$$f(c, T) = \min_u J(u) \tag{8.2}$$

the principle of optimality, cf. Bellman,[1,2] yields the nonlinear partial differential equation

$$f_T = \min_v [g(c, v) + vf_c], \qquad f(c, 0) = 0 \tag{8.3}$$

From this equation the familiar Euler equation can readily be obtained, cf. Dreyfus[4] and Bellman.[5] For computational purposes, it is frequently better to use the discrete approximation

$$f(c, T + \Delta) = \min_v [g(c, v)\Delta + f(c + v\Delta, T)] \tag{8.4}$$

$T = 0, \Delta, 2\Delta, \cdots$, cf. Bellman[2] and Bellman and Dreyfus.[3]

The solution obtained in this way requires the tabulation of two sequences of functions of one variable, the functions $\{f(c, T\}$ and the "policy functions," $v = v(c, T)$. It is thus a routine problem as far as modern digital computers are concerned. For a discussion of the advantages of this approach as opposed to the usual approach of the calculus of variations, see Bellman.[2]

8.4 Constraint—I

If we add a constraint such as

$$| u' | \leq m, \qquad 0 \leq t \leq T \tag{8.5}$$

Eq. (8.3) is replaced by

$$f_T = \min_{|v| \leq m} [g(c, v) + vf_c] \tag{8.6}$$

The corresponding version of (8.4) is

$$f(c, T + \Delta) = \min_{|v| \leq m} [g(c, v)\Delta + f(c + v\Delta, T)] \tag{8.7}$$

The minimization is carried out by a search process over some finite set of v-values lying in the interval $[-m, m]$. In many cases, sophisticated techniques can be used to reduce greatly the number of values that must be examined, cf. Bellman and Dreyfus.[3] Observe that the presence of the constraint simplifies the solution by dynamic programming techniques since it serves to reduce the number of feasible policies, which is to say, the possible choices of v.

8.5 Constraint—II

Suppose that the problem is that of minimizing $J(u)$, as given in Section 8.3, subject to the additional constraint

$$\int_0^T h(u, u') \, dt \leq k \tag{8.8}$$

In place of adding another state variable, we employ a Lagrange multiplier and consider the new problem of minimizing the functional

$$\int_0^T [g(u, u') - \lambda h(u, u')] \, dt \tag{8.9}$$

subject only to the conditions

(a) $u(0) = c,$

$$\tag{8.10}$$

(b) $| u'(t) | \leq m, \qquad 0 \leq t \leq T$

Writing

$$f(c, T) = \min_u \left[\int_0^T [g(u, u') - \lambda h(u, u')] \, dt \right] \tag{8.11}$$

we have, for each fixed value of λ, the discrete recurrence relation

$$f(c, T + \Delta) = \min_{|v| \leq m} [(g(c, v) - \lambda h(c, v)) + f(c + v\Delta, T)] \qquad (8.12)$$

from which the numerical solution can be obtained easily. The value of λ, a "price," is then varied until the original constraint is attained.

8.6 Discussion

We may conclude that the general one-dimensional variational problem of minimizing

$$J(u) = \int_0^T g(u, u') \, dt \qquad (8.13)$$

subject to

(a) $$\int_0^T h(u, u') \, dt \leq k$$

(b) $$u(0) = c \qquad (8.14)$$

(c) $$|u'(t)| \leq m$$

is a routine problem which can quickly and accurately be solved using dynamic programming techniques in conjunction with digital computers. For some results, see Bellman and Dreyfus.[3]

Minor modifications handle the case where there is a boundary condition at $t = T$

$$r(u(T), u'(T)) = 0 \qquad (8.15)$$

the case where the integrand depends explicitly upon t, and the more general case where it is desired to minimize

$$J(u) = \int_0^T g(u, v) \, dt \qquad (8.16)$$

over all functions v where u and v are connected by the differential equation

$$\frac{du}{dt} = h(u, v), \qquad u(0) = c \qquad (8.17)$$

8.7 Two-Dimensional Problems

Let us now consider the problem of minimizing the functional

$$J(u_1, u_2) = \int_0^T g(u_1, u_2, u_1', u_2') \, dt \qquad (8.18)$$

where u_1 and u_2 are subject to the initial conditions

$$u_1(0) = c_1, \qquad u_2(0) = c_2 \qquad (8.19)$$

Setting

$$f(c_1, c_2, T) = \min_{u_1, u_2} J(u_1, u_2) \qquad (8.20)$$

we obtain as before the nonlinear partial differential equation

$$\frac{\partial f}{\partial t} = \min_{v_1, v_2} \left[g(c_1, c_2, v_1, v_2) + v_1 \frac{\partial f}{\partial c_1} + v_2 \frac{\partial f}{\partial c_2} \right], \quad f(c_1, c_2, 0) = 0 \qquad (8.21)$$

For computational purposes we can employ the recurrence relation

$$f(c_1, c_2, T + \Delta) = \min_{v_1, v_2} \left[g(c_1, c_2, v_1, v_2) \Delta + f(c_1 + v_1\Delta, c_2 + v_2\Delta, T) \right] \qquad (8.22)$$

$T = 0, \Delta, 2\Delta, \cdots$, with the initial condition $f(c_1, c_2, 0) = 0$, or standard methods for the numerical solution of partial differential equations.

The numerical solution along the foregoing lines involves the tabulation and storage of sequences of functions of two variables. This introduces some complications. Consider, to illustrate this point, a situation in which c_1 and c_2 are both allowed to assume one hundred different values. Since the number of different sets of c_1 and c_2 values is now 10^4, the tabulation of the values of $f(c_1, c_2, T)$ for a particular value of T requires a memory of 10^4. Moreover, since the recurrence relation requires that f at T be stored while the values for $T+\Delta$ are calculated, and since the two policies $v_1 = v_1(c_1, c_2, T)$ and $v_2 = v_2(c_1, c_2, T)$ must also be stored, we see that we need a memory of at least 4×10^4.

Let us note that when we use the term "memory," we always mean *fast memory*. There is, of course, no limit on the slow memory that is available.

There are many ways of cutting down the number of grid-points. These are discussed in Bellman and Dreyfus.[3] Generally speaking, with the current digital computers with memories of 32,000 words, we can handle two-dimensional variational problems in one way or another. The situation becomes very much worse, however, as we turn to higher dimensions. A three-dimensional trajectory problem, involving three position variables and three velocity variables, leads by way of the dynamic programming approach to functions of six phase variables, or "state variables." Even if each variable is allowed to take only 10 different values, this leads to 10^9 values, an absurdly large number.

We wish to employ a different idea, the technique of *polynomial approximation*. This will enable us to tabulate functions of several variables in a quick and efficient way, and allow us to use the functional equation approach to solve multidimensional variational problems.

8.8 One-Dimensional Case

In order to present the idea in a simple form, let us begin with the one-dimensional problem discussed above. We wish to obtain a numerical solution of the recurrence relation

$$f(c, T + \Delta) = \min_{v} \left[g(c, v)\Delta + f(c + v\Delta, T) \right] \tag{8.23}$$

$T = 0, \Delta, 2\Delta, \cdots$, with $f(c, 0) = 0$. To simplify the notation, let us write

$$f(c, k\Delta) = f_k(c) \tag{8.24}$$

Let us agree to consider only values of c lying in a fixed interval, which with suitable normalization we can take to be $[-1, 1]$. To ensure that c remains in this interval, we add a constraint on v, namely,

$$-1 \le c + v\Delta \le 1 \tag{8.25}$$

By taking the interval sufficiently large, we can ensure that the effect at the boundaries will be negligible as far as the internal values are concerned. In many cases, a constraint of the foregoing nature exists as part of the original problem.

We now approximate to each member of the sequence $\{f_k(c)\}$ by a polynomial in the state variable c. Instead of writing this in the usual polynomial form, we write it in terms of orthonormal Legendre polynomials,

$$f_k(c) = \sum_{n=0}^{N} a_{kn} P_n(c) \tag{8.26}$$

where the coefficients depend upon k. The advantage of using Legendre polynomials in place of the usual powers of c lies in the fact that we can use the formula

$$a_{kn} = \int_{-1}^{1} f_k(c) P_n(c) \, dc \tag{8.27}$$

to determine the coefficients rather than relying upon a differentiation process.

The point of the representation of Eq. (8.26) is that the function $f_k(c)$ is now represented for *all* points in the interval $[-1, 1]$ by the set of $N + 1$ coefficients $\{a_{kn}\}$. Once these $N + 1$ values have been stored, we can then calculate the value of $f_k(c)$ for any value of c in this interval. This calculation is naturally approximate, but we can expect to obtain excellent agreement by choosing N to be of the order of magnitude of 10 or so.

How do we actually calculate the sequence of coefficients $\{a_{kn}\}$? If we use a Riemann approximation

$$\int_{-1}^{1} f_k(c)\, P_n(c)\, dc \cong \delta \sum_{r=-M}^{M} f_k(r\delta)\, P_n(r\delta) \qquad (8.28)$$

we may end up either tabulating as many values of $f_k(c)$ as before, or suffer serious inaccuracies. In place of evaluating the integral as in Eq. (8.28), we use a quadrature technique. If the points t_j and the weights w_j are chosen suitably, we may write

$$\int_{-1}^{1} g(c)\, dc \cong \sum_{j=1}^{M} w_j g(t_j) \qquad (8.29)$$

an approximation formula which is *exact* if $g(c)$ is a polynomial of degree $2M - 1$ or less.

It is easy to show that the t_j are the M roots of the Legendre polynomial of degree M, and the w_j are constants determined by the Legendre polynomials, the Christoffel numbers. The parameters are readily available up to quite large values of M.

It follows that the values of $f_k(c)$ for all points in $[-1, 1]$ are determined by the values of $f_k(t_j)$, $j = 1, 2, \cdots, M$, since these values determine the coefficients a_{kn} in Eq. (8.28), and these coefficients determine $f_k(c)$ by way of Eq. (8.26).

Let us now see how this simplifies the determination of the sequence $\{f_k(c)\}$. Starting with the known function $f_1(c)$, obtained from

$$f_1(c) = \min_{v} g(c, v) \qquad (8.30)$$

we convert $f_1(c)$ into the sequence $[a_{11}, a_{21}, \cdots, a_{N1}]$ by using the relations

$$a_{k1} = \int_{-1}^{1} f_1(c)\, P_n(c)\, dc$$
$$= \sum_{j=1}^{M} w_j f_1(t_j)\, P_k(t_j) \qquad (8.31)$$

Since w_j and $P_k(t_j)$ are fixed constants, calculated once and for all, we can store their product, b_{kj}, and write

$$a_{k1} = \sum_{j=1}^{M} b_{kj} f_1(t_j), \qquad k = 1, 2, \cdots, N \tag{8.32}$$

Turning to the determination of $f_2(c)$ from the relation

$$f_2(c) = \min_v \left[g(c, v)\Delta + f_1(c + v\Delta) \right] \tag{8.33}$$

we note first of all that we need only compute the M values $f_2(t_j)$, $j = 1, 2, \cdots, M$. The value of $f_1(t_j + v\Delta)$ is obtained for each value of v examined by use of the formula

$$f_1(t_j + v\Delta) = \sum_{j=1}^{M} a_{k1} P_k(t_j + v\Delta) \tag{8.34}$$

The evaluation of this expression is not too much more difficult than that of a polynomial since the Legendre polynomial $P_n(x)$ satisfies a simple 3-term recurrence relation which makes its evaluation very simple starting from the initial values $P_0(x) = 1$, $P_1(x) = x$.

Having calculated the M values $\{f_2(t_j)\}$, $j = 1, 2, \cdots, M$, we determine the coefficients $\{a_{k2}\}$, $k = 1, 2, \cdots, N$,

$$a_{k2} = \sum_{j=1}^{M} w_j f_2(t_j) P_k(t_j) \tag{8.35}$$

The values $\{f_2(t_j)\}$ are now discarded and the sequence $\{a_{k2}\}$, $k = 1, 2, \cdots, N$ is stored. All values of $f_2(c)$ required for the determination of $f_3(c)$ from the equation

$$f_3(c) = \min_v \left[g(c, v)\Delta + f_2(c + v\Delta) \right] \tag{8.36}$$

are now obtained by means of the relation

$$f_2(c) = \sum_{j=1}^{N} a_{k2} P_k(c) \tag{8.37}$$

We compute the M values $\{f_3(t_j)\}$ and continue in this fashion.

8.9 Discussion

It will be seen that the memory requirements for this process are quite small. We store only the sequence $\{a_{kR}\}$ at the Rth stage, as well as the constants b_{kj} and the instructions for the machine to carry out the indicated operations. For $M, N \le 20$, this is a negligible total.

The choice of M and N is a matter of convenience and experience. It is generally true in variational problems that regardless of the behavior of the policy function, $v = v(c, T)$, the return function $f(c, T)$ is quite smooth. This is to be expected from physical reasons (stability under small changes) and from mathematical reasoning as well. Consequently, we can expect a polynomial approximation of say degree $N = 10$ to yield very accurate results. Some preliminary results and comparisons with an exact solution are given in Bellman and Dreyfus.[3,6]

The determination of the policy function can be accomplished in two ways. We can either compute all the polynomial approximations the first time around, store the coefficients, and then compute the policy functions, $v_k = v_k(c, T)$, from the recurrence relation Eq. (8.23), or we can compute the policy functions as we go along and print out the values.

8.10 Two-Dimensional Case

Let us now consider the two-dimensional problem discussed in Section 8.6. We approximate to a function of two variables $f(c_1, c_2)$ by a polynomial in c_1 and c_2, most conveniently taken to be of the form

$$f(c_1, c_2) = \sum_{k,l=1}^{N} a_{kl} P_k(c_1) P_l(c_2) \tag{8.38}$$

The coefficients are determined by the relation

$$a_{kl} = \int_{-1}^{1} f(c_1, c_2) P_k(c_1) P_l(c_2) \, dc_1 \, dc_2$$

$$= \sum_{j=1}^{M} \sum_{r=1}^{M} f(t_{1j}, t_{2r}) P_k(t_{1j}) P_l(t_{2j}) w_j w_r \tag{8.39}$$

where the weights w_j and interpolation points t_{1j} are as before.

We see then that the function $f(c_1, c_2)$ is determined for storage purposes by the N^2 coefficients $\{a_{kl}\}$, $k, l = 1, 2, \cdots, N$, which in turn are determined by the values $f(t_{1j}, t_{2r})$.

The recurrence relation Eq. (8.16) may be written

$$f_{n+1}(c_1, c_2) = \min_{v_1, v_2} \left[g(c_1, c_2, v_1, v_2)\Delta + f_n(c_1 + v_1\Delta, c_2 + v_2\Delta) \right] \tag{8.40}$$

As before, we start with the function $f_n(c_1, c_2)$ in the form of the coefficients $\{a_{kl}^{(n)}\}$ and use these to compute the values of f_n needed to determine $\{ f_{n+1}(t_{1j}, t_{2r}) \}$. From these we evaluate $\{a_k^{(9n+1)}\}$ and so on.

A function of two variables over $-1 \leq c_1, c_2 \leq 1$ is stored by means of the N^2 coefficients $\{a_{kl}\}$. If $N = 10$, an approximation which should yield quite accurate results, we need only 100 values.

8.11 Discussion

Proceeding along the same lines, we see that the general trajectory problem in the plane could be treated in terms of polynomial approximation to functions of four variables, requiring N^4 coefficients. If $N = 10$, this requires not only a large memory, but an enormous amount of time for the evaluation of particular functional values. If we decrease N to 5, we reduce the number to N^4 to 625, a more reasonable quantity.

Similarly, if we turn to three-dimensional trajectory problems, involving functions of six variables, we see that a choice of $N = 4$ yields the figure $4^6 = 1024$.

We may expect to get by with polynomials of lower degree as we increase the number of state variables.

What we have presented above is an outline of the general idea of polynomial approximation. Combining it with various other techniques such as successive approximations, in the form of approximation in policy space or otherwise, we feel that it is reasonable at the present time to think in terms of routine solutions of three-dimensional trajectory problems involving six state variables. With the computers of 10 years hence, with memories 10–30 times larger and speeds 10–30 times faster, we can consider routine solutions of problems involving other state variables such as fuel, mass, and so on.

References

1. R. Bellman, "Dynamic Programming." Princeton Univ. Press, Princeton, New Jersey, 1957.
2. R. Bellman, "Adaptive Control Processes: A Guided Tour." Princeton Univ. Press, Princeton, New Jersey, 1961.
3. R. Bellman and S. E. Dreyfus, "Applied Dynamic Programming." Princeton Univ. Press, Princeton, New Jersey, 1962.
4. S. Dreyfus, Dynamic programming and the calculus of variations, *J. Math. Anal. and Appl.* **1,** 228–239 (1960).
5. R. Bellman, Dynamic programming of continuous processes, Rept. R-271, The RAND Corporation, Santa Monica, California (1954).
6. R. Bellman and S. Dreyfus, Functional approximations and dynamic programming, *Math. Tables and Other Aids to Computation* **13,** 247–251 (1959).

—9—

Computational Considerations for Some Deterministic and Adaptive Control Processes

ROBERT KALABA

The RAND Corporation, Santa Monica, California

9.1 Introduction

A fundamental problem common to all branches of engineering is this: given certain resources, design a system which maximizes a prescribed figure of merit. With relatively simple and inexpensive systems the desired optimization can be achieved through use of experience and experimentation, only a modicum of theory being required. For complex and expensive systems, such as modern missile systems, where only limited experience is available and experimentation is costly and perhaps dangerous, there is a premium on being able to carry out the desired optimization theoretically and at relatively small cost. In preliminary design such capability is useful for investigatigating the very feasibility of a proposed system. A number of outstanding engineers, including C. Steinmetz and R. Goddard, have emphasized this view.

Generally speaking, modern mathematics is not capable of dealing with the problems which arise in cursory attempts to synthesize or analyze complex electrical, mechanical, and thermal systems, where a variety of economic factors must also be taken into account. These problems are much more delicate than the usual problems treated in classical mathematical physics, where, as a rule, only several variables occur. To deal with these new problems new fields of mathematics have been cultivated. These include linear and dynamic programming. A common feature is that heavy emphasis is laid on the modern high-speed digital computer from the time the analysis of a physical situation is begun until the analysis is concluded. Intelligent use of such computers frequently makes possible the consideration of mathematical models which are sufficiently realistic to be interesting from the engineering and operations research viewpoints, yet which are capable of treatment with reasonable expenditures of computational effort.

It frequently happens that classical mathematical techniques are not the ones best suited for obtaining desired insights via high-speed computation. Often a blend of the old and the new can be very efficacious.

Section 9.2 is concerned with the determination of an optimal control policy for a problem typical of many occurring in engineering and economics, provided one can assume known cause and effect, known objective, and so on. Following the general discussion, based on use of the Bellman principle of optimality, some generalizations are indicated and some special examples are worked in detail. In Section 9.210 a quasi-linearization technique, which holds promise insofar as the numerical resolution of the nonlinear two-point boundary-value problems to which the classical variational approach often leads, is applied to a special problem.

Section 9.3 is devoted to the formulation and solution of a problem of adaptive control. The point of view taken is that an adaptive controller has the capability of "learning" about certain initially unknown factors in the course of the control process. The controller thus both learns and controls in an effort to best achieve an objective.

9.2 Some Deterministic Control Processes

9.21 Formulation

Let us first consider the problem of determining a function $v(t)$ on the interval $0 \leq t \leq T$ which minimizes the functional $J[v]$, where

$$J[v] = \int_0^T F(x, v) \, dt \tag{9.1}$$

and where
$$\frac{dx}{dt} = G(x, v) \tag{9.2}$$

and
$$x(0) = c \tag{9.3}$$

As we shall see, the most effective means of solution of this problem depends very much on the precise nature of the information about the optimizing function v which is desired.

A variety of optimization problems in economics and engineering are of the general type sketched above. The parameter c represents the initial state of a system, and $x(t)$ represents the state at time t. The decision made at time t is $v(t)$. The rate at which the cost of the process increases at time t is $F(x(t), v(t))$, and so depends on the current state and control decision. The function $G(x, v)$ provides the rate of change of the state of the system in the event that it is in state x and decision v is made, and so specifies the dynamics of the process under consideration. We desire to determine an optimal choice of the decision as a function of time; that is, we seek an optimal decision function $v(t)$, $0 \leq t \leq T$. Various restraints on v will normally be imposed, but we do not consider them here.

We shall now turn to a discussion of several modes of solution.

9.22 Dynamic Programming Approach

We observe that the value of the minimum of the functional $J[v]$ is solely a function of c and T:

$$\min_v J[v] = f(c, T) \tag{9.4}$$

We can now derive a partial differential equation which is satisfied by the function $f(c, T)$. This is done by comparing the minimal costs of processes of duration $T + \Delta$ against those of duration T and using the Bellman principle of optimality.[1] This principle can be formulated thusly: An optimal decision process has the property that whatever the initial decisions are, the remaining decisions must be optimal with respect to the state resulting from the initial decisions. Let us note that Eq. (9.4) can be written

$f(c, T) =$ the cost of a control process in which the initial state of
the system is c, the duration is T, and an optimal choice $\quad$ (9.5)
of the control function v is made on the interval $(0, T)$

Our key equation is

$$f(c, T + \Delta) = \min_w \{F(c, w)\Delta + f(c + G(c, w)\Delta, T) + o(\Delta)\} \tag{9.6}$$

The first term on the right-hand side is the cost of the first Δ time units of the process under the assumption that v is chosen equal to w during this interval. The second term represents the minimal cost of a process in which the initial state of the system is $c + G(c, w)\Delta$ and the duration is T. The last term, $o(\Delta)$, is a term having the property that $(o(\Delta)/\Delta) \to 0$ as $\Delta \to 0$. A minimization over w is involved since a best initial choice of v must be made. Expanding, using Taylor's theorem, we find

$$f(c, T) + f_T \Delta + o(\Delta) = \min_{w} \{ F(c, w)\Delta + f(c, T)$$

$$+ G(c, w)\Delta f_c + o(\Delta) \} \quad (9.7)$$

Finally, upon subtracting $f(c, T)$ from both sides of the equation, dividing by Δ, and letting Δ tend to zero, we obtain the equation

$$f_T = \min_{w} \{ F(c, w) + G(c, w)f_c \} \quad (9.8)$$

where the subscripts denote partial derivatives. In addition, we note that zero cost is associated with processes of zero duration, according to Eq. (9.1) so that

$$f(c, 0) = 0 \quad (9.9)$$

Our object, then, becomes the investigation of the solution of Eq. (9.8) subject to the condition (9.9). Before entering into this, though, let us give another derivation of Eq. (9.8), one that emphasizes the intuitive content of the equation.

Consider an optimal choice of the decision function $v = v(t)$, and let $x = x(t)$ be the corresponding function determined by the differential equation (9.2). The rate of decrease of the cost of the remaining portion of the process at any time t is equal to $F(x(t), v(t))$, i.e.,

$$-\frac{d}{dt} f(x(t), T - t) = F(x(t), v(t)) \quad (9.10)$$

On the other hand, no other choice of v can yield a greater rate of decrease, so that

$$-\frac{d}{dt} f(x(t), T - t) \leq F(x(t), v(t)) \quad (9.11)$$

$$-f_c(x(t), v(t)) \frac{dx}{dt} + f_T(x(t), v(t)) \leq F(x(t), v(t)) \quad (9.12)$$

Now we use the equation

$$\frac{dx}{dt} = G(x, v) \tag{9.13}$$

to obtain the relationship

$$f_T \leq F + f_c G \tag{9.14}$$

and finally the desired equation

$$f_T = \min_{v} \{F + f_c G\} \tag{9.15}$$

which is Eq. (9.8).

9.23 Sketch of Numerical Solution

We now consider in elementary fashion the numerical solution of the first-order quasi-linear partial differential equation derived earlier:

$$f_T = \min_{w} \{F(c, w) + G(c, w)f_c\} \tag{9.16}$$

where the initial condition

$$f(c, 0) = 0 \tag{9.17}$$

is prescribed. We first note that $f(c, T)$ is known to be zero at the points $c = \pm k\delta$, $T = 0$, where $k = 0, 1, 2, \cdots, K$. In addition, f_c is zero at these points. Next we evaluate the given function $F(c, w)$ at the points $c = k\delta$ and $w = \pm m\Delta$, $m = 1, 2, \cdots, M$. We can then determine the smallest of these functional values (and also record the value of w that minimizes) and set this value equal to f_T. This is done for $k = 0, \pm 1, \cdots, \pm K$. The result is that an approximation to the partial derivative f_T is then known for $T = 0$ and $c = k\delta$, $k = 0, \pm 1, \pm 2, \cdots, \pm K$. These results are then used to determine approximations to the function $f(c, T)$ for $T = h$ by using the formula

$$f(c, h) = f(c, 0) + hf_T(c, 0) \tag{9.18}$$

In this way an approximate solution is obtained at the points $(\pm k\delta, h)$. Furthermore, approximations to the derivatives at these points can be obtained, e.g., by using the relationship

$$f_c(k\delta, h) = \frac{f((k + 1)\delta, h) - f(k\delta, h)}{h} \tag{9.19}$$

Then by repeating this operation the solution for $T = 2h$ can be obtained for a certain set of c values. The calculation proceeds until the function f and the optimal decisions to make are determined at all the grid points of a desired region of the $c - T$ plane. It is to be expected that individual problems will present their own special difficulties with regard to determination of the grid-size parameters δ, Δ, and h, and the precise finite difference formulas to use. Furthermore, in some cases additional analytic progress is possible, which lightens the ultimate computational problem. For example, it may be possible to carry out the minimization explicitly, and then use the theory of characteristic curves[2] for first-order partial differential equations as a starting point for numerical resolution. See Collatz[3] and Kamke[4] for additional discussion. Lastly, let us note that Eq. (9.6) can be made the basis of an efficient numerical scheme.

9.24 Lagrange Multipliers and Euler Equations

We return to the problem sketched in Section 9.21 and show how Eq. (9.8) can be used to derive the usual Euler equations for such problems. We assume that the optimal choice of w is obtained through solving the equation

$$F_w + G_w f_c = 0 \tag{9.20}$$

which is obtained by setting the partial derivative with respect to w of the expression in brackets in Eq. (9.8) equal to zero. For this choice of w we obtain

$$f_T = F + Gf_c \tag{9.21}$$

We can obtain an equation for the function f_c by taking the total derivative of f_c with respect to the time elapsed during an optimal process t,

$$\frac{d}{dt}(f_c) = f_{cc}\frac{dc}{dt} + f_{cT}\frac{dT}{dt} \tag{9.22}$$

$$= f_{cc}G - f_{cT}$$

Taking the partial derivatives of both sides of Eq. (9.21) with respect to c, we find

$$f_{Tc} = F_c + F_w w_c + (G_c + G_w w_c)f_c + Gf_{cc} \tag{9.23}$$

Making use of Eq. (9.20) we find

$$f_{Tc} = F_c + G_c f_c + Gf_{cc} \tag{9.24}$$

Thus Eq. (9.22) becomes

$$\frac{d}{dt}(f_c) = -F_c - G_c(f_c) \tag{9.25}$$

Now let us put

$$\lambda = f_c \tag{9.26}$$

and observe that

$$f_c(c, 0) = 0 \tag{9.27}$$

or

$$\lambda \mid_{t=T} = 0 \tag{9.28}$$

Consequently we obtain the system of two equations for x and λ,

$$\frac{dx}{dt} = G(x, w), \qquad x(0) = c$$

$$\tag{9.29}$$

$$\frac{d\lambda}{dt} = -F_x - G_x\lambda, \qquad \lambda(T) = 0$$

which are augmented by the algebraic relation

$$F_w + G_w\lambda = 0 \tag{9.30}$$

thus providing w as a function of x and λ.

The problem discussed in Section 9.210 corresponds to the case in which

$$G(x, w) = w \tag{9.31}$$

and

$$F(x, w) = \tfrac{1}{2}w^2 + e^x \tag{9.32}$$

so that Eqs. (9.29) and (9.30) become

$$\frac{dx}{dt} = w, \qquad x(0) = c$$

$$\frac{d\lambda}{dt} = e^x, \qquad \lambda(T) = 0 \tag{9.33}$$

$$w + \lambda = 0$$

These are equivalent to Eq. (9.83). Other results are available in the paper by Dreyfus.[5]

9.25 Generalization to Vector Systems

The conceptual considerations of Section 9.22 are readily generalized to the case in which the state of the system is a vector, $x = (x_1, x_2, \cdots, x_M)$, and the choice variable is also a vector, $v = (v_1, v_2, \cdots, v_R)$. The function $F(x, v)$ is a scalar function of its vector arguments, and $G(x, v)$ is an M-dimensional vector $(g_1, g_2, \cdots, g_M)$. We once again define

$$f(c, T) = \min_v J[v] \tag{9.34}$$

where

$$J[v] = \int_0^T F(x, v) \, dt \tag{9.35}$$

and

$$\frac{dx}{dt} = G(x, v), \qquad x(0) = c \tag{9.36}$$

The analog of Eq. (9.8) is

$$f_T = \min_w \left[F(c, w) + \sum_{i=1}^M G_i f_{c_i} \right] \tag{9.37}$$

and the terminal condition is

$$f(c, 0) = 0 \tag{9.38}$$

As M increases from 1 to 2 and goes beyond 2, the analytic and computational difficulties increase rapidly. This is the problem of dimensionality which itself has been the subject of much study.[6,7]

9.26 An Example: Linear System and Quadratic Cost Functional

We shall now consider an example which is simple enough so that the problem can be resolved analytically. We wish to find a function $g(t)$ which minimizes the integral

$$J[g] = \int_0^T \{u^2 + g^2\} \, dt \tag{9.39}$$

where

$$\frac{du}{dt} = \dot{u} = g, \qquad 0 < t \le T \tag{9.40}$$

and

$$u(0) = c \tag{9.41}$$

Upon introducing the cost function $f(c, T)$, we find that this function satisfies the equation

$$f_T = \min_w \left\{ c^2 + w^2 + w \frac{\partial f}{\partial c} \right\} \tag{9.42}$$

and the subsidiary condition

$$f(c, 0) = 0 \tag{9.43}$$

These are special cases of Eqs. (9.37) and (9.38).

Since f and f_c are functions of c and T and do not contain w explicitly, we may carry out the optimization of the quadratic function of w in the brackets of Eq. (9.42) by setting the derivative equal to zero, which yields the optimal control law

$$w_{min} = -\tfrac{1}{2} f_c \tag{9.44}$$

This is most important information from the point of view of feedback control, for it tells what the optimal choice of w to make is with the system in any state c and any particular time T remaining in the process, assuming that the function $f_c(c, T)$ is known. We now use the information that the minimizing choice of w is given by Eq. (9.44) to transform Eq. (9.42) into the quasi-linear equation

$$f_T = c^2 + \tfrac{1}{4} f_c^2 - \tfrac{1}{2} f_c^2 \tag{9.45}$$

or

$$f_T = c^2 - \tfrac{1}{4} f_c^2 \tag{9.46}$$

To proceed further we can use the method of separation of variables and write

$$f(c, T) = \varphi(T) c^2 \tag{9.47}$$

where, according to Eq. (9.43),

$$f(c, 0) = 0 = \varphi(0) \tag{9.48}$$

The reason for trying the particular form in Eq. (9.47) will be given later. According to Eqs. (9.46) and (9.47), $\varphi(T)$ satisfies the Riccati equation and initial condition

$$\frac{d\varphi}{dT} = 1 - \varphi^2, \qquad \varphi(0) = 0 \tag{9.49}$$

The explicit solution can be given in terms of the hyperbolic tangent function and is

$$\varphi(T) = \tanh T \tag{9.50}$$

Consequently, the cost function $f(c, T)$ is found to be

$$f(c, T) = c^2 \tanh T \tag{9.51}$$

The optimal control law is then found from Eq. (9.44); it is

$$w_{\min} = -c \tanh T \tag{9.52}$$

showing that optimal control is a linear function of the state, the factor of proportionality being a function of the time remaining in the process. Thus, a linear time-varying filter is required for optimal control.

We note that if the process is a short one, we may approximate to an optimal policy by putting

$$w = 0 \tag{9.53}$$

This leads to a cost of

$$\int_0^T (c^2 + 0^2)\, dt = c^2 T \tag{9.54}$$

If the process is a long one, then Eq. (9.52) indicates that we may try

$$w = -c \tag{9.55}$$

For such a control policy the equation of motion is

$$\dot{u} = -u, \qquad 0 < t \le T \tag{9.56}$$

and

$$u(0) = c \tag{9.57}$$

which has as solution

$$u(t) = ce^{-t} \tag{9.58}$$

The cost in this case is

$$\int_0^T \{c^2 e^{-2t} + c^2 e^{-2t}\}\, dt = c^2(1 - e^{-2T}) \tag{9.59}$$

For large T, this cost is not too much different from the minimal cost given by Eq. (9.51), but the costs of actual physical implementation of the two control schemes, one time–varying, the other not, could be quite different. One of the advantages in solving the optimization problem is that one is better able to assess the worth of suboptimal, but particularly simple, control policies.

9.27 The Classical Approach

We can also analyze the control process of the previous section using classical ideas from the calculus of variations.[2] We are confronted with the problem of finding a function $u(t)$, $0 \le t \le T$, which minimizes the integral

$$J[u] = \int_0^T \{u^2 + \dot{u}^2\} \, dt \tag{9.60}$$

subject to the boundary condition

$$u(0) = c \tag{9.61}$$

The Euler equation for this problem is the linear equation

$$\ddot{u} = u \tag{9.62}$$

[The linearity of this equation and the quadratic nature of $J[u]$ suggested the formula (9.47).] In addition to the condition of Eq. (9.61) there is a free boundary condition at $t = T$,

$$\dot{u}(T) = 0 \tag{9.63}$$

Since

$$\dot{u} = g \tag{9.64}$$

Eq. (9.63) simply requires that $g = 0$ at $t = T$. This is also implied by Eq. (9.52), for in this case

$$w_{\min} = -c \tanh 0 = 0 \tag{9.65}$$

We are now confronted with a two-point boundary value problem which requires solution. In general this is impossible analytically and very difficult computationally. The linearity of the Euler equation (9.62) enables us to see that

$$u(t) = c \, \frac{\cosh \, (t - T)}{\cosh T} \tag{9.66}$$

so that the function g [see Eq. (9.40)] is given by

$$g(t) = c \, \frac{\sinh \, (t - T)}{\cosh T} \tag{9.67}$$

The above equation gives the time history of the optimal control as a function of c, the initial state, T, the duration of the process, and t, the time elapsed. For purposes of open loop control this is just the information that is required.

We can combine ideas to rederive Eq. (9.66) in the following manner. Equation (9.52) implies that

$$\dot{u}(t) = -u(t) \tanh \, (T - t) \tag{9.68}$$

Since t does not appear explicitly in the integrand of Eq. (9.60), we know a first integral of the Euler equation, namely,

$$\dot{u}^2(t) - u^2(t) = \text{const}$$

$$= \dot{u}^2(0) - u^2(0) \qquad (9.69)$$

$$= c^2\{\tanh^2 T - 1\}$$

Elimination of $\dot{u}(t)$ between Eqs. (9.68) and (9.69) then yields the desired result

$$u(t) = \frac{c \cosh (T - t)}{\cosh T} \qquad (9.70)$$

9.28 The Pontryagin Maximum Principle[8]

A discussion of this problem from still another viewpoint, that of the maximum principle of Pontryagin, is given by Rozonoer.[9]

9.29 Terminal Control

Let us slightly modify the cost associated with the control process by adding to the original integral the term $u^2(T)$, a measure of the cost of terminal deviations from zero. If we now define the function $f(c, T)$ to be

$$f(c, T) = \min_{g} J[g] \qquad (9.71)$$

where

$$J[g] = \int_0^T \{u^2 + g^2\} \, dt + u^2(T) \qquad (9.72)$$

and

$$\dot{u} = g, \qquad 0 < t \le T \qquad (9.73)$$

$$u(0) = c \qquad (9.74)$$

then the analysis proceeds exactly as in Section 9.26. The function f satisfies the same partial differential equation,

$$f_T = c^2 - \tfrac{1}{4}f_c^2 \qquad (9.75)$$

but now the terminal condition is

$$f(c, 0) = c^2 \qquad (9.76)$$

The solution for the function $f(c, T)$ is

$$f(c, T) = c^2 \qquad (9.77)$$

9.210 A Special Case with Nonlinear Euler Equation

Let us return to the remark made above concerning the difficulty of solving the two-point boundary-value problems for nonlinear Euler differential equations. We wish to show that in some fortunate cases a quasi-linearization technique introduced by Kalaba[10] and Bellman[11] does lead to efficient computational methods. We consider the integral $J[g]$,

$$J[g] = \int_0^T \{\tfrac{1}{2}g^2 + e^u\} \, dt \tag{9.78}$$

and the dynamical equations

$$\frac{du}{dt} = g, \qquad 0 < t \le T \tag{9.79}$$

$$u(0) = c \tag{9.80}$$

We wish to determine the function g so as to minimize the functional $J[g]$. Substituting from Eq. (9.79) into Eq. (9.78), we find we are to minimize

$$I[u] = \int_0^T \{\tfrac{1}{2}\dot{u}^2 + e^u\} \, dt \tag{9.81}$$

where

$$u(0) = c \tag{9.82}$$

The Euler equation for this problem is the nonlinear equation

$$\ddot{u} = e^u \tag{9.83}$$

and the free boundary condition at $t = T$ is

$$\dot{u}(T) = 0 \tag{9.84}$$

Equations (9.83), (9.84), and (9.80) can be resolved in closed form, a point which does not interest us here, for we wish to discuss their numerical solution via modern high-speed digital computing machinery. A similar problem is discussed by Kalaba[10] where many extensions are also indicated (see also Bellman[11]). We choose

$$c = 0, \qquad T = 1 \tag{9.85}$$

for the sake of definiteness.

Our approach is a method of successive approximations having the property that each additional iteration approximately doubles the number of correct digits in the approximation. Given the nth approximation $u_n(t)$, the next approximation $u_{n+1}(t)$ is taken as the solution of the linear boundary-value problem

$$\frac{d^2 u_{n+1}}{dt^2} = e^{u_n} + e^{u_n}(u_{n+1} - u_n) \tag{9.86}$$

$$u_{n+1}(0) = \dot{u}_{n+1}(T) = 0 \tag{9.87}$$

As initial approximation, $u_0(t)$, we may take

$$u_0(t) \equiv 0 \tag{9.88}$$

The solution for $u_{n+1}(t)$ is effected by first solving the linear initial value problem

$$\frac{d^2 y_{n+1}}{dt^2} = e^{u_n} y_{n+1} \tag{9.89}$$

$$y_{n+1}(0) = 0, \qquad \dot{y}_{n+1}(0) = 1 \tag{9.90}$$

(a solution of the homogeneous equation) and then finding the solution of the initial value problem

$$\frac{d^2 z_{n+1}}{dt^2} = e^{u_n} + e^{u_n}(z_{n+1} - z_n) \tag{9.91}$$

$$z_{n+1}(0) = \dot{z}_{n+1}(0) = 0 \tag{9.92}$$

The function $u_{n+1}(t)$ is then represented in the form

$$u_{n+1}(t) = z_{n+1}(t) + k y_{n+1}(t) \tag{9.93}$$

The condition $u_{n+1}(0)$ is automatically satisfied, and the constant k is determined by the condition

$$0 = \dot{z}_{n+1}(1) + k \dot{y}_{n+1}(1) \tag{9.94}$$

The above considerations reduce the solution of a nonlinear two-point boundary-value problem to the solution of a rapidly converging sequence of solutions of linear initial value problems. The initial value problems are readily solved by the computing machine; the boundary-value problem is not.

Table I gives the results of a numerical experiment carried out on the IBM 7090 computer. Dr. B. Kotkin programmed the solution of the Eqs. (9.86)–(9.88) using the method sketched above. A Runge-Kutta integration routine employing double precision arithmetic was used, and a grid size of $2^{-7} = 0.0078125$ was employed. Only a few seconds of running time were required.

TABLE I

RESULTS OF A NUMERICAL EXPERIMENT

t	$u_0(t)$	$u_1(t)$	$u_2(t)$	$u_3(t)$
0.0	0.0	0.0	0.0	0.0
0.09375	0.0	−0.067104	−0.069276	−0.069279
0.203125	0.0	−0.135064	−0.139758	−0.139765
0.3046875	0.0	−0.188878	−0.195866	−0.195876
0.40625	0.0	−0.234318	−0.243486	−0.243500
0.5000	0.0	−0.269237	−0.280253	−0.280270
0.6015625	0.0	−0.299821	−0.312591	−0.312611
0.703125	0.0	−0.323177	−0.337380	−0.337402
0.8046875	0.0	−0.339546	−0.354803	−0.354827
0.90625	0.0	−0.349096	−0.364988	−0.365013
1.0	0.0	−0.351946	−0.368031	−0.367056

9.3 Adaptive Control Processes

9.31 Basic Concepts

In earlier sections we confined ourselves to some deterministic control processes for which the state of the system at every instant of time is assumed known, the outcome of every control decision is known, the objective is known, and so on. The emphasis was upon determining efficient computational procedures. We now turn our attention to a class of control processes of quite a different nature. In particular, we wish to consider processes in which the controller suffers from an initial lack of knowledge concerning some aspects of the process, but is able to "learn" about these unknown factors during the course of the process. In this way, hopefully, it improves the quality of its control. Such control processes we refer to as adaptive control processes. A further discussion of these processes can be found in the works of Bellman[12] and Bellman and Kalaba.[13−16] In this field one of the gravest difficulties consists in attempting to formulate concepts and equations which put the physical process in mathematical form.

9.32 Formulation[17]

Let us consider the case of a controller that is called upon to estimate the value of an unknown probability p. We shall assume that p is the unknown probability that a certain random variable takes the value unity, and $1 − p$ is the probability that it takes the value zero. The controller is to conduct a series of experiments, record the outcomes, and make an estimate of p on the basis of this experience plus any a priori information available. There are costs which are associated with making each experiment and with making wrong estimates of p. We wish to determine when the experiments should be stopped and what estimate should be made by the controller. This is clearly a prototype problem of importance in the theory of experimentation.

Sequential estimation and related sequential detection processes of this type occur in communication and radar technology when the receiver uses variable rather than fixed sample sizes. As we shall see, the principle of optimality provides a guide to the mathematical formulation and the numerical resolution.

We must now specify matters in more detail. We shall assume that before the decision process begins, the controller is in possession of the a priori information that n ones out of s trials have been observed. Then, insofar as observation of the outcomes of the process itself is concerned, we assume that m of r trials have resultsd in a one. Of course, we are disregarding information concerning the order in which the events occurred, but there is a corresponding great simplification in the specification of the controller's knowledge. Since p is unknown, we regard it as a random variable with a distribution function which changes during the course of the process. Solely on the basis of the a priori information we consider this distribution function to be given by

$$dG(p) = \frac{p^{n-1}(1-p)^{s-n-1}}{B(n, s-n)} \, dp \tag{9.95}$$

where B is the beta function, a Bayes approach. Then, after m ones have been observed in r additional trials we consider it to be

$$dG_{r,m}(r) = \frac{p^m(1-p)^{r-m}dG(p)}{\int_0^1 p^m(1-p)^{r-m}dG(p)} \tag{9.96}$$

We let $c_{r,m}$ denote the expected cost of incorrect estimation after r additional trials have resulted in ones and set

$$c_{r,m} = \alpha \int_0^1 (p_{r,m} - p)^2 dG_{r,m}(p) \tag{9.97}$$

where $p_{r,m}$ is the estimate which minimizes $c_{r,m}$. This value of $p_{r,m}$ is given by the formula

$$p_{r,m} = \int_0^1 p \, dG_{r,m}(p)$$

$$= \frac{m+n}{r+s} \tag{9.98}$$

which certainly yields an intuitively reasonable estimate for p. A calculation then shows that

$$c_{r,m} = \alpha \frac{m+n}{r+s} \left[\frac{m+n+1}{r+s+1} - \frac{m+n}{r+s} \right] \tag{9.99}$$

We shall also assume that if m experiments have been performed, then the cost of the next experiment is $k(m)$, noting that the cost per experiment is permitted to vary during the process, a feature which gives rise to many interesting possibilities. Next we shall assume that in the absence of additional information estimated probabilities are to be regarded as true probabilities. Lastly, we wish to require that no more than R experiments be performed, so that the process must be truncated should this point be reached. We now turn to the determination of an optimal control policy.

9.33 Dynamic Programming Treatment

Let us introduce the cost function $f_r(m)$ by means of the definition

$$f_r(m) = \text{the expected cost of a process beginning with } m \text{ ones} \atop \text{in } r \text{ experiments having been observed, and using} \atop \text{an optimal sequence of decisions} \tag{9.100}$$

Then the principle of optimality yields the functional equation

$$f_r(m) = \min \begin{cases} C: \ k(r) + p_{r,m} f_{r+1}(m+1) + (1 - p_{r,m}) f_{r+1}(m) \\[2ex] S: \ \alpha \dfrac{m+n}{r+s} \left[\dfrac{m+n+1}{r+s+1} - \dfrac{m+n}{r+s} \right] \end{cases} \tag{9.101}$$

which holds for $m = 0, 1, 2, \cdots, r$ and $r = R - 1, R - 2, \cdots, 0$. In view of the truncation assumption we also have

$$f_R(m) = \alpha \frac{m+n}{R+s} \left[\frac{m+n+1}{R+s+1} - \frac{m+n}{R+s} \right] \tag{9.102}$$

The above relations quickly enable us to calculate the sequence of functions $f_R(m), f_{R-1}(m), \cdots, f_0(m)$. At the same time we determine whether to stop (S) or continue (C), and what estimate to make of p in the event the process is terminated.

9.34 Numerical Results

The functional equations of the previous section were investigated computationally for a wide variety of values for the parameters α and R, and for several cost functions, $k(r)$. When the cost of experimentation was constant from experiment to experiment, or when it increased, and when one out of two ones had been observed *a priori*, we found that the optimal policy consisted essentially in:

(1) continuing the experiments if r was small (not enough information present on which to base an estimate),

(2) stopping the experiments if r was sufficiently large, and

(3) continuing the experiments for intermediate values of r, unless extreme runs of either zeros or ones occurred, and stopping otherwise.

On the other hand, in the case of a decreasing cost of experiment for each new experiment,

$$k(r) = \exp\left(1 - \frac{r}{15}\right) \tag{9.103}$$

we find the optimal control policy is much more complex. The case in which $n = 1$, $s = 2$, $\alpha = 1500$, and $R = 40$ illustrates this nicely. When r is 19 or less, that is, when 19 or less experiments have been performed, generally speaking the rule is to do at least one more experiment. When r lies between 20 and 33 the rule is to stop immediately and make the appropriate estimate. If r is between 34 and 39 and approximately half the observations have been ones, then once again the rule is to do at least one more experiment. The reason for this behavior, of course, is that the cost of experimentation has dropped so low that it is profitable to do at least one more experiment before making the estimate. When r is 40, the process must terminate, by agreement.

REFERENCES

1. R. Bellman, "Dynamic Programming." Princeton Univ. Press, Princeton, New Jersey, 1957.
2. R. Courant and D. Hilbert, "Methoden der Mathematischen Physik," Vols. I and II. Springer-Verlag, Berlin, 1931.
3. L. Collatz, "The Numerical Treatment of Differential Equations." Springer-Verlag, Berlin, 1959.
4. E. Kamke, "Differentialgleichungen Lösungsmethoden und Lösungen." Akad. Verlag, Leipzig, 1959.
5. S. E. Dreyfus, Dynamic programming and the calculus of variations, *J. Math. Anal. and Appl.* **1**, 228–239 (1960).

6. R. Bellman, Some new techniques in the dynamic programming solution of variational problems, *Quart. Appl. Math.* **16,** 295–305 (1958).

7. R. Bellman and R. Kalaba, Reduction of dimensionality, dynamic programming, and control processes, Paper No. P-1964, The RAND Corporation (April, 1960).

8. V. G. Boltyanskii, R. V. Gamkrelidze, and L. S. Pontryagin, The theory of optimal processes. I. The maximum principle, *Izvest. Akad. Nauk S.S.S.R. Ser. Mat.* **24,** 3–42 (1960).

9. L. I. Rozonoer, L. S. Pontryagin maximum principle in the theory of optimal systems. I. *Automation Remote Control* **20,** 1288–1302 (1959).

10. R. Kalaba, On nonlinear differential equations, the maximum operation, and monotone convergence, *J. Math. and Mech.* **8,** 519–574 (1959).

11. R. Bellman, Functional equations in the theory of dynamic programming. V. Positivity and quasilinearity, *Proc. Natl. Acad. Sci. U.S.* **41,** 743–746 (1955).

12. R. Bellman, "Adaptive Control Processes: A Guided Tour." Princeton Univ. Press, Princeton, New Jersey, 1961.

13. R. Bellman and R. Kalaba, Dynamic programming and adaptive processes: mathematical foundation, *IRE Trans. on Automatic Control*, **AC-5,** 5–10 (1960).

14. R. Bellman and R. Kalaba, On communication processes involving learning and random duration, 1958 IRE Natl. Convention Record, part 4, 16–21 (1958).

15. R. Bellman and R. Kalaba, On adaptive control processes, 1959 IRE Natl. Convention Record, part 4, 2–11 (1959).

16. R. Bellman and R. Kalaba, A mathematical theory of adaptive control processes, *Proc. Natl. Acad. Sci. U.S.* **45,** 1288–1290 (1959).

17. R. Bellman, R. Kalaba, and D. Middleton, Dynamic programming, sequential estimation and sequential detection processes, *Proc. Natl. Acad. Sci. U. S.* **47,** 338–341 (1961).

—*10*—

General Imbedding Theory

C. M. KASHMAR and E. L. PETERSON

General Electric Company, Santa Barbara, California

10.1 Introduction

The general problem of missile system optimization involves a number of equations of motion which must necessarily be satisfied by a group of variables in terms of which the motion can be described. In addition, there is a mass flow equation, necessary to generate the maneuvering thrust, as well as the possibility of other restrictions such as guidance laws, acceleration limits, or realistic engine performance: In most problems of this type, the number of variables exceeds the number of equations to be satisfied. Thus if there are n equations to be satisfied by m variables, where $m > n$, one is free to choose $m - n$ of the variables in a rather arbitrary manner and attempt to solve for the remaining variables. If for every choice made for $m - n$ of the variables, there exists a unique solution for the remaining variables, there are obviously many solutions to choose from thus giving rise to the opportunity of making the choice optimal in some sense.

In rocket powered flight in space one might require that the powered flight be conducted in such a way as to obtain the smallest expenditure of fuel. Alternatively, one might consider the shortest time of flight, the largest displacement, the greatest change in velocity, or some weighted combination of these. In short one might desire to minimize or maximize any arbitrary function of the problem variables. We have freedom to select certain of the problem variables, for example, the thrust program in

311

rocket flight, and the minimization must be carried out under the constraints of the equations describing the physical phenomena.

Many situations require that the problem variables be forced to satisfy some boundary conditions. In a space interception we care only that the position of the two objects be brought into correspondence. The time duration of the encounter might be specified or we may be free to bring it about in any arbitrary time interval but the final velocity is of no concern. On the other hand, in the case of rendezvous between two objects, both the position and the velocity of the two objects must be brought into correspondence.

10.2 Problem Formulation

The mathematical transliteration of this problem may be accomplished by considering a system whose vector state at any time, $\bar{x}(t)$ is governed by the nonlinear dynamic process

$$\frac{d\bar{x}(t)}{dt} = \bar{G}(\bar{x}, \bar{y}, t) \qquad \bar{x}(0) = \bar{a} \tag{10.1}$$

where for any particular element of $\bar{x}(t)$, say $x_i(t)$, one has

$$\frac{dx_i}{dt} = G_i(x_1, x_2, \cdots, x_p, y_1, y_2, \cdots, y_q, t)$$

$$x_i(0) = a_i; \qquad i = 1, 2, 3, \cdots, p \tag{10.2}$$

The state vector $\bar{x}(t)$ is p-dimensional where p is indicative of the number of available equations, and the choice vector, $\bar{y}(t)$ is q-dimensional where q indicates the excess of variables over equations. Let the final values at time $t = T$ be specified for k elements of the state vector $\bar{x}(t)$, such that

$$x_i(T) = b_i(T), \qquad i = 1, 2, 3, \cdots, k \leq p \tag{10.3}$$

where the functions $b_i(t)$ are specified for all t in the interval $(0, T)$. Let l elements of the choice vector, $\bar{y}(t)$, be bounded in the interval $(0, T)$ according to specified limits $c_i(t)$ and $d_i(t)$ such that

$$c_i(t) \leq y_i(t) \leq d_i(t), \qquad i = 1, 2, 3, \cdots, l \leq q. \tag{10.4}$$

Suppose that we are required to minimize some function

$$J(\bar{y}) = \int_0^T F(x_1, x_2, \cdots, x_p, y_1, y_2, \cdots, y_q, t) \, dt \tag{10.5}$$

We then have a rather general formulation of a multidimensional, non-linear, boundary-valued variational problem.

10.3 Elimination of Boundary Valuedness

Since the process as described in Eq. (10.1) is nonlinear, the relationship between the initial values, $\bar{x}(0)$, and the final values, $\bar{x}(T)$ is difficult to derive. The q-dimensional choice vector, $\bar{y}(t)$, must be chosen in such a way that the minimization in Eq. (10.5) is carried out subject to the final conditions (10.3).

One method of attacking these difficulties is to imbed the original problem within a more general class of problems for which the constraints (10.2) and (10.4) apply but the function to be minimized is taken to be

$$J_1(\bar{y}) = \int_0^T F(x_1, x_2, \cdots, x_p, y_1, y_2, \cdots, y_q, t) \, dt$$

$$+ \lambda(r) \left\{ \sum_{i=1}^k [x_i(T) - b_i(T)]^2 \right\} \qquad (10.6)$$

where the final value constraints (10.3) have been removed by incorporating them in the function to be minimized, Eq. (10.6). This is accomplished through the introduction of the multiplier, $\lambda(r)$.

It is clear that Eq. (10.6) can be expressed as

$$J_1(\bar{y}) = J(\bar{y}) + \lambda(r) \left\{ \sum_{i=1}^k [x_i(T) - b_i(T')]^2 \right\} \qquad (10.7)$$

If $\lambda(r)$ is chosen so as to increase without bound as r vanishes, and if $J_1(\bar{y})$ is bounded, the limiting form of Eq. (10.7) produces the conclusions that

$$\lim_{r \to 0} \lambda(r) \sum_{i=1}^k [x_i(T) - b_i(T)]^2 = 0 \qquad (10.8)$$

and

$$\lim_{r \to 0} J_1(\bar{y}) = J(\bar{y}) \qquad (10.9)$$

Obviously Eq. (10.8) can be satisfied for functions $\lambda(r)$, unbounded for vanishing values of r, only in the event that

$$\sum_{i=1}^k [x_i(T) - b_i(T)]^2 = 0 \qquad (10.10)$$

The sum of the squares in Eq. (10.10) vanishes if and only if

$$x_i(T) = b_i(T) \text{ for every } i = 1, 2, \cdots, k \qquad (10.11)$$

which are precisely the boundary conditions (10.3) of the original problem. Notice that Eq. (10.9) also implies that the solution of the transformed problem for vanishing values of r, renders the minimization of $J_1(\bar{y})$ exactly the same as the original problem of minimizing $J(\bar{y})$.

In effect, the original boundary problem has been imbedded within the framework of a more general class of problems by increasing dimensionality (the new variable r has been added) in such a way that the special case, $r = 0$, corresponds to the original problem.

Notice from Eq. (10.7), that when one minimizes $J_1(\bar{y})$ for various values of r, the quantity being minimized is actually a combination of the desired quantity and the terminal errors. By performing the minimization over a range of values of $\lambda(r)$, one obtains a trade-off between the quantity of interest and the terminal error. Using sufficiently large value of λ causes the terminal errors to become arbitrarily small, vanishing in the limit as λ increases without bounds.

Besides eliminating the two-point boundary aspects of the problem, this imbedding procedure opens up additional applications. Consider, for example, a problem which is simply boundary valued. Such a problem is one for which constraints such as (10.1)–(10.4) apply, but we have no variational minimization constraint such as (10.5). Under the imbedding procedure, the problem is viewed as a variational minimization problem in terms of Eq. (10.6) where F is taken to be identically equal to zero.

10.4 Reduction to Final Value Problem

The requirement of minimizing the function in Eq. (10.6) can be translated into a requirement for minimizing the final value of a single state variable. For example, suppose that the dimensionality of the vector $\bar{x}$ is increased by adding additional state variables (an embodiment of invariant imbedding). Let

$$\frac{dx_{p+1}(t)}{dt} = F(\bar{x}, \bar{y}, t), \; x_{p+1}(0) = a_{p+1} = 0 \qquad (10.12)$$

We can also take

$$x_{p+2}(t) = \lambda(r) \sum_{i=1}^{k} [x_i(t) - b_i(t)]^2 \qquad (10.13)$$

or, equivalently,

$$\frac{dx_{p+2}(t)}{dt} = 2\lambda(r) \sum_{i=1}^{k} [x_i(t) - b_i(t)][G_i(\bar{x}, \bar{y}, t) - \dot{b}_i(t)]$$

(10.14)

$$x_{p+2}(0) = \lambda(r) \sum_{i=1}^{k} [a_i - b_i(0)]^2 = a_{p+2}$$

With

$$x_{p+3}(t) = x_{p+1}(t) + x_{p+2}(t)$$

(10.15)

so that, equivalently,

$$\frac{dx_{p+3}(t)}{dt} = G_{p+1}(\bar{x}, \bar{y}, t) + G_{p+2}(\bar{x}, \bar{y}, t), \ x_{p+3}(0) = a_{p+3} = a_{p+2}$$

(10.16)

The constraints added to the original problem are

$$\frac{dx_{p+1}(t)}{dt} = G_{p+1}(\bar{x}, \bar{y}, t) \qquad x_{p+1}(0) = 0$$

$$\frac{dx_{p+2}(t)}{dt} = G_{p+2}(\bar{x}, \bar{y}, t) \qquad x_{p+2}(0) = a_{p+2}$$

(10.17)

$$\frac{dx_{p+3}(t)}{dt} = G_{p+3}(\bar{x}, \bar{y}, t) \qquad x_{p+3}(0) = a_{p+3}$$

and the function to be minimized is

$$J_1(\bar{y}) = x_{p+3}(T)$$

(10.18)

the final value of the p + 3rd state variable.

It seems clear that almost any function to be minimized or maximized can be reduced to the problem of seeking the extreme final value of a single state variable. The problem of minimum time for example can be replaced by the problem of minimizing $x_{p+1}(T)$ when the additional constraint

$$\frac{dx_{p+1}(t)}{dt} = 1, \qquad x_{p+1}(0) = 0$$

(10.19)

is added to the original problem constraints. Similarly, the problem of minimizing the final value of some arbitrary function of the state variables can be replaced by the problem of minimizing

$$x_{p+1}(T) = \varphi[x_1(T), x_2(T), \cdots, x_p(T)]$$

(10.20)

with the added constraint

$$\frac{dx_{p+1}(t)}{dt} = \sum_{i=1}^{p} \frac{\partial \varphi[\bar{x}(t)]}{\partial x_i} G_i(\bar{x}, \bar{y}, t), \; x_{p+1}(0) = \varphi[\bar{x}(0)] \quad (10.21)$$

Thus, almost any optimization problem can be reduced to the form

$$\frac{d\bar{x}}{dt} = \bar{G}(\bar{x}, \bar{y}, t), \qquad \bar{x}(0) = \bar{a} \qquad (10.22)$$

with the requirement to either minimize or maximize

$$J(\bar{y}) = x_n(T) \qquad (10.23)$$

the final value of the nth element of the state vector $\bar{x}$.

We have observed how a wide variety of optimization problems can be reduced effectively to final value minimizations or maximizations; in fact, the maximization or minimization of the final value of only a single state variable. Through the concept of invariant imbedding, a problem which is originally boundary valued in nature is viewed as imbedded in a class of more general problems of which the boundary problem is simply a special limiting case.

The reason for elimination of boundary-valuedness, of course, is an attempt to achieve a reduction in complexity associated with the numerical solution of two-point boundary problems. However, the transformation of a boundary problem into an initial-valued minimization or maximization of a final element of state is retained, from a computational point of view, only when the numerical solution is undertaken by means of dynamic programming. Whether or not the original problem is boundary-valued, the computational solution by classical procedures is always boundary valued.

10.5 The Classical Solution

For example, suppose that the problem whose numerical solution is being sought takes the general form given by Eqs. (10.22) and (10.23), where it is required that the selection of the elements $y_i(t)$ of the vector-valued point function $\bar{y}(t)$ in the time interval $0 \leq t \leq T$ be made in such a way that the final value of the nth element of the state vector $\bar{x}(t)$, denoted by $x_n(T)$, assumes its minimum value. If the elements $y_i(t)$ are unrestricted [that is, $-\infty \leq y_i(t) \leq \infty$], then the classical method of solution follows the well-known problem of Mayer[1] in variational calculus. A more general approach using classical methods, which permits arbitrary restrictions on the choice vector $\bar{y}(t)$ [that is, $c_i \leq y_i(t) \leq d_i$] is provided by the so-called "maximum principle" of the Soviet mathematician Pontryagin.[2] A special case of the maximum principle, as described by Rozonoer,[3] applies to the problem of final value minimizations.

In terms of Rozoneor's formulation for the minimization of $x_n(T)$, the function

$$H(\bar{x}, \bar{p}, \bar{y}, t) = \sum_{j=1}^{n} p_j G_j \qquad (10.24)$$

must be maximized in $\bar{y}$ for any vector functions $\bar{x}$ and $\bar{p}$ satisfying the Hamilton system of equations

$$\frac{dx_i}{dt} = \frac{\partial H}{\partial p_i} = G_i(\bar{x}, \bar{y}, t); x_i(0) = a_i, \qquad i = 1, 2, \cdots, n \quad (10.25)$$

and

$$\frac{dp_i}{dt} = -\frac{\partial H}{\partial x_i} = -\sum_{j=1}^{n} p_j \frac{\partial G_j(\bar{x}, \bar{y}, t)}{\partial x_i}; \qquad p_i(T) = 0; i = 1, 2, \cdots, n - 1$$

$$p_n(T) = -1 \qquad (10.26)$$

Equations (10.25) and (10.26) represent a $2n$-dimensional two-point boundary-valued problem with the elements of $\bar{x}$ known at $t = 0$ and the elements of $\bar{p}$ known at $t = T$. The elements $\bar{y}$ must satisfy the maximization of Eq. (10.24), or when they are not on the boundary

$$\frac{\partial H}{\partial y_i} = \sum_{j=1}^{n} p_j \frac{\partial G_j(\bar{x}, \bar{y}, t)}{\partial y_i} = 0, \qquad i = 1, 2, \cdots, m \quad (10.27)$$

which implies that the m elements of $\bar{y}$ satisfy a functional relation

$$y_i = \psi_i(\bar{x}, \bar{p}, t) \qquad (10.28)$$

If the m equations of (10.27) could be solved explicitly for the m quantities y_i, functions of the form given by Eq. (10.28) would be obtained. Equations (10.28), when substituted into (10.25) and (10.26), give a $2n$-dimensional boundary-valued problem in the pair of n-dimensional vectors $\bar{x}$ and $\bar{p}$.

There are difficulties in separating the elements y_i satisfying Eq. (10.27) into the explicit functional form of Eq. (10.28) except in the simplest cases, but even when it is possible to do so there remains the problem of integrating the coupled pair of equations (10.25) and (10.26). Rarely is it possible to integrate these latter two equations in closed form and even with machine integration there remains the fact that $\bar{x}(t)$ and $\bar{p}(t)$ are specified at opposite ends of the time interval $0 \leq t \leq T$.

The difficulty with all classical approaches to the solution of the problem results from the necessity of formulating an auxiliary set of equations, whether it be the Euler-Lagrange equations in the problem of Mayer with unrestricted variations or the Hamilton system of equations in the maximum principle which includes restricted variations. These auxiliary equations together with the original constraint equations always lead to the computational requirement of solving a two-point boundary problem. One method of getting around the boundary valuedness has been suggested by Kelley[4] who takes a solution which satisfies the boundary conditions and iterates that solution to force satisfaction of the equations between the boundaries.

10.6 The Dynamic Programming Solution

The dynamic programming approach, while presenting certain computational peculiarities of its own is not, however, plagued by the two-point boundary problem. If the final problem formulation is not boundary valued, then no boundary valuedness is encountered in the computational solution by the method of dynamic programming.

In the dynamic programming solution of the problem with constraints

$$\frac{d\bar{x}}{dt} = \bar{G}(\bar{x}, \bar{y}, t) ; \bar{x}(0) = \bar{a}$$

$$\min_{\bar{y}} [x_n(T)] \quad \text{with} \quad \bar{c} \leq \bar{y}(t) \leq \bar{d} \tag{10.29}$$

one can regard the end time $t = T$ as being variable and consider a range of starting times $t = \rho$, where $0 \leq \rho \leq T$. The problem in Eq. (10.29) then becomes imbedded in the general problem

$$\frac{d\bar{x}}{dt} = \bar{G}(\bar{x}, \bar{y}, t) ; \bar{x}(\rho) = \bar{a}; 0 \leq \rho \leq T$$

$$\min_{\bar{y}} [x_n(T)] \quad \text{with} \quad \bar{c} \leq \bar{y}(t) \leq \bar{d} \tag{10.30}$$

the functional equation is defined by the return function

$$f(\bar{a}, \rho, T) = \min_{\bar{y}} [x_n(T)] \tag{10.31}$$

In terms of first-order difference equations

$$\bar{x}^{k+1} = \bar{x}^k + \bar{G}(\bar{x}^k, \bar{y}^k, \rho + k\Delta) \Delta, \rho + k \Delta \leq T \tag{10.32}$$

The functional recurrence equations of dynamic programming become

$$f(\bar{a}, \rho, \rho + \Delta) = f_1(\bar{a}; \rho) = \min_{\bar{y}} \left[a_n + G_n(\bar{a}, \bar{y}, \rho) \Delta \right] \quad (10.33)$$

whose solution is $\bar{y}^{01}(\bar{a}; \rho)$ and

$$f(\bar{a}, \rho, \rho + N \Delta)$$
$$= f_N(\bar{a}; \rho) = \min_{\bar{y}} \left[f_{N-1}(\bar{a} + \bar{G}(\bar{a}, \bar{y}, \rho) \Delta; \rho + (N - 1) \Delta) \right] \quad (10.34)$$

whose solution is $\bar{y}^{0N}(\bar{a}; \rho)$.

The complete solution for a problem in which $\rho = 0$, $\bar{x}(0) = \bar{a}$, and $T = N \Delta$ can then be determined by a sequence of operations with the functions $\bar{y}^{0i}(\bar{a}; \rho)$. For example,

$$f(\bar{a}, 0, N \Delta) = f_N(\bar{a}; 0) = \min_{\bar{y}} \left[x_n(T) \right] \quad (10.35)$$

and if $\bar{x}^*(t)$ and $\bar{y}^*(t)$ denote the optimal state and choice, respectively, then

$$\bar{x}^*(0) = \bar{a}$$
$$\bar{y}^*(0) = \bar{y}^{0N}(\bar{a}; 0) \quad (10.36)$$

Using the values of Eq. (10.36) one then obtains

$$\bar{x}^*(\Delta) = \bar{a} + \bar{G}(\bar{a}, \bar{y}^*(0), \Delta) \Delta$$
$$\bar{y}^*(\Delta) = \bar{y}^{0(N-1)}(\bar{x}^*(\Delta); \Delta) \quad (10.37)$$

Similarly, one finds

$$\bar{x}^*(2\Delta) = \bar{x}^*(\Delta) + \bar{G}(\bar{x}^*(\Delta), \bar{y}^*(\Delta), \Delta) \Delta$$
$$\bar{y}^*(2\Delta) = y^{0(N-2)}(\bar{x}^*(2\Delta); 2\Delta) \quad (10.38)$$

One continues in a similar fashion, finding values of $\bar{x}^*(t)$ and $\bar{y}^*(t)$ at intervals of Δ in the interval $0 \leq t \leq T$.

The preceding discussion has been carried out in terms of first-order difference equations. There can arise questions with regard to the increment size Δ for satisfactory convergence. However, second, third, or higher ordered difference equations could also be employed if needed. On the other hand, it is not necessary to use difference equations at all. While it is always necessary to place the problem in discrete form for digital computation, difference equations represent only one such form. Several methods of rendering problems discrete are discussed by Greenstadt[5] including difference equations, the Fourier method, and the method of cells.

The most difficult problem in the computational solution by dynamic programming stems from the multidimensionality of the functional recurrence formulas (10.33) and (10.34). It is not practical to store functions of more than two-dimensions because of limited memory capacity even with currently available large scale digital computers. Consequently, any approach to a workable computational solution must embody reduction in dimensionality.

There are at least three known methods of reducing dimensionality. These include coarsening the grid, polynomial approximation, and linearization, and successive approximation. Each of the methods reduces dimensionality by exchanging computation for memory.

Coarsening of the grid can be described in the following way. Suppose, for example, we are concerned with a three-dimensional function and that we are interested in 100 values for each of its three dimensions. The storage requirements for such a case require a 10^6-element memory capacity. If instead, we at first satisfy ourselves with only 10 values for each dimension of the function, the storage requirements reduce to only 10^3 elements. One first finds a "coarse" solution and then seeks successive refinements of the "coarse" solution.

Polynomial approximation can be described the following way. Suppose that even a one-dimensional function is approximated by an nth degree polynomial. It seems likely that functions for most physical problems could be reasonably approximated by a 10th degree polynomial. The problem of storing the function for 100 values of its argument is replaced by storing 10 coefficients of the polynomial and computing the value of the function for any given value of its argument. Similarly, if a multi-dimensional function were approximated by a polynomial of finite degree in the variables upon which it is dependent, vast reductions in memory capacity are realized. As a matter of fact, special cases are known to exist for which the minimum or maximum return function is specified exactly by a polynomial of the second degree. Merriam[6] shows that if the function whose extreme is sought has a quadratic form, then the extreme of the function also exists in quadratic form.

Bellman[7] provides a detailed discussion of the method of linearization and successive approximation. Briefly, an arbitrary zero-order solution $[\bar{x}^0(t), \bar{y}^0(t)]$ is assumed. The constraint equations are then linearized about this zero-order solution. The final value $x_n(T)$ can now be computed for the perturbed set of linearized equations. Even more important, the contribution to $x_n(T)$ from the initial conditions and the restricted choice vector can be completely separated using the vector-matrix solution for a set of simultaneous linear time-varying differential equations. Furthermore, $\bar{x}(0) = \bar{a}$ enters the determination of $x_n(T)$ as a function of u where u is an explicitly determinable function of $\bar{a}$. The value of $\bar{y}(t)$ which gives the extreme value of the first perturbed value of $x_n(T)$ is $\bar{y}^1(t)$ the best first-order choice. If $\bar{y}^1(t)$ is substituted into the original constraint equations, they can be integrated to give $\bar{x}^1(t)$. The constraint equations are then linearized about the first-order solution $[\bar{x}^1(t), \bar{y}^1(t)]$. The procedure continues as before, determining $[\bar{x}^k(t), \bar{y}^k(t)]$ until there is negligible difference between the kth return and the $(k-1)$st return. The extreme return function now depends upon u, which in turn is an explicitly determinable function of a. There are also, of course, questions of convergence with the successive approximations.

10.7 Summary

In any event, we can conclude with the following remarks. Almost any optimization problem can be viewed as a search for the extreme final value of a single state variable. The numerical solution of such problems can be undertaken by two different methods, each of which possesses difficulties that are by no means trivial. In the classical solution, using variational principles, the primary difficulty is the two-point boundary problem. In the dynamic programming solution, the primary difficulty is the multidimensionality of the return function. The method used for any particular problem will no doubt depend upon the particular problem, the ingenuity of the analyst and his familiarity with either method.

REFERENCES

1. G. A. Bliss, "Lectures on the Calculus of Variations." Univ. Chicago Press, Chicago, Illinois, 1946.
2. L. S. Pontryagin, Optimal Control Processes, *Automation Express* **1**, 15 (1959).
3. L. I. Rozonoer, L. S. Pontryagin maximum principle in the theory of optimum systems. I. *Automation Remote Control U.S.S.R.* **20**, 10 (1959).
4. H. J. Kelley, Gradient theory of optimal flight paths, *ARS Journal* **30**, 947 (1960).
5. J. Greenstadt, On the reduction of continuous problems to discrete form, *IBM J. Research and Develop.* **3**, 355 (1959).
6. C. W. Merriam, III, A class of optimum control systems, *J. Franklin Inst.* **267**, 267 (1959).
7. R. Bellman, Some new techniques in the dynamic programming solution of variational problems, *Quart. Appl. Math.* **16**, 295 (1958).

—11—

Impulsive Transfer between Elliptical Orbits

DEREK F. LAWDEN

University of Canterbury, Christchurch, New Zealand

11.1 Introduction

The solution to the general problem of programming the propellant expenditure and thrust direction for a rocket vehicle so that transfer between two specified points in a given gravitational field is effected most economically is given elsewhere.[1] In the same article, the results of the general theory were applied in the particular case of a simple inverse square law field to obtain conditions governing the optimal mode of transfer between two coplanar elliptical orbits. It was shown that, provided the magnitude of the motor thrust could be regarded as unlimited, optimal conditions were attained by the application of impulsive thrusts at certain *junction points*, the vehicle coasting freely between these points under the action of gravity alone. In this chapter it will be demonstrated that, provided the assumption is made that the motor thrusts are invariably impulsive, the conditions determining the positions of the junction points for optimal transfer between coplanar elliptical orbits can be obtained by employing an elementary method and without reference to the general theory.

323

The problem of optimal transfer between orbits in an inverse square law field was first studied by Hohmann[2] in the particular case when the orbits are coplanar and circular. Transfer between elliptical orbits has been investigated by Lawden,[1,3-7] Long,[8] Smith,[9] and Plimmer.[10] Vargo,[11] Munick *et al.*,[12] and Horner[13] have considered the related problem of optimal transfer between two *terminals* in an inverse square law field, a terminal being completely specified by its distance from the center of attraction and a velocity vector, i.e., the angle subtended at the center of attraction by two terminal points is assumed to be open to choice. The question of the number of impulsive thrusts which is optimal for a maneuver of this type has been taken up by Edelbaum,[14] Hoelker and Silber,[15] and Rider,[16] and it has been demonstrated that, in certain circumstances, as many as four impulses are necessary to achieve absolute minimal expenditure of fuel. This important question will not be pursued further in this chapter; for it will always be assumed that the number of impulses (usually two) has been decided prior to our calculations and that the problem is to discover the junction points at which these are to be applied and their magnitudes and directions at these points.

11.2 Impulsive Change in Orbital Elements

Let O be a center of inverse square law attraction, γ/r^2 being the attraction per unit mass at a distance r from the center. Let (r, θ) be polar coordinates with respect to O as pole in a given plane through this point. Then the polar equation for the orbit of a body which moves in this plane under the action of the attraction alone can be written

$$\frac{l}{r} = 1 + e \cos (\theta - \tilde{\omega}) \tag{11.1}$$

where l is the semilatus rectum, e is the eccentricity, and $\tilde{\omega}$ is the longitude of perihelion. It will be convenient to put

$$\frac{1}{r} = s, \quad \frac{1}{l} = p, \quad \frac{e}{l} = q \tag{11.2}$$

so that Eq. (11.1) becomes

$$q \cos (\theta - \tilde{\omega}) = s - p \tag{11.3}$$

The parameters $(p, q, \tilde{\omega})$ completely determine the orbit in the given plane.

If P is the position of the body at any instant and $(1/s, \theta)$ are its polar coordinates, let (v_r, v_θ) be the components of the body's velocity along and perpendicular (in the sense of the motion) to OP, respectively. Then it is a well-known consequence of the theory of orbits that

$$v_r = q \sqrt{\frac{\gamma}{p}} \sin (\theta - \tilde{\omega}) \tag{11.4}$$

$$v_\theta = \sqrt{\frac{\gamma}{p}} \{p + q \cos (\theta - \tilde{\omega})\} = s \sqrt{\frac{\gamma}{p}} \tag{11.5}$$

Let V be the component of the body's velocity at P in a direction making

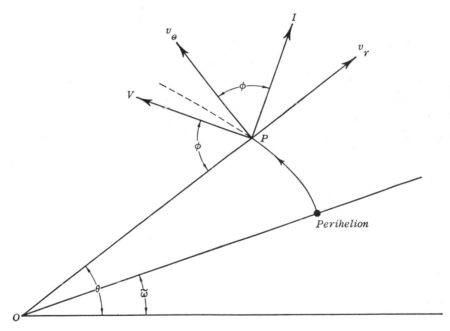

FIG. 1. Junction point.

an angle ϕ with PO (see Fig. 1). Then it follows from Eqs. (11.4) and (11.5) that

$$V = v_\theta \sin \phi - v_r \cos \phi$$

$$= s \sqrt{\frac{\gamma}{p}} \sin \phi - q \sqrt{\frac{\gamma}{p}} \sin (\theta - \tilde{\omega}) \cos \phi \tag{11.6}$$

By rearrangement, Eq. (11.6) can be expressed in the form

$$q \sin (\theta - \tilde{\omega}) = (s - Zp^{1/2}) \tan \phi \qquad (11.7)$$

where

$$Z = V/\gamma^{1/2} \sin \phi \qquad (11.8)$$

Suppose, now, that an impulse I is applied to the orbiting body when it is at the point P and in a direction making an angle ϕ with the transverse velocity component v_θ. The component V of the body's velocity perpendicular to I will be unaffected by the impulse. It follows that Z, as given by Eq. (11.8), will be unaltered. Further, (s, θ) will undergo no appreciable change during the short period of thrust. Hence the values of the orbital parameters $(p, q, \tilde{\omega})$ relating to the new orbit into which the body has been transferred by the impulse will still satisfy Eq. (11.7). By a similar argument it follows that these parameters will also satisfy Eq. (11.3).

To sum up, therefore, the parameters $(p, q, \tilde{\omega})$ of any orbit into which the body may be transferred by application of an impulse at a point P $(1/s, \theta)$ in the direction making an angle ϕ with v_θ satisfy the equations

$$q \cos (\theta - \tilde{\omega}) = s - p \qquad (11.9)$$

$$q \sin (\theta - \tilde{\omega}) = (s - Zp^{1/2}) \tan \phi \qquad (11.10)$$

where Z is related to the body's velocity component V in the direction perpendicular to the impulse by Eq. (11.8). The requirement that the three parameters $(p, q, \tilde{\omega})$ should satisfy Eqs. (11.9) and (11.10) leaves these quantities one degree of freedom. The parameters will be specified completely when the *magnitude* of the impulse is given.

A convenient graphical means of determining all those orbits $(p, q, \tilde{\omega})$ into which an orbiting body may be transferred by application of a single impulse in a given direction at a given point is as follows: Construct the graph of the functional relationship $y = x^2$ (see Fig. 2). Fix the point A on the x-axis at a distance from the origin O given by the equation

$$OA = \frac{s}{Z^2 \tan \phi} \qquad (11.11)$$

and erect the perpendicular AB to OA such that

$$AB = \frac{s}{Z^2 \tan^2 \phi} \qquad (11.12)$$

Let P be a point (x, y) on the curve $y = x^2$ and let PN be the perpendicular

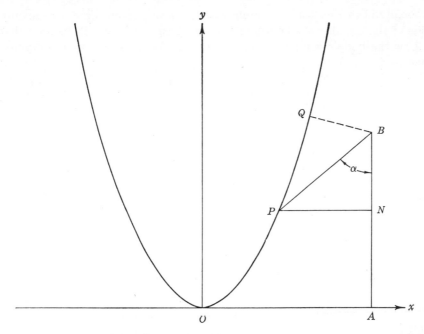

FIG. 2. Nomogram for orbital elements.

from P on to AB. Denoting $\angle PBA$ by α, we have by simple geometry

$$PB \cos \alpha = AB - y \tag{11.13}$$

$$PB \sin \alpha = OA - x = OA - y^{1/2} \tag{11.14}$$

If, therefore, we interpret PB, α, and y thus,

$$PB = \frac{q}{Z^2 \tan^2 \phi}, \quad \alpha = \theta - \bar{\omega}, \quad y = \frac{p}{Z^2 \tan^2 \phi} \tag{11.15}$$

Eqs. (11.13) and (11.14) are seen to be identical with Eqs. (11.9) and (11.10), respectively. It now follows that, as P describes the curve $y = x^2$, possible sets of values of the parameters $(p, q, \bar{\omega})$ are given for any position of P by AN, PB, and α in accordance with Eqs. (11.15). When an impulse of given magnitude is applied, the effect in the diagram will be to move P from one point to another along the curve. The possible ranges of values of $(p, q, \bar{\omega})$ for impulses applied at a given point on a body's orbit and in a given direction are now immediately obvious from inspection of the diagram. For example, the minimum value of q which can be attained corresponds to BQ.

Finally in this section, a formula will be obtained from which the magnitude of the impulse can be found. Referring to Fig. 1, it will be seen that if U is the body's component of velocity in the direction of the impulse, then

$$v_\theta = U \cos \phi + V \sin \phi \qquad (11.16)$$

Employing Eq. (11.5), this implies that

$$U = s \sqrt{\frac{\gamma}{p}} \sec \phi - V \tan \phi \qquad (11.17)$$

At the termination of the impulse, suppose (p, U) have new values (p', U'). (s, V) will be unaltered in value and the equation corresponding to (11.17), but applying to conditions immediately after the impulse, will be

$$U' = s \sqrt{\frac{\gamma}{p'}} \sec \phi - V \tan \phi \qquad (11.18)$$

Subtracting Eq. (11.17) from (11.18) we now find that

$$\Delta U = U' - U = \gamma^{1/2} s (p'^{-1/2} - p^{-1/2}) \sec \phi \qquad (11.19)$$

This last equation fixes the velocity increment caused by the impulse and hence its magnitude.

11.3 Dependence of Impulse on Orbital Elements

Suppose that a body moving in an orbit $(p, q, \tilde{\omega})$ is transferred by a single impulse into a coplanar orbit $(p', q', \tilde{\omega}')$. This impulse must be applied at a point of intersection (assumed real) of the two orbits. Let $(1/s, \theta)$ be the polar coordinates of this point and let ϕ be the angle made by the direction of the impulse with the perpendicular to the radius vector from the center of attraction. Equations (11.9) and (11.10) must be satisfied by the parameters of both orbits, thus yielding the equations

$$q \cos (\theta - \tilde{\omega}) = s - p \qquad (11.20)$$

$$q \sin (\theta - \tilde{\omega}) = (s - Z p^{1/2}) \tan \phi \qquad (11.21)$$

$$q' \cos (\theta - \tilde{\omega}') = s - p' \qquad (11.22)$$

$$q' \sin (\theta - \tilde{\omega}') = (s - Z p'^{1/2}) \tan \phi \qquad (11.23)$$

where Z is the quantity defined by Eq. (11.8) for this maneuver. Regarding the parameters determining the two orbits as given quantities, the four equations (11.20)–(11.23) can be solved for the four unknowns (s, θ, Z, ϕ), thus expressing these quantities as functions of $p, q, \tilde{\omega}, p', q', \tilde{\omega}'$. The velocity increment $\Delta \bar{U} = \gamma^{1/2} X$ resulting from the impulse then follows from Eq. (11.19), viz.

$$\Delta \bar{U} = \gamma^{1/2} X = \gamma^{1/2} s (p'^{-1/2} - p^{-1/2}) \sec \phi \qquad (11.24)$$

and X can also be expressed as a function of the six orbital parameters. Thus

$$X = X(p, q, \tilde{\omega}, p', q', \tilde{\omega}'). \qquad (11.25)$$

It is our purpose in this section to investigate this functional dependence of X upon the parameters by calculating expressions for the partial derivatives of X with respect to its six arguments.

Differentiating Eqs. (11.20)–(11.23) partially with respect to p, it will be seen that

$$-q \sin (\theta - \tilde{\omega}) \frac{\partial \theta}{\partial p} = \frac{\partial s}{\partial p} - 1 \qquad (11.26)$$

$$q \cos (\theta - \tilde{\omega}) \frac{\partial \theta}{\partial p} = \left(\frac{\partial s}{\partial p} - \frac{\partial Z}{\partial p} p^{1/2} - \tfrac{1}{2} Z p^{-1/2} \right) \tan \phi$$

$$+ (s - Z p^{1/2}) \sec^2 \phi \frac{\partial \phi}{\partial p} \qquad (11.27)$$

$$-q' \sin (\theta - \tilde{\omega}') \frac{\partial \theta}{\partial p} = \frac{\partial s}{\partial p} \qquad (11.28)$$

$$q' \cos (\theta - \tilde{\omega}') \frac{\partial \theta}{\partial p} = \left(\frac{\partial s}{\partial p} - \frac{\partial Z}{\partial p} p'^{1/2} \right) \tan \phi + (s - Z p'^{1/2}) \sec^2 \phi \frac{\partial \phi}{\partial p}$$

$$(11.29)$$

By solving Eqs. (11.26) and (11.28) for $\partial s/\partial p$ and $\partial \theta/\partial p$ and employing Eqs. (11.21) and (11.23), it is easy to show that

$$\frac{\partial s}{\partial p} = \frac{s - Z p'^{1/2}}{Z(p^{1/2} - p'^{1/2})} \qquad (11.30)$$

$$\frac{\partial \theta}{\partial p} = \frac{\cot \phi}{Z(p'^{1/2} - p^{1/2})} \qquad (11.31)$$

By substituting for $\partial s/\partial p$ and $\partial \theta/\partial p$ in Eqs. (11.27) and (11.29), making use of Eqs. (11.20) and (11.22), and then eliminating $\partial Z/\partial p$ between these equations, it will be found that

$$sZ(p'^{1/2} - p^{1/2}) \tan \phi \sec^2 \phi \, \frac{\partial \phi}{\partial p}$$

$$= \left(s - Zp'^{1/2} + \frac{Z^2 \dot{p}'^{1/2}}{2p^{1/2}}\right) \tan^2 \phi + s + (pp')^{1/2} \qquad (11.32)$$

thus determining $\partial \phi/\partial p$.

Differentiating Eq. (11.24) with respect to p, we obtain

$$\frac{\partial X}{\partial p} = \frac{\partial s}{\partial p}(p'^{-1/2} - p^{-1/2}) \sec \phi + \tfrac{1}{2}sp^{-3/2} \sec \phi$$

$$+ s(p'^{-1/2} - p^{-1/2}) \sec \phi \tan \phi \, \frac{\partial \phi}{\partial p} \qquad (11.33)$$

Upon substitution for $\partial s/\partial p$ and $\partial \phi/\partial p$ from Eqs. (11.30) and (11.32), respectively, this last result reduces to

$$\frac{\partial X}{\partial p} = \left\{\frac{s}{2p^{3/2}} \sec^2 \phi - \frac{Z}{2p} \tan^2 \phi - \frac{1}{p^{1/2}} - \frac{1}{Z}\right\} \cos \phi \qquad (11.34)$$

By a very similar procedure, expressions for the partial derivatives of X with respect to q and $\tilde{\omega}$ may be found in the form

$$\frac{\partial X}{\partial q} = -\frac{1}{p^{1/2}q} \left\{(s - p)\left(1 + \frac{p^{1/2}}{Z}\right) \cos \phi + (s - p^{1/2}Z) \tan \phi \sin \phi\right\}$$

$$\hspace{10cm} (11.35)$$

$$\frac{\partial X}{\partial \tilde{\omega}} = \left(Z - \frac{s}{Z}\right) \sin \phi \qquad (11.36)$$

If, now, the two sets of variables $(p, q, \tilde{\omega})$ and $(p', q', \tilde{\omega}')$ are interchanged in Eqs. (11.20)–(11.23), s, θ, Z, ϕ being unaltered, the same set of equations results. However, the sign of X as given by Eq. (11.24) is reversed. It follows that a repetition of the above argument will yield expressions for $\partial X/\partial p'$, $\partial X/\partial q'$, and $\partial X/\partial \tilde{\omega}'$ which are identical with those for $\partial X/\partial p$, $\partial X/\partial q$, and $\partial X/\partial \tilde{\omega}$, respectively, as given by Eqs. (11.34)–(11.36), with the exceptions that the quantities $(p, q, \tilde{\omega})$ will be replaced by the corresponding quantities $(p', q', \tilde{\omega}')$ and the signs of the right-hand members will be reversed.

11.4 Optimal n-Impulse Transfer between Two Terminal Orbits

Suppose that a rocket is to be transferred between the coplanar orbits $(p_0, q_0, \bar{\omega}_0)$ and $(p_n, q_n, \bar{\omega}_n)$ by the application of a series of n impulsive thrusts. Let the first thrust effect transfer from the orbit $(p_0, q_0, \bar{\omega}_0)$ to the orbit $(p_1, q_1, \bar{\omega}_1)$ and be applied at the point having polar coordinates $(1/s_1, \theta_1)$, the second effect transfer from the orbit $(p_1, q_1, \bar{\omega}_1)$ to the orbit $(p_2, q_2, \bar{\omega}_2)$ and be applied at the point $(1/s_2, \theta_2)$, and so on, the nth impulse being applied at the point $(1/s_n, \theta_n)$ and finally transferring the rocket into the orbit $(p_n, q_n, \bar{\omega}_n)$. Let $\gamma^{1/2}X_i$ be the velocity increment due to the ith impulse so that, by Eq. (11.19),

$$X_i = s_i(p_i^{-1/2} - p_{i-1}^{-1/2}) \sec \phi_i \qquad (11.37)$$

where ϕ_i is the angle determining the direction of the thrust. The characteristic velocity for the over-all maneuver is then given by the equation

$$W = \gamma^{1/2} \sum_{i=1}^{n} X_i \qquad (11.38)$$

As explained in the last section, X_i is a function of the six orbital parameters $(p_{i-1}, q_{i-1}, \bar{\omega}_{i-1}, p_i, q_i, \bar{\omega}_i)$ and hence W is a function of the $3n - 3$ variables $(p_1, q_1, \bar{\omega}_1, \cdots, p_{n-1}, q_{n-1}, \bar{\omega}_{n-1})$, the quantities $(p_0, q_0, \bar{\omega}_0, p_n, q_n, \bar{\omega}_n)$ being given constants. W is stationary with respect to its variable arguments provided

$$\frac{\partial W}{\partial p_i} = \frac{\partial W}{\partial q_i} = \frac{\partial W}{\partial \bar{\omega}_i} = 0 \qquad (11.39)$$

for $i = 1, 2, \cdots, (n - 1)$. The values of the parameters $(p_i, q_i, \bar{\omega}_i)$ $(i = 1, 2, \cdots, (n - 1))$ determining the optimal n-impulse mode of transfer must necessarily satisfy the Eqs. (11.39). Hence, by solving these equations and computing the value of W to which each solution leads, this optimal mode can, in principle, be determined.

Now

$$\frac{\partial W}{\partial p_i} = \gamma^{1/2} \left(\frac{\partial X_i}{\partial p_i} + \frac{\partial X_{i+1}}{\partial p_i} \right) \qquad (11.40)$$

with similar expressions for $\partial W/\partial q_i$ and $\partial W/\partial \bar{\omega}_i$. It follows from the results obtained in the last section that

$$\frac{\partial X_i}{\partial p_i} = -\left\{ \frac{s_i}{2p_i^{3/2}} \sec^2 \phi_i - \frac{Z_i}{2p_i} \tan^2 \phi_i - \frac{1}{p_i^{1/2}} - \frac{1}{Z_i} \right\} \cos \phi_i \qquad (11.41)$$

$$\frac{\partial X_{i+1}}{\partial p_i} = \left\{ \frac{s_{i+1}}{2p_i^{3/2}} \sec^2 \phi_{i+1} - \frac{Z_{i+1}}{2p_i} \tan^2 \phi_{i+1} - \frac{1}{p_i^{1/2}} - \frac{1}{Z_{i+1}} \right\} \cos \phi_{i+1}$$

Z_i and Z_{i+1} being the Z-values appropriate to the ith and $(i + 1)$th impulses, respectively. It follows that $\partial W/\partial p_i$ vanishes if

$$\left\{\frac{s_i}{2p_i^{3/2}} \sec^2 \phi_i - \frac{Z_i}{2p_i} \tan^2 \phi_i - \frac{1}{p_i^{1/2}} - \frac{1}{Z_i}\right\} \cos \phi_i$$

$$= \left\{\frac{s_{i+1}}{2p_i^{3/2}} \sec^2 \phi_{i+1} - \frac{Z_{i+1}}{2p_i} \tan^2 \phi_{i+1} - \frac{1}{p_i^{1/2}} - \frac{1}{Z_{i+1}}\right\} \cos \phi_{i+1} \qquad (11.42)$$

Similarly, it may be proved that $\partial W/\partial q_i$ and $\partial W/\partial \tilde{\omega}_i$ vanish if

$$(s_i - p_i)\left(1 + \frac{p_i^{1/2}}{Z_i}\right) \cos \phi_i + (s_i - p_i^{1/2}Z_i) \tan \phi_i \sin \phi_i$$

$$\qquad (11.43)$$

$$= (s_{i+1} - p_i)\left(1 + \frac{p_i^{1/2}}{Z_{i+1}}\right) \cos \phi_{i+1} + (s_{i+1} - p_i^{1/2}Z_{i+1}) \tan \phi_{i+1} \sin \phi_{i+1}$$

$$\left(Z_i - \frac{s_i}{Z_i}\right) \sin \phi_i = \left(Z_{i+1} - \frac{s_{i+1}}{Z_{i+1}}\right) \sin \phi_{i+1} \qquad (11.44)$$

Equations (11.20)–(11.23) determine the values of the quantities $(s_i, \theta_i, Z_i, \phi_i)$ appropriate to the ith impulse and take the form

$$q_{i-1} \cos (\theta_i - \tilde{\omega}_{i-1}) = s_i - p_{i-1} \qquad (11.45)$$

$$q_{i-1} \sin (\theta_i - \tilde{\omega}_{i-1}) = (s_i - Z_i p_{i-1}^{1/2}) \tan \phi_i \qquad (11.46)$$

$$q_i \cos (\theta_i - \tilde{\omega}_i) = s_i - p_i \qquad (11.47)$$

$$q_i \sin (\theta_i - \tilde{\omega}_i) = (s_i - Z_i p_i^{1/2}) \tan \phi_i \qquad (11.48)$$

With $i = 1, 2, \cdots, (n - 1)$, Eqs. (11.42)–(11.48) are $7n - 7$ in number and determine the $7n - 7$ unknowns $p_i, q_i, \tilde{\omega}_i, s_i, \theta_i, Z_i, \phi_i$ $(i = 1, 2, \cdots, (n - 1))$ for an optimal n-impulse mode transfer between the given orbits.

Equation (11.42) can be replaced by a simpler, but equivalent, condition as follows: Multiply Eq. (11.42) through by $2p_i^{3/2}$ and subtract from Eq. (11.43); the result will be found to be

$$p_i\left(1 + \frac{s_i + p_i}{Z_i p_i^{1/2}}\right) \cos \phi_i = p_i\left(1 + \frac{s_{i+1} + p_i}{Z_{i+1}p_i^{1/2}}\right) \cos \phi_{i+1}$$

or

$$\left(1 + \frac{s_i + p_i}{Z_i p_i^{1/2}}\right) \cos \phi_i = \left(1 + \frac{s_{i+1} + p_i}{Z_{i+1}p_i^{1/2}}\right) \cos \phi_{i+1} \qquad (11.49)$$

11.5 Optimal Two-Impulse Transfer

Transfer between two coplanar orbits by means of a single impulsive thrust is only possible in the case when the orbits intersect and in this case there is no optimization problem since the impulse necessary at a point of intersection is completely fixed by the two given terminal orbits.

The next simplest mode is that of two-impulse transfer and this is always possible between any two terminal orbits. It will be convenient to denote the orbital parameters for the terminals by $(p_1, q_1, \tilde{\omega}_1)$ and $(p_2, q_2, \tilde{\omega}_2)$ and the parameters for the single variable transfer orbit by $(p, q, \tilde{\omega})$. Equations determining the optimal mode can then be written down as explained in the previous section. These take the form

$$q_1 \cos (\theta_1 - \tilde{\omega}_1) = s_1 - p_1 \tag{11.50}$$

$$q_1 \sin (\theta_1 - \tilde{\omega}_1) = (s_1 - Z_1 p_1^{1/2}) \tan \phi_1 \tag{11.51}$$

$$q \cos (\theta_1 - \tilde{\omega}) = s_1 - p \tag{11.52}$$

$$q \sin (\theta_1 - \tilde{\omega}) = (s_1 - Z_1 p^{1/2}) \tan \phi_1 \tag{11.53}$$

$$q \cos (\theta_2 - \tilde{\omega}) = s_2 - p \tag{11.54}$$

$$q \sin (\theta_2 - \tilde{\omega}) = (s_2 - Z_2 p^{1/2}) \tan \phi_2 \tag{11.55}$$

$$q_2 \cos (\theta_2 - \tilde{\omega}_2) = s_2 - p_2 \tag{11.56}$$

$$q_2 \sin (\theta_2 - \tilde{\omega}_2) = (s_2 - Z_2 p_2^{1/2}) \tan \phi_2 \tag{11.57}$$

$$(s_1 - p)\left(1 + \frac{p^{1/2}}{Z_1}\right) \cos \phi_1 + (s_1 - Z_1 p^{1/2}) \sin \phi_1 \tan \phi_1$$

$$= (s_2 - p)\left(1 + \frac{p^{1/2}}{Z_2}\right) \cos \phi_2 + (s_2 - Z_2 p^{1/2}) \sin \phi_2 \tan \phi_2, \tag{11.58}$$

$$\left(Z_1 - \frac{s_1}{Z_1}\right) \sin \phi_1 = \left(Z_2 - \frac{s_2}{Z_2}\right) \sin \phi_2 \tag{11.59}$$

$$\left(1 + \frac{s_1 + p}{Z_1 p^{1/2}}\right) \cos \phi_1 = \left(1 + \frac{s_2 + p}{Z_2 p^{1/2}}\right) \cos \phi_2 \tag{11.60}$$

where $s_1, \theta_1, Z_1, \phi_1$ refer to the first impulse and $s_2, \theta_2, Z_2, \phi_2$ to the second. These are 11 equations for the 11 unknowns $p, q, \tilde{\omega}, s_1, \theta_1, Z_1, \phi_1, s_2, \theta_2, Z_2, \phi_2$.

The solution to Eqs. (11.50)–(11.60) is not known for the general case, but it has been obtained in a number of special cases and these we proceed to consider in the following sections.

11.6 Optimal Slewing of the Orbital Axis

Suppose that it is desired to rotate the major axis of a body's orbit through an angle 2α in the orbital plane, the shape and size of the orbit to remain unaffected. This is the problem of transferring a body from an orbit $(P, Q, -\alpha)$ to an orbit (P, Q, α). These orbits intersect, so that it is possible for the transfer to be effected by the application of a single impulse. However, this mode of transfer proves invariably to be un-

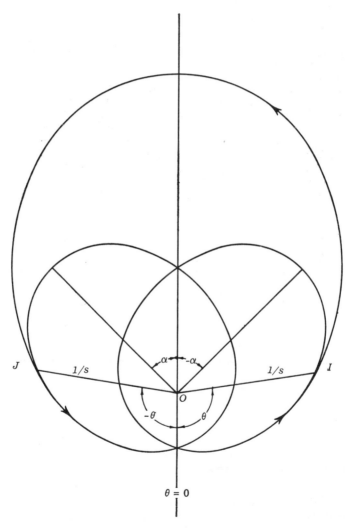

Fig. 3. Transfer between equal ellipses.

economical by comparison with the optimal two-impulse mode and we shall therefore concentrate our attention upon the latter.

In view of the symmetry which exists about the line $\theta = 0$, it will be assumed that the intermediate ellipse of transfer has parameters $(p, q, 0)$ or (p, q, π), i.e., that its major axis lies along the axis of symmetry. The transfer ellipse will then intersect the terminal ellipses in two junction points I, J (Fig. 3) having polar coordinates $(1/s, \theta)$, $(1/s, -\theta)$, respectively. By further consideration of the symmetry, it will be evident that the values of Z at the junction points as given by Eq. (11.8) are identical and that, if ϕ determines the direction of the thrust at the first junction point, $\pi - \phi$ determines the direction at the second junction point. Equations (11.50)–(11.53) now become identical with Eqs. (11.54)–(11.57), condition (11.59) is automatically satisfied, and hence there remain the equations

$$Q \cos (\theta + \alpha) = s - P \tag{11.61}$$

$$Q \sin (\theta + \alpha) = (s - ZP^{1/2}) \tan \phi \tag{11.62}$$

$$q \cos \theta = s - p \tag{11.63}$$

$$q \sin \theta = (s - Zp^{1/2}) \tan \phi \tag{11.64}$$

$$(s - p)\left(1 + \frac{p^{1/2}}{Z}\right) \cos \phi + (s - Zp^{1/2}) \sin \phi \tan \phi = 0 \tag{11.65}$$

$$\left(1 + \frac{s + p}{Zp^{1/2}}\right) \cos \phi = 0 \tag{11.66}$$

When deriving these equations it has been assumed that the transfer ellipse has parameters $(p, q, 0)$. Since the transfer ellipse (p, q, π) is identical with the ellipse $(p, -q, 0)$, both possibilities are allowed for by Eqs. (11.61)–(11.66), provided negative values of q are permitted. These six equations then determine the six unknowns p, q, s, θ, Z, ϕ.

Rejecting the possiblity $\cos \phi = 0$, since this would require $\tan \phi$ to be infinite, Eq. (11.66) requires that

$$\frac{Z}{p^{1/2}} = -\frac{(x + 1)}{x} \tag{11.67}$$

where

$$x = \frac{p}{s} = \frac{r}{l} \quad \text{(by Eq. (11.2))} \tag{11.68}$$

Substituting for $Z/p^{1/2}$ in Eq. (11.65), it will be found that

$$\tan^2 \phi = \frac{x - 1}{(x + 1)(x + 2)} \tag{11.69}$$

and, clearly therefore, $x \geq 1$. It will be found that $\tan^2 \phi$ is a maximum for $x = 1 + \sqrt{6} = 3 \cdot 449 \cdots$. Thus, when ϕ is positive acute, $\phi_{max} = 17°38'$. Equations (11.63) and (11.64) can be written in the form

$$e \cos \theta = \frac{1}{x} - 1 \tag{11.70}$$

$$e \sin \theta = \frac{x + 2}{x} \tan \phi \tag{11.71}$$

where $e = q/p$ is the eccentricity of the transfer ellipse. Dividing Eq. (11.71) by Eq. (11.70), we also obtain

$$\tan \theta = -\frac{x + 2}{x - 1} \tan \phi \tag{11.72}$$

Similarly, Eqs. (11.61) and (11.62) are equivalent to the following equations:

$$E \cos (\theta + \alpha) = \frac{y^2}{x} - 1 \tag{11.73}$$

$$E \sin (\theta + \alpha) = \frac{y(x + y + 1)}{x} \tan \phi \tag{11.74}$$

where $E = Q/P$ is the eccentricity of the terminal ellipses and

$$y = \sqrt{\frac{p}{P}} \tag{11.75}$$

Division of Eq. (11.74) by Eq. (11.73) yields

$$\tan (\theta + \alpha) = \frac{y(x + y + 1)}{y^2 - x} \tan \phi \tag{11.76}$$

Given E and α, Eqs. (11.69)–(11.74) determine x, y, e, θ, ϕ. Equation (11.19) then gives the characteristic velocity for the maneuver to be $\gamma^{1/2}X$, where

$$P^{-1/2}X = \frac{2}{x}(1 - y)y \sec \phi \tag{11.77}$$

The form taken by Eqs. (11.69)–(11.74) implies that if, when

$$E = E_0, \qquad \alpha = \alpha_0 \qquad\qquad (11.78)$$

these equations are satisfied by

$$x = x_0, \quad y = y_0, \quad e = e_0, \quad \theta = \theta_0, \quad \phi = \phi_0 \qquad (11.79)$$

then, when

$$E = E_0, \qquad \alpha = \pi - \alpha_0 \qquad\qquad (11.80)$$

the equations are satisfied by

$$x = x_0, \quad y = y_0, \quad e = -e_0, \quad \theta = \pi - \theta_0, \quad \phi = 2\pi - \phi_0 \qquad (11.81)$$

Also, when

$$E = E_0, \qquad \alpha = \pi + \alpha_0 \qquad\qquad (11.82)$$

the equations are satisfied by

$$x = x_0, \quad y = y_0, \quad e = -e_0, \quad \theta = \pi + \theta_0, \quad \phi = \phi_0 \qquad (11.83)$$

and, when

$$E = E_0, \qquad \alpha = 2\pi - \alpha_0 \qquad\qquad (11.84)$$

the equations are satisfied by

$$x = x_0, \quad y = y_0, \quad e = e_0, \quad \theta = 2\pi - \theta_0, \quad \phi = 2\pi - \phi_0 \qquad (11.85)$$

Also, if the solution (11.79) leads to a positive value for X from Eq. (11.77) (as is necessary), each of the solutions (11.81), (11.83), and (11.85) will also yield a positive value of the same magnitude. It follows that any solution to a problem of the type we are considering immediately provides solutions to three related problems. The four cases (11.78), (11.80), (11.82), and (11.84), together with the appropriate transfer orbits, are shown in Figs. 4(i)–(iv), respectively. It will be observed that cases (i) and (iii) differ only in respect to orientation and are essentially identical, as also are cases (ii) and (iv). Further, cases (i) and (iv) differ only in that the orbit of departure in the first case is the orbit of arrival in the second and complementary major and minor arcs of a single ellipse are employed to effect transfer; cases (ii) and (iii) are similarly related. It follows from these considerations that it is only necessary for us to consider the possibility that α is a positive acute angle, for if α lies outside this range the solution can be derived from the corresponding acute angle configuration.

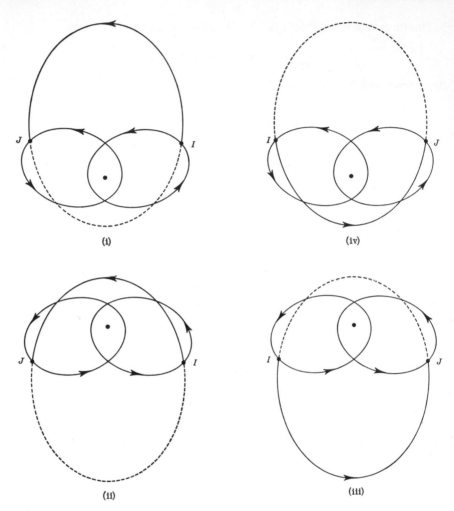

FIG. 4.   Similar transfers between equal ellipses.

Assuming, then, that $0 \leq \alpha \leq \frac{1}{2}\pi$, Eqs. (11.69)–(11.74) are solved most easily by an indirect procedure as follows: Assume a pair of values for the quantities x, y and derive the corresponding value of ϕ from Eq. (11.69). This must be chosen to be such that the value of X given by Eq. (11.77) is positive; this condition will restrict ϕ to lie in one of two quadrants but will leave the sign of $\tan \phi$ undetermined. For each sign of $\tan \phi$, Eq. (11.72) now yields a value of $\tan \theta$ and hence two distinct values of θ differing by π. Of the four alternative values of θ, only two can yield a positive acute value of α when substituted in Eq. (11.76), and of these two only one will yield a positive value for E from either of the equations (11.73) or (11.74). At this stage all ambiguities can be resolved and a solution of the type being sought can be written down.

This procedure has been followed through for a large number of pairs of values of x and y and from these data the families of curves $x =$ constant, $y =$ constant have been drawn in the αE-plane (Fig. 5). It was found that, in most cases, to each pair of values of α, E, there corresponded two pairs of values of x, y; in one pair y was less than unity and in the other greater.

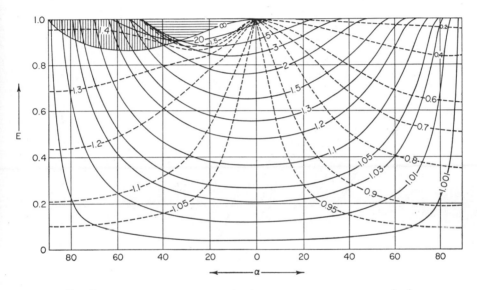

FIG. 5. ———, curves $x =$ constant; – – – –, curves $y =$ constant.

These two types of solution have been separated in Fig. 5 by employing an α-axis proceeding to the right in the case of solutions for which $y < 1$ and an α-axis proceeding to the left in the case of solutions for which $y > 1$. This arrangement is made very convenient by the facts that the E-axis is also the curve $y = 1$ and that the curves $x =$ constant are continuous across this axis. The curve $x = 1$ comprises the two vertical lines $\alpha = 90°$ and the horizontal line $E = 0$. The curve $y = 0$ comprises that portion of the line $E = 1$ which lies in the right-hand quadrant. The constant values of x and y appropriate to the remaining curves have been marked on each. It will be observed that, in the left-hand quadrant, the curves $x = x_0$ with $x_0 > 3$, intersect some of the curves $x = x_0$ with $x_0 < 3$. This implies that, in the region bounded by the curves $x = 3$ (approximately), $x = \infty$ and $E = 1$, and indicated by vertical shading, each point (α, E) lies on two distinct curves $x =$ constant and hence that, in such

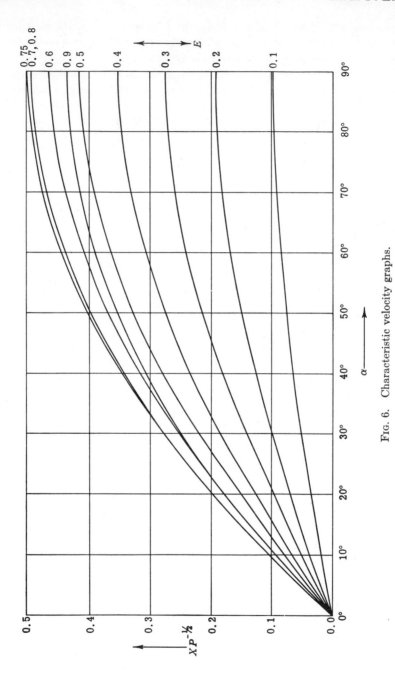

Fig. 6. Characteristic velocity graphs.

cases, two solutions are available from the left-hand quadrant, making a total of three possible solutions altogether. By contrast, the region bounded by the same curves and indicated by horizontal shading is traversed by no curves x = constant and it follows that for values of α, E corresponding to points in this region, only one solution is possible; this is provided by the curves in the right-hand quadrant.

To calculate an optimal transfer with the aid of these curves, it is necessary to identify the two points having coordinates (α, E) and then to estimate which curves of the two families pass through these points, thus yielding appropriate values for x and y. These can be refined in accuracy by substitution into Eqs. (11.69)–(11.74) and subsequent adjustment and the values of e, θ, ϕ, X determined. The solution providing the least value for X is, of course, the absolute optimal solution. Calculation suggests that this absolute optimal solution will invariably be found in the right-hand quadrant of Fig. 5.

For each value of E in the range $0 \cdot 1 (0 \cdot 1) 0 \cdot 9$, values of $XP^{-1/2}$ were calculated for a number of values of α and from the results the family of curves shown in Fig. 6 were constructed. These indicate that, for a given elliptical orbit, the propellant expenditure necessary to bring about a rotation of its axis increases with the angle of rotation 2α, reaching a maximum when $\alpha = 90°$. For a given value of α, the propellant expenditure is greatest when $E = \frac{3}{4}$. The curves $E = 0 \cdot 7$ and $0 \cdot 8$ are indistinguishable at the scale to which Fig. 6 has been drawn. It was found that the formula

$$XP^{-1/2} = 2 \cdot 469 (1 - E)^{1/2} \{1 - (1 - E)^{1/2}\} \alpha (180 - \alpha) \times 10^{-4} \quad (11.86)$$

where α is to be measured in degrees, is in agreement with data obtained from Fig. 6 to an accuracy of within 10% and often to an accuracy of better than 2%.

Further numerical data relating to the problem of this section will be found in the paper by Plimmer.[10]

11.7 Transfer between Orbits Whose Axes Are Aligned

Another special case in which a solution to Eqs. (11.50)–(11.60) can be found without difficulty is that where the axes of the terminal orbits $(p_1, q_1, \bar{\omega}_1)$ and $(p_2, q_2, \bar{\omega}_2)$ are aligned. This case has been studied by Smith[9] and Plimmer.[10] As has already been remarked, the orbits $(p, q, \bar{\omega} + \pi)$ and $(p, -q, \bar{\omega})$ are identical and hence, provided negative q-values are permitted, if the axes of the terminal orbits are aligned, we may take $\bar{\omega}_1 = \bar{\omega}_2$. Then, if q_1 and q_2 are of like sign, the orbital axes will be in the same sense, whereas, if the signs of q_1 and q_2 are opposite, the senses of the axes will also be opposite. It will then be convenient to choose the direction of the reference line $\theta = 0$ so that $\tilde{\omega}_1 = \tilde{\omega}_2 = 0$.

It has been shown by Plimmer[10] that if one of the terminal orbits is a circle, so that one of q_1 or q_2 vanishes, Eqs. (11.50)–(11.60) are easily

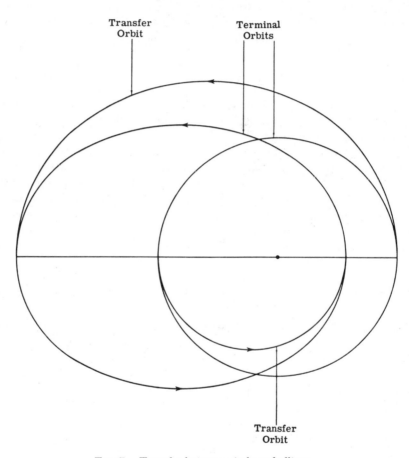

Transfer
Orbit

Terminal
Orbits

Transfer
Orbit

Fig. 7.   Transfer between circle and ellipse.

solved. The optimal transfer ellipse is then tangential at its two apses to the terminal orbits and its axis is aligned with that of the elliptical terminal. There are always two possible such transfer orbits as indicated in Fig. 7, but, in both cases, the impulsive thrusts are applied at its apses and are in a direction perpendicular to the radius from the center of attraction, i.e., ϕ_1, ϕ_2 take the values 0 or π. In case both terminals are ellipses, Eqs. (11.50)–(11.60) have not yet been solved directly. However, it is clear that, in these circumstances also, it is possible to find two transfer ellipses which are tangential at both their apses to the terminals. The previous result then renders it probable that optimal transfer will be effected along one of these ellipses by the application of two impulses in a direction perpendicular to the radius from the center of attraction. We shall accordingly seek solutions of Eqs. (11.50)–(11.60) for which ϕ_1, $\phi_2 = 0$ or π. It is conjectured that, in the conditions being considered in this section, any other type of solution (if such exists) will lead to a higher characteristic velocity.

With $\bar{\omega}_1 = \bar{\omega}_2 = 0$ and ϕ_1, $\phi_2 = 0$ or π, Eqs. (11.50)–(11.60) reduce to the set

$$q_1 \cos \theta_1 = s_1 - p_1, \qquad q_1 \sin \theta_1 = 0$$

$$q \cos (\theta_1 - \bar{\omega}) = s_1 - p, \qquad q \sin (\theta_1 - \bar{\omega}) = 0 \qquad (11.87)$$

$$q \cos (\theta_2 - \bar{\omega}) = s_2 - p, \qquad q \sin (\theta_2 - \bar{\omega}) = 0$$

$$q_2 \cos \theta_2 = s_2 - p_2, \qquad q_2 \sin \theta_2 = 0$$

$$\frac{s_1 + p}{Z_1 p^{1/2}} + 1 = \pm\left(\frac{s_2 + p}{Z_2 p^{1/2}} + 1\right) \qquad (11.88)$$

$$\left(1 + \frac{p^{1/2}}{Z_1}\right)(s_1 - p) = \pm\left(1 + \frac{p^{1/2}}{Z_2}\right)(s_2 - p) \qquad (11.89)$$

where the positive sign is to be taken in Eqs. (11.88) and (11.89) if $\phi_1 = \phi_2$ and the negative sign otherwise. It follows from the right-hand set of equations (11.87) that θ_1, θ_2, $\bar{\omega}$ are all integral multiples of π. If negative values of q are permitted, there is no loss of generality in taking $\bar{\omega} = 0$. If $\theta_1 = \theta_2 = 0$ (or π), the transfer ellipse has degenerated into a straight line which is coincident with the axes of the terminals. To effect transfer into this orbit by an impulse for which $\phi_1 = 0$ or π, it would be necessary to bring the rocket to rest; the rocket would then fall freely towards the center of attraction and, provided its path intersected the second terminal, a second impulse could be employed to establish it in the required orbit. However, this impulse would not be in a direction perpendicular to the radius from the center of attraction. It follows that $\theta_1 \neq \theta_2$ and there are only two cases to consider, viz., *case I*, $\theta_1 = 0$, $\theta_2 = \pi$ and *case II*, $\theta_1 = \pi$,

$\theta_2 = 0$. Substituting for θ_1, θ_2, $\bar{\omega}$, in the left-hand set of equations (11.87), it will be found that:

Case I. $\quad s_1 = p_1 + q_1, \quad s_2 = p_2 - q_2$

$$p = \tfrac{1}{2}(p_1 + p_2 + q_1 - q_2)$$

$$q = \tfrac{1}{2}(p_1 - p_2 + q_1 + q_2)$$

Case II. $\quad s_1 = p_1 - q_1, \quad s_2 = p_2 + q_2$

$$p = \tfrac{1}{2}(p_1 + p_2 - q_1 + q_2)$$

$$q = \tfrac{1}{2}(-p_1 + p_2 + q_1 + q_2)$$

Having satisfied Eqs. (11.87), the remaining conditions (11.88) and (11.89) can be satisfied by appropriate choice of Z_1, Z_2 and serve, in fact, to determine these quantities; their values are of no interest.

Equation (11.19) now specifies the characteristic velocity for the transfer maneuver. Denoting this by $\gamma^{1/2}X$ and writing

$$a = p_1 - q_1, \qquad b = p_2 - q_2$$

$$a' = p_1 + q_1, \qquad b' = p_2 + q_2 \tag{11.90}$$

it will be found that in case I

$$X = X_1 = \sqrt{2}a' \left| \frac{1}{(a + a')^{1/2}} - \frac{1}{(a' + b)^{1/2}} \right|$$

$$+ \sqrt{2}b \left| \frac{1}{(b + b')^{1/2}} - \frac{1}{(a' + b)^{1/2}} \right| \tag{11.91}$$

and in case II

$$X = X_2 = \sqrt{2}a \left| \frac{1}{(a + a')^{1/2}} - \frac{1}{(a + b')^{1/2}} \right|$$

$$+ \sqrt{2}b' \left| \frac{1}{(b + b')^{1/2}} - \frac{1}{(a + b')^{1/2}} \right| \tag{11.92}$$

a, b, a', b' are the reciprocals of the distances from the center of attraction of the four apses on the terminals.

Suppose, first, that the axes of the terminals are directed in the same sense. Then there are two possibilities: (a) the orbits intersect or (b) the orbits do not intersect. These alternative possibilities are illustrated in Fig. 8. The initial orbit will be taken to be that marked "A" and the final

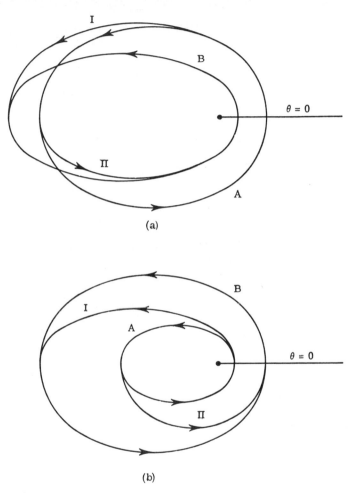

(a)

(b)

FIG. 8.   Ellipses with axes in identical senses.

orbit to be that marked "B"; reversal of the roles of the two orbits or of the senses of both their axes are trivial modifications which do not lead to any essentially distinct possibilities. The transfer orbits corresponding to the cases I and II solutions are also indicated in the figure.

In Fig. 8a, it is clear that $a > b$, $a' < b'$, $a < a'$, $b < b'$. Employing these inequalities to resolve the ambiguous senses of the differences in Eqs. (11.91) and (11.92), it will be found upon subtraction that

$$\frac{1}{\sqrt{2}} (X_1 - X_2) = (a' + b)^{1/2} - (a' + a)^{1/2} - (b' + b)^{1/2} + (b' + a)^{1/2}$$

$$= f(a', a, b) - f(b', a, b) \tag{11.93}$$

where

$$f(x, a, b) = (x + b)^{1/2} - (x + a)^{1/2} \tag{11.94}$$

It is shown in the Appendix at the end of this chapter that, when $a > b$, f is an increasing function of x. It accordingly follows from Eq. (11.93) that, since $a' < b'$, then $X_1 - X_2 < 0$. Thus $X_1 < X_2$ and in Fig. 8a the transfer orbit I is the more economical.

In Fig. 8b the following inequalities are valid: $a > b$, $a' > b'$, $a < a'$, $b < b'$. From Eqs. (11.91) and (11.92), it now follows that

$$\frac{1}{\sqrt{2}} (X_1 - X_2) = \frac{a' - b}{(a' + b)^{1/2}} - \frac{a' - a}{(a' + a)^{1/2}} - \frac{b' - b}{(b' + b)^{1/2}} + \frac{b' - a}{(b' + a)^{1/2}}$$

$$= g(a', a, b) - g(b', a, b) \tag{11.95}$$

where

$$g(x, a, b) = \frac{x - b}{(x + b)^{1/2}} - \frac{x - a}{(x + a)^{1/2}} \tag{11.96}$$

It is also shown in the Appendix that, when $a > b$, the graph of $g(x, a, b)$ for $x \geq b$ has the form indicated in Fig. 9, i.e., g first increases monotonically as x increases to the value ξ and then decreases monotonically so that $g \to 0$ as $x \to \infty$. It is also clear that $g(a, a, b) = g(b, a, b) = G$. It now follows from Fig. 9 that, since $a' > a$ and $a' > b'$, therefore

$$g(a', a, b) < g(b', a, b) \tag{11.97}$$

Thus, from Eq. (11.95), we deduce that $X_1 - X_2 < 0$ and transfer orbit I is again the more economical.

Now suppose that the axes of the terminal orbits are directed in opposite senses. We shall consider the intersecting and nonintersecting cases shown in Figs. 10a and 10b, respectively. No other possibilities are essentially distinct from these two.

In Fig. 10a we have $a > b$, $a' < b'$, $a > a'$, $b < b'$ and Eq. (11.93) follows as before. The inequality $X_1 < X_2$ may now be deduced as already

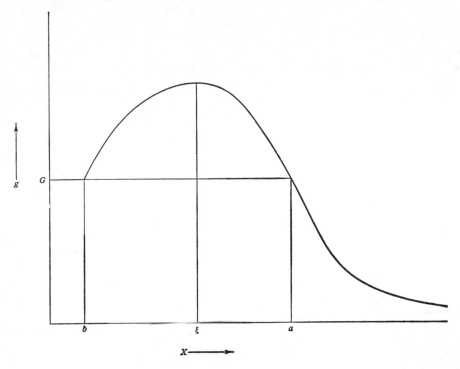

FIG. 9. Graph of $g(x, a, b)$.

explained. Again, therefore, the transfer orbit I has been proved to be the over-all optimal.

In Fig. 10b we have $a > b$, $a' > b'$, $a > a'$, $b < b'$ and Eq. (11.95) is accordingly valid. However, in this instance, a' and b' both lie in the interval (a, b) and it follows from Fig. 9 that either of the inequalities $X_1 < X_2$, $X_1 > X_2$ may be valid depending upon the values of the quantities a' and b'. In this case there appears to be no simple criterion by which the smaller of X_1, X_2 may be selected and each individual case must accordingly be decided by substitution of numerical values in Eq. (11.95).

The findings of this section may be summarized thus: *If two orbits have their axes aligned and the orbits either intersect or have their axes directed in the same sense, then the over-all optimal transfer orbit is that which is tangential to both terminals at an apse on each and which passes through the apse most distant from the center of attraction. In cases where the terminals have their axes directed in opposite senses and are nonintersecting, the optimal transfer orbit may be either of the two ellipses tangential to the terminals at apses depending upon the relative dimensions of the terminals.*

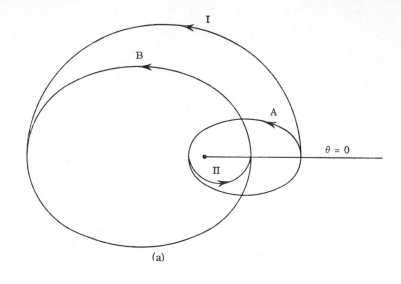

(a)

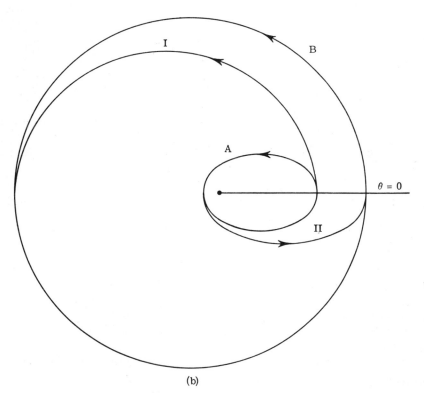

(b)

FIG. 10.   Ellipses with axes in opposite senses.

11.8 Appendix

11.81 The Function $f(x, a, b)$

This function is defined by the equation

$$f(x, a, b) = (x + b)^{1/2} - (x + a)^{1/2} \qquad (11.98)$$

Differentiating with respect to x, it will be found that

$$\frac{\partial f}{\partial x} = \tfrac{1}{2}(x + b)^{-1/2} - \tfrac{1}{2}(x + a)^{-1/2} \qquad (11.99)$$

Thus, if $a > b$ and x is positive, then $\partial f/\partial x > 0$ and hence f is an increasing function of x.

11.82 The Function $g(x, a, b)$

This function is defined by the equation

$$g(x, a, b) = \frac{x - b}{(x + b)^{1/2}} - \frac{x - a}{(x + a)^{1/2}} \qquad (11.100)$$

We shall suppose that a, b are given fixed quantities such that $a > b > 0$ and shall abbreviate $g(x, a, b)$ to $g(x)$.

Then $g(a) = g(b)$ and it therefore follows from Rolle's theorem that a number ξ can be found such that $b < \xi < a$ and $g'(\xi) = 0$.

Now

$$g'(x) = \frac{x + 3b}{2(x + b)^{3/2}} - \frac{x + 3a}{2(x + a)^{3/2}} \qquad (11.101)$$

Writing $h(x) = x^{1/2}g'(x)$ and differentiating then yields the following result:

$$h'(x) = \frac{3b(b - x)}{4x^{1/2}(x + b)^{5/2}} + \frac{3a(x - a)}{4x^{1/2}(x + a)^{5/2}} \qquad (11.102)$$

Hence, provided $b \leq x \leq a$, then $h'(x) < 0$, i.e., $h(x)$ is decreasing. But $h(\xi) = 0$ and consequently $h(x) > 0$, provided $b \leq x < \xi$, and $h(x) < 0$, when $\xi < x \leq a$. It now follows immediately that

$$g'(x) > 0, \qquad b \leq x < \xi$$
$$< 0, \qquad \xi < x \leq a \qquad (11.103)$$

Now suppose that x is fixed and a is variable and put

$$k(a) = \frac{x + 3a}{(x + a)^{3/2}} \qquad (11.104)$$

Then, differentiating with respect to a, we obtain

$$k'(a) = \frac{3(x - a)}{2(x + a)^{5/2}} \qquad (11.105)$$

and hence $k'(a) > 0$, provided $a < x$. This implies that $k(a)$ is an increasing function for such values of a and thus, if $b < a < x$, we have

$$k(b) < k(a) \qquad (11.106)$$

It now follows from Eq. (11.101) that

$$g'(x) = \tfrac{1}{2}\{k(b) - k(a)\} < 0 \qquad (11.107)$$

provided $x > a$.

Finally, it is easy to prove that $g(x) \to 0$ as $x \to \infty$. Taking this result in conjunction with Ineqs. (11.103) and (11.107), it will be immediately obvious that the graph of the function $g(x, a, b)$ takes the form shown in Fig. 9.

REFERENCES

1. D. F. Lawden, Interplanetary Rocket Trajectories, *Advances in Space Sci.* **1,** 1, Academic Press, New York (1959).
2. W. Hohmann, 'Die Erreichbarkeit der Himmelskörper,' Oldenbourg, Munich (1925).
3. D. F. Lawden, Optimal transfer via tangential ellipses, *J. Brit. Interplanet. Soc.* **11,** 278 (1952).
4. D. F. Lawden, Inter-orbital transfer of a rocket, *J. Brit. Interplanet. Soc.* **11,** 321 (1952).
5. D. F. Lawden, The determination of minimal orbits, *J. Brit. Interplanet. Soc.* **11,** 216 (1952).
6. D. F. Lawden, Minimal rocket trajectories, *J. Am. Rocket Soc.* **23,** 360 (1953).
7. D. F. Lawden, Fundamentals of space navigation, *J. Brit. Interplanet. Soc.* **13,** 87 (1954).
8. R. S. Long, Transfer between non-coplanar elliptical orbits, *Astronaut. Acta* **6,** 167 (1960).
9. G. C. Smith, The calculation of minimal orbits, *Astronaut. Acta* **5,** 253 (1959).
10. R. N. A. Plimmer, Fuel requirements for inter-orbital transfer of a rocket, *Proc. 10th Intern. Astronaut. Congr., London,* 1959 (1960).
11. L. G. Vargo, Optimal transfer between two coplanar terminals in a gravitational field, *Am. Astronaut. Soc. Preprint* No. 58–20 (1958).
12. H. Munick, R. McGill and G. E. Taylor, Minimization of characteristic velocity for two-impulse orbital transfer, *ARS Journal* **30,** 638 (1960).

13. J. M. Horner, Optimum orbital transfer, Personal communication from ABMA, Huntsville, Alabama (1960).
14. T. N. Edelbaum, Some extensions of the Hohmann transfer maneuver, *ARS Journal* **29,** 864 (1959).
15. R. F. Hoelker and R. Silber, The bi-elliptical transfer between circular coplanar orbits, *DA Tech. Memo.* No. 2–59, Army Ballistic Missile Agency (1959).
16. L. Rider, Ascent from inner circular to outer coplanar elliptic orbits, *ARS Journal* **30,** 254 (1960).

—12—

The Optimum Spacing of Corrective Thrusts in Interplanetary Navigation

JOHN BREAKWELL

Lockheed Missiles and Space Division, Sunnyvale, California

12.1 Discussion and Results

Suppose that a spaceship is in free flight (i.e., unpowered flight) on its way from earth to a planet such as Mars. Except in the immediate vicinity of earth and the planet, its trajectory is essentially a heliocentric ellipse. Let us pretend that the orbits of earth and the planet and the "transfer ellipse" are coplanar. Now the actual transfer trajectory, if uncorrected beyond some point P_n, will miss the destination planet by a distance D_{n-1} to which we may attach a sign, e.g., $\pm$ according as the spaceship passes to the left or right of the planet (see Fig. 1). Suppose that a corrective velocity impulse $\mathbf{v}_n^{(c)}$ is to be applied at the point P_n on the transfer trajectory. This, of course, effectively includes the application of a finite thrust over a duration very much smaller than the flight duration. The amount of velocity correction $\mathbf{v}_n^{(c)}$ is computed as follows: (i) make an estimate $\hat{D}_{n-1}$ of D_{n-1} based on measurements (probably angular) determining present and past positions; (ii) compute $\mathbf{v}_n^{(c)}$ so that (in a linearized error theory)

$$\frac{\partial D}{\partial \mathbf{v}}(t_n) \cdot \mathbf{v}_n^{(c)} = -\hat{D}_{n-1} \tag{12.1}$$

353

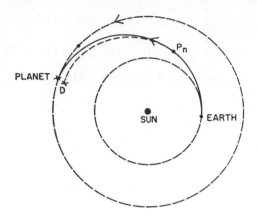

Fig. 1.   Interplanetary trajectory.

It should be mentioned here that errors in the estimate $\hat{D}_{n-1}$ may include biases in the subsequent trajectory calculation due, for example, to over-simplifying the computation. Our main concern, however, will be with random errors in $\hat{D}_{n-1}$ due to random measurement errors

Now the "control effectiveness" $\partial D(t)/\partial \mathbf{v}$ certainly decreases toward zero as the spaceship moves from earth to the destination planet. Consequently, if D_{n-1} were correctly estimated, the economical thing to do in terms of fuel expended on velocity correction would be to correct as soon as possible.

On the average, however, D_{n-1} is not correctly estimated. This means that a correction at P_n still leaves us with a miss distance D_n which may have to be reduced by further corrections. This supposedly reduced miss distance is

$$D_n = D_{n-1} - \hat{D}_{n-1} + \frac{\partial D}{\partial \mathbf{v}}(t_n) \cdot \mathbf{v_n}' \tag{12.2}$$

where the last term is due to a possible velocity mechanization error $\mathbf{v_n}'$. Moreover, we may expect that the error in estimating D_{n-1}, like the control effectiveness, decreases toward zero as we approach the target planet.

The problem we face is that of choosing the correction points $P_1, P_2, \cdots, P_N$, so as to achieve in some average sense a required terminal accuracy with a minimum total velocity correction and hence a minimum expenditure of fuel for corrective thrusts.

The problem as we have described it so far is two-dimensional. Actually the true situation is three-dimensional, even if the "nominal" transfer trajectory is coplanar with the orbit of the destination planet, since it will be necessary to consider an "out-of-plane" miss-distance component related to out-of-plane position and velocity components. The out-of-plane one-dimensional correction problem is independent of the "in-plane" correction problem, except that both kinds of correction are made simultaneously so as to economize on

$$\sum_{n=1}^{N} |\mathbf{v}_n^{(c)}|$$

Returning to our two-dimensional problem, we note that the velocity correction $\mathbf{v}_n^{(c)}$ is not uniquely determined by Eq. (12.1). Naturally we resolve this choice by minimizing the individual velocity correction magnitude $|\mathbf{v}_n^{(c)}|$. It is easy to see that this amounts to choosing $\mathbf{v}_n^{(c)}$ either parallel or antiparallel to the vector $\partial D(t_n)/\partial \mathbf{v}$, depending on the sign of $\hat{D}_{n-1}$. It then follows that

$$|\mathbf{v}_n^{(c)}| = \frac{|\hat{D}_{n-1}|}{|\partial D(t_n)/\partial \mathbf{v}|} \tag{12.3}$$

The control-effectiveness vector $\partial D(t)/\partial \mathbf{v}$ is to be evaluated along the nominal correction-free transfer orbit. Its magnitude and direction are indicated in Fig. 2 for the case of a "Hohmann transfer" from earth to Mars, i.e., a 180° transfer along an ellipse cotangential to the earth and Mars orbits, treated as coplanar heliocentric circles. The gravitational fields of earth and Mars themselves were ignored in the calculation of $\partial D(t)/\partial \mathbf{v}$. The abscissa in Fig. 2, the so-called mean anomaly, increases uniformly with time from 0° to 180°. It appears, then, that the effectiveness magnitude $|\partial D(t)/\partial \mathbf{v}|$ decreases to zero essentially linearly with time, while the direction of $\partial D(t)/\partial \mathbf{v}$, measured from the "transverse" direction perpendicular to the radius from the sun, increases essentially linearly with time from 0° to 90°. Thus, as might be anticipated, an early correction is made forward or backward along the transfer orbit while the last correction is made perpendicular to the motion.

We may use Eq. (12.3), with n increased by 1, together with Eq. (12.2) to express $|\mathbf{v}_{n+1}^{(c)}|$ in terms of errors at P_n and P_{n+1}. In particular, if we neglect the mechanization errors $\mathbf{v}'$, we may obtain

$$|\mathbf{v}_{n+1}^{(c)}| = \frac{1}{|\partial D(t_{n+1})/\partial \mathbf{v}|} |(\hat{D}_n - D_n) - (\hat{D}_{n-1} - D_{n-1})| \tag{12.4}$$

This tells us, for example, that if the latest miss distance is correctly estimated $(\hat{D}_n = D_n)$, the corrective velocity depends only on the last previous error in miss-distance estimation, regardless of how many correc-

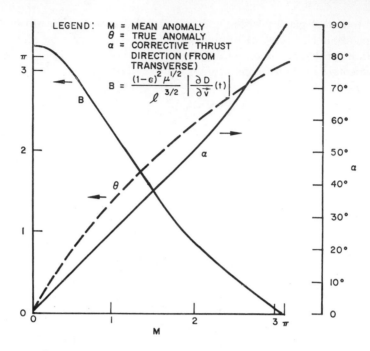

Fig. 2.   Guidance chart for earth-Mars Hohmann transfer.

tions have been made. On the other hand, if the last previous miss-distance estimate were correct, the new correction would be due only to an incorrect new estimate of a miss distance which is really zero.

If we now disregard any biases in the estimates $\hat{D}$, we may assume that the differences $(\hat{D} - D)$ are normally distributed with zero mean and with variances and covariances which may be obtained in a straightforward manner from assumed variances in the various independent angular measurements involved, whose errors are presumably normal with zero bias.

The in-plane velocity correction magnitude $|\mathbf{v}_{n+1}^{(c)}|$ is thus expressed by means of Eq. (12.4) as the absolute value of a normal random variable with zero mean and computable variance.

Meanwhile we may use Eq. (12.2) to establish a time t_N for the last correction such that any earlier time would lead to an expected miss $\mathcal{E}\{|D_N|\}$ in excess of some allowed terminal error. The "launching" error D_0 before the first correction may be presumed to be, on the average, far greater in absolute value than the allowed terminal error.

What we would like to do, given t_N and an rms launching error σ_{D_0}, is to choose a sequence of times t_1, t_2, $\cdots$, t_N, with the integer N *not* specified, so that the 90 percentile, say, of the distribution of

$$\sum_{n=1}^{N} |\mathbf{v}_n^{(c)}|$$

is as small as possible. This, however, is an awkward quantity to compute because of the correlation between successive terms in the sum. A more workable, and closely related, criterion is the minimization of the sum

$$S_N = \sum_{n=1}^{N} \mathcal{E}\{|\mathbf{v}_n^{(c)}|\} \tag{12.5}$$

We may take advantage here of the fact that the expected magnitude $\mathcal{E}\{|x|\}$ of a normal random variable x with zero mean and variance σ_x^2 is just $\sigma_x \sqrt{2/\pi}$.

The three-dimensional situation is as follows: If we denote the out-of-plane miss by D' and choose the z-direction perpendicular to the plane of motion, the out-of-plane velocity correction at P_{n+1} is

$$|\dot{z}_{n+1}^{(c)}| = \left| \left\{ \frac{\hat{D}_n' - D_n'}{\partial D'(t_{n+1})/\partial \dot{z}} - \dot{z}_{n+1}' \right\} - \frac{\partial D'(t_n)/\partial \dot{z}}{\partial D'(t_{n+1})/\partial \dot{z}} \left\{ \frac{\hat{D}_{n-1}' - D_{n-1}'}{\partial D'(t_n)/\partial \dot{z}} - \dot{z}_n' \right\} \right| \tag{12.6}$$

where small mechanization errors $\dot{z}'$ are now included. The in-plane velocity correction becomes

$$\sqrt{(\dot{x}_{n+1}^{(c)})^2 + (\dot{y}_{n+1}^{(c)})^2}$$

$$= \left| \left\{ \frac{\hat{D}_n - D_n}{\partial D(t_{n+1})/\partial v} - w_{n+1}' \right\} - \frac{\partial D(t_n)/\partial v}{\partial D(t_{n+1})/\partial v} \left\{ \frac{\hat{D}_{n-1} - D_{n-1}}{\partial D(t_n)/\partial v} - w_n' \right\} \right| \tag{12.7}$$

where $\partial D(t)/\partial v$ denotes $\sqrt{[\partial D(t)/\partial \dot{x}]^2 + [\partial D(t)/\partial \dot{y}]^2}$ and where w' denotes the component of the mechanization error $\mathbf{v}'$ in the direction of the in-plane vector $(\partial D/\partial \dot{x}, \partial D/\partial \dot{y})$.

Since $\sqrt{(\dot{x}_{n+1}^{(c)})^2 + (\dot{y}_{n+1}^{(c)})^2 + (\dot{z}_{n+1}^{(c)})^2}$ no longer has a simple statistical distribution in spite of the assumed normality of the mechanization errors as well as the measurement errors, we replace the criterion Eq. (12.5) by a related criterion, namely, that of minimizing:

$$S_N = \sum_{n=1}^{N} \sqrt{(\mathcal{E}\{[\dot{x}_n^{(c)}]^2 + [\dot{y}_n^{(c)}]^2\}^{\frac{1}{2}})^2 + (\mathcal{E}\{|\dot{z}_n^{(c)}|\})^2} \tag{12.8}$$

which is more easily computable.

To carry out a minimization of S_N without a digital computer we shall have to make some simplifying assumptions relative to the miss-distance estimates $\hat{D}$. We shall consider two examples. As our first example, in two dimensions, let us suppose the estimate $\hat{D}_{n-1}$ is based on measurements rather close to the position P_n so that they effectively measure position and velocity at P_n with an uncertainty in velocity which will have a substantially greater effect on miss distance than will the uncertainty in position. In this case:

$$\sigma_{\hat{D}_{n-1}} \cong \sigma_v \frac{\partial D}{\partial v} (t_n) \tag{12.9}$$

where σ_v is the rms velocity measurement uncertainty in the direction of $\partial D(t_n)/\partial \mathbf{v}$, which uncertainty we shall further suppose to be, like the rms value of σ' of w', independent of time.

The sum S_N now simplifies to

$$S_N = \sqrt{\frac{2}{\pi}} \left\{ \sqrt{\sigma_v{}^2 + \sigma'^2 + \frac{\sigma_{D_0}^2}{[\partial D(t_1)/\partial v]^2}} \right.$$
$$\left. + \sqrt{\sigma_v{}^2 + \sigma'^2} \sum_{n=2}^{N} \sqrt{1 + \left[\frac{\partial D(t_{n-1})/\partial v}{\partial D(t_n)/\partial v} \right]^2} \right\} \tag{12.10}$$

It is shown in Section 12.2 that for sufficiently large rms launching error, in fact if $\sigma_{D_0} > 3\sqrt{\sigma_v{}^2 + \sigma'^2} \, \partial D(0)/\partial v$, the optimum choice of correction times t_n must be such that $t_1 = 0$ (or as soon as feasible) and

$$\frac{\partial D(t_{n-1})/\partial v}{\partial D(t_n)/\partial v} = \rho \tag{12.11}$$

a value independent of n, and that the optimum integer N is determined approximately by the condition $\rho = 3.0$. In the case of the Hohmann transfer from earth to Mars, the approximate linearity of $\partial D/\partial v$ as a function of time leads to the following rough description of the optimum spacing of corrections: Make the first correction as soon as feasible; after any correction proceed two-thirds of the way to the target (e.g., wait for two-thirds of the remaining time) before the next correction. Figure 3 shows that the behavior of S_N as a function of ρ is not very sensitive to changes in "spacing ratio" from the optimum value of 3.

This "cascading" of corrections is surprisingly effective in reducing errors. Suppose that our terminal accuracy is restricted by the criterion, which is a stringent one, is that in aiming to "bounce off" the planet in a particular direction along the "other asymptote" (e.g., enroute to another planet), our error in the subsequent velocity vector shall be on the average

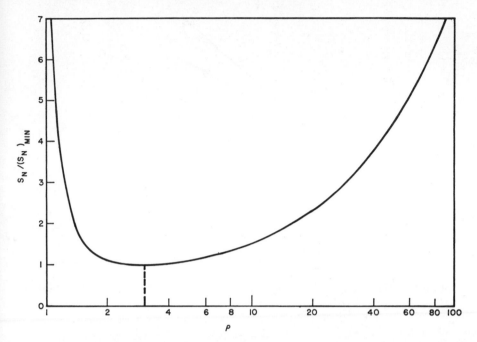

FIG. 3. Fuel expenditure versus spacing ratio (example 1).

no greater than the velocity penalty incurred at correction points on our way to the planet.

From Eqs. (12.2) and (12.9),

$$\mathcal{E}(|\,D_N\,|) = \sqrt{\frac{2}{\pi}} \sqrt{\sigma_v{}^2 + \sigma'^2}\, \frac{\partial D}{\partial v}\,(t_N) \tag{12.12}$$

Now the distance D from the center of the planet to the approach asymptote (see Fig. 4), the angle ψ turned through (as seen relative to the planet), and the distance R of nearest approach to the planet's center are all related to the eccentricity ϵ_1 and semitransverse axis a_1 of the hyperbola of passage around the planet, as follows:

$$D = a_1 \sqrt{\epsilon_1{}^2 - 1}$$

$$\psi = 2 \sin^{-1}\left(\frac{1}{\epsilon_1}\right)$$

$$R = a_1(\epsilon_1 - 1)$$

while the semitransverse axis a_1 is related to the velocity v_R of approach

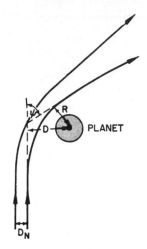

FIG. 4.   Trajectory near planet.

relative to the planet (measured before the gravitational field of the planet affects this velocity) by

$$\frac{Gm}{a_1} = v_R^2$$

G being the universal gravitational constant and m the mass of the planet. It follows that the error in the velocity vector of departure along the other asymptote is

$$|\Delta \mathbf{v}| = v_R |\Delta \psi| = \frac{2v_R |\Delta \epsilon_1|}{\epsilon_1 \sqrt{\epsilon_1^2 - 1}} = \frac{2v_R (|D_N|/a_1)}{(1 + (R/a_1))^2} = \frac{(2v_R^3/Gm)|D_N|}{(1 + (Rv_R^2/Gm))^2}$$

$$(12.13)$$

But from Eqs. (12.10) and (12.11), with $\rho = 3.0$, the velocity penalty incurred from previous velocity mechanization errors was

$$\mathcal{E}(|\Delta \mathbf{v}|) \cong 3.2 \sqrt{\frac{2}{\pi}} \sqrt{\sigma_v^2 + \sigma'^2} \tag{12.14}$$

Combining Eqs. (12.12)–(12.14), our criterion for choosing t_N is thus

$$\frac{\partial D}{\partial v}(t_N) = 1.6 \frac{Gm}{v_R^3} \left(1 + \frac{Rv_R^2}{Gm}\right)^2 \tag{12.15}$$

In the case of the earth-Mars Hohmann transfer, it is known that $v_R \cong 8800$ ft/sec and that the eccentricity ϵ of the transfer orbit is approximately 0.21.

But from Fig. 2 we see that, for times t close to the time t_f of arrival at the planet:

$$0.89\omega \frac{\partial D}{\partial v}(t) = B \cong \frac{2(t_f - t)}{T}$$

where ω is the mean heliocentric angular velocity of the interplanetary trajectory, and T is the total travel time, equal to 259 days. Since $\omega T = \pi$, we find from Eq. (12.15) that

$$\frac{v_R(t_f - t_N)}{R} = 0.7\pi \frac{Gm}{v_R^2 R}\left(1 + \frac{Rv_R^2}{Gm}\right)$$

The most stringent requirement clearly corresponds to the smallest allowable distance R of nearest approach, which we shall take to be 2500 miles. The last correction is thus made at a distance of about 23,000 miles from the center of Mars, or $3\frac{3}{4}$ hours before arrival.

The total number of corrective thrusts on the way to Mars is given by

$$N = 1 + \log_3\left[\frac{\partial D}{\partial v}(0) \bigg/ \frac{\partial D}{\partial v}(t_N)\right]$$

which is now calculable from Fig. 2. It is $N = 8$.

The weak assumption in this first example is the assumption that D_{n-1} is estimated on the basis of observations close to P_n. It is certainly more plausible to assume that D_{n-1} is estimated from measurements at least as far back as P_{n-1} if not all the way back to the start, the estimation in the latter case taking account of the previous corrective velocities.

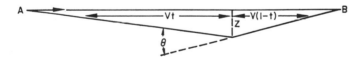

FIG. 5. Position determination by subtended angle.

To see the effect this might have on the optimum spacing, we choose for our second example a rather different "one-dimensional" situation (see Fig. 5). Suppose that a vehicle has a nominal straight-line motion from A to B with constant speed V in unit time, but that its actual position at time t has a small lateral component z perpendicular to AB in a fixed plane. Suppose further that lateral position z at any time is measured by means of the exterior subtended angle θ whose standard deviation σ_θ is assumed to be independent of time. It is then easy to show that the standard deviation of lateral position determination z is

$$\sigma_z = Vt(1 - t)\sigma_\theta \qquad (12.16)$$

which is, of course, largest midway from A to B. Perfectly mechanized corrective thrusts are to be applied perpendicular to AB. It is shown in Section 12.3 that, if miss distance is estimated at any time from closely spaced measurements of z all the way back to A, the optimum choice of correction times t_n is such that

$$\frac{1 - t_{n-1}}{1 - t_n} \to 2.62 \quad \text{as} \quad t_n \to 1 \qquad (12.17)$$

Figure 6, which is analogous to Fig. 3, shows again that the expected fuel consumption for corrections is not very sensitive to a change of the spacing ratio ρ from the optimum value, in this case 2.62. Also, included in Fig. 6 is a curve representing the relative fuel expenditure, computed for a general constant spacing-ratio ρ, for the case in which miss distance is estimated only on the basis of closely spaced measurements since the last correction (see Section 12.5).

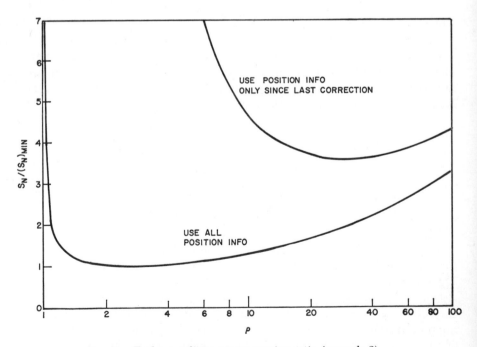

FIG. 6.   Fuel expenditure versus spacing ratio (example 2).

It is interesting here that because of the closeness of the last corrections and in spite of the assumed improvement in measurement as we approach B, the neglect of position information prior to the previous correction is costly.

It is also interesting that the optimum spacing is not substantially different from that in the first example.

12.2 Development of the Optimum Spacing in Example 1

Let us denote

$$\frac{\partial D(t_n)/\partial v}{\partial D(0)/\partial v}$$

by τ_n, and

$$\frac{\sigma_{D_0}^2}{(\sigma_v{}^2 + \sigma'^2)[\partial D(0)/\partial v]^2}$$

by K^2. Our problem is to find N and a sequence $\tau_1 > \tau_2 > \cdots > \tau_N$, with $\tau_1 \leq 1$ and τ_N given, so as to minimize

$$F_1 = \sqrt{1 + \frac{K^2}{\tau_1{}^2}} + \sum_{n=2}^{N} \sqrt{1 + \frac{\tau_{n-1}^2}{\tau_n{}^2}} \qquad (12.18)$$

Denoting τ_{n-1}/τ_n by ρ $(n = 2, \cdots, N)$, we may write

$$F_1 = \sqrt{1 + \frac{K^2}{\tau_1{}^2}} + \sum_{n=2}^{N} \sqrt{1 + \rho_n{}^2}$$

where

$$\prod_{n=2}^{N} \rho_n = \frac{\tau_1}{\tau_N}, \quad \text{i.e.,} \quad \sum_{n=2}^{N} \ln \rho_n = \ln \tau_1 - \ln \tau_N$$

Differentiation of the function $F_1 - \lambda \, \Sigma_{n=2}^{N} \ln \rho_n$, where λ is a Lagrange multiplier, shows that, for fixed τ_1 and τ_N, F_1 can only be minimum when

$$\rho_2 = \rho_3 = \cdots = \rho_N = \left(\frac{\tau_1}{\tau_N}\right)^{1/(N-1)} \qquad (12.19)$$

On the other hand, minimization of F_1 in Eq. (12.18) with respect to τ_1 (≤ 1), for fixed $\tau_2, \tau_3, \cdots, \tau_N$, requires that $\rho_2 = \tau_1/\tau_2 = K/\tau_1$ if this yields $\tau_1 \leq 1$ and otherwise, $\tau_1 = 1$.

It follows that

$$\tau_1 = \min \left[1, \, K^{(N-1)/N} \tau_N^{1/N}\right] \qquad (12.20)$$

Thus F_1 is reduced to a function of N only, defined by

$$
F_1 = \begin{cases}
\sqrt{1 + K^2} + (N-1)\{1 + \tau_N^{-2/(N-1)}\}^{1/2} \\
\quad \text{if} \quad N - 1 \geq \ln(1/\tau_N)/\ln K \quad \text{and thus} \quad \tau_1 = 1 \\[2mm]
N\{1 + K^{2/N}\}^{1/2} \\
\quad \text{if} \quad N - 1 < \ln(1/\tau_N)/\ln K
\end{cases}
\tag{12.21}
$$

Looking first at the second form for F_1 in Eq. (12.21), regarding N as a continuous variable, and re-introducing the ratio

$$
\rho = K^{1/N}\tau_N^{-1/N}
$$

we have

$$
N = \frac{\ln (K/\tau_N)}{\ln \rho}
$$

and, hence,

$$
\ln F_1 = \ln \ln \left(\frac{K}{\tau_N}\right) - \ln \ln \rho + \tfrac{1}{2} \ln (1 + \rho^2)
$$

which, regarded as a function of a continuous variable ρ, is easily shown to be minimum when

$$
\ln \rho = 1 + \frac{1}{\rho^2}
$$

i.e.,

$$
\rho \cong 3.0
$$

in which case

$$
N = \frac{\ln (K/\tau_N)}{\ln (3.0)} \quad \text{and} \quad F_1 = 2.9 \ln \left(\frac{K}{\tau_N}\right)
\tag{12.22}
$$

The second term in the first form for F_1 in Eq. (12.21) may be treated accordingly, simply by replacing K by 1 and N by $N - 1$. We thus retain $\ln \rho = 1 + 1/\rho^2$, whereas N and F_1 are now given by

$$
N = 1 + \frac{\ln (1/\tau_N)}{\ln (3.0)} \quad \text{and} \quad F_1 = \sqrt{1 + K^2} + 2.9 \ln \left(\frac{1}{\tau_N}\right)
\tag{12.23}
$$

Comparison of Eqs. (12.22) and (12.23) with the ranges for $N - 1$ specified in Eq. (12.21) shows that the first and second forms in Eq. (12.21) correspond, respectively, to $K > 3.0$ and $K < 3.0$.

12.3 Development of the Optimum Spacing in Example 2

The information about D may be described as follows: The estimated miss-distance $\hat{D}_{n-1}$ at time t_n is given by

$$\hat{D}_{n-1} = \frac{\partial D}{\partial z_n} \hat{z}_n + \frac{\partial D}{\partial \dot{z}_n} \hat{z}_n^- \tag{12.24}$$

where $\hat{z}_n$ and $\hat{z}_n^-$ are the estimated position and velocity, based on measurements $\bar{z}$ of positions $z(t)$ at various times t prior to t_n. Furthermore, $z(t)$ itself is a linear function of z_n and $\dot{z}_n^-$:

$$z(t) = \frac{\partial z(t)}{\partial z_n} z_n + \frac{\partial z(t)}{\partial \dot{z}_n} \dot{z}_n^- + b_n(t) \tag{12.25}$$

where

$$\frac{\partial z(t)}{\partial z_n} = 1$$

$$\frac{\partial z(t)}{\partial \dot{z}_n} = -(t_n - t) \tag{12.26}$$

$$b_n(t) = + \sum_{\substack{i \\ t_i < t < t_n}} v_i^{(c)}(t_i - t)$$

The estimates $\hat{z}_n$ and $\hat{z}_n^-$ are obtained by a weighted least-squares fit of Eq. (12.25) to the observed $\bar{z}(t)$'s, i.e., they minimize the sum:

$$\Sigma = \sum_n \sum_{t < t_n} \left[\frac{1}{\sigma_{\bar{z}(t)}} \left(\frac{\partial z(t)}{\partial z_n} \hat{z}_n + \frac{\partial z(t)}{\partial \dot{z}_n} \hat{z}_n^- + b_n(t) - \bar{z}(t) \right) \right]^2 \tag{12.27}$$

where $\sum_{t < t_n}$ denotes summation over all observation times prior to t_n. Assuming independence of the measurements $\bar{z}(t)$, it follows from statistical theory (see Section 12.4) that the 2×2 covariance matrix for the estimates $\hat{z}_n$ and $\hat{z}_n^-$ is just the inverse of the following "information matrix":

$$\| M^{(n)} \| = \left\| \begin{array}{cc} \displaystyle\sum_{t < t_n} \frac{1}{\sigma_{\bar{z}(t)}^2} \left(\frac{\partial z(t)}{\partial z_n} \right)^2 & \displaystyle\sum_{t < t_n} \frac{1}{\sigma_{\bar{z}(t)}^2} \frac{\partial z(t)}{\partial z_n} \frac{\partial z(t)}{\partial \dot{z}_n} \\[4ex] \displaystyle\sum_{t < t_n} \frac{1}{\sigma_{\bar{z}(t)}^2} \frac{\partial z(t)}{\partial z_n} \frac{\partial z(t)}{\partial \dot{z}_n} & \displaystyle\sum_{t < t_n} \frac{1}{\sigma_{\bar{z}(t)}^2} \left(\frac{\partial z(t)}{\partial \dot{z}_n} \right)^2 \end{array} \right\| \tag{12.28}$$

The variance of the estimate $\hat{D}_{n-1}$ of Eq. (12.24) is thus

$$\sigma^2_{\hat{D}_{n-1}} = \| M^{(n)} \|^{-1}_{11} \left(\frac{\partial D}{\partial z_n}\right)^2 + 2 \| M^{(n)} \|^{-1}_{12} \left(\frac{\partial D}{\partial z_n}\right)\left(\frac{\partial D}{\partial \dot{z}_n}\right) + \| M^{(n)} \|^{-1}_{22} \left(\frac{\partial D}{\partial \dot{z}_n}\right)^2$$

(12.29)

Here we must use

$$\frac{\partial D}{\partial \dot{z}_n} = 1 - t_n$$

(12.30)

$$\frac{\partial D}{\partial z_n} = 1$$

To evaluate Eq. (12.28) we substitute from Eqs. (12.26) and, assuming that measurements are made at frequent (equal) intervals of time, we replace

$$\sum_{t<t_n} \text{ by } \lambda_0 \int_0^{t_n} dt, \qquad \lambda_0 \text{ being an "observation rate"} \qquad (12.31)$$

and Eq. (12.16) by $\sigma_{\tilde{z}(t)} = \kappa(1 - t)$, valid near $t = 1$, where $\kappa = V\sigma_\theta$. We thus obtain

$$\| M^{(n)} \| = \frac{\lambda_0}{\kappa^2} \left\| \begin{matrix} \dfrac{t_n}{1 - t_n} & t_n - \ln \dfrac{1}{1 - t_n} \\[3mm] t_n - \ln \dfrac{1}{1 - t_n} & t_n(2 - t_n) - 2(1 - t_n)\ln \dfrac{1}{1 - t_n} \end{matrix} \right\|$$

(12.32)

The inverse matrix is

$$\| M^{(n)} \|^{-1} = \frac{\kappa^2}{\lambda_0 \left(\dfrac{t_n^2}{1 - t_n} - \ln^2 \dfrac{1}{1 - t_n}\right)}$$

$$\cdot \left\| \begin{matrix} t_n(2 - t_n) - 2(1 - t_n)\ln \dfrac{1}{1 - t_n} & -t_n + \ln \dfrac{1}{1 - t_n} \\[4mm] -t_n + \ln \dfrac{1}{1 - t_n} & \dfrac{t_n}{1 - t_n} \end{matrix} \right\|$$

(12.33)

Substitution of Eqs. (12.30) and (12.33) into Eq. (12.29) yields

$$\sigma^2_{\hat{D}_{n-1}} = \frac{(\kappa^2/\lambda_0)\,t_n}{\dfrac{t_n{}^2}{1 - t_n} - \ln^2 \dfrac{1}{1 - t_n}} \tag{12.34}$$

To evaluate $\mathcal{E}\{|\,\dot{z}^{(c)}_{n+1}\,|\}$ in Eq. (12.6) with mechanization errors $\dot{z}'$ omitted, we need not only the variance Eq. (12.34) of $\hat{D}_{n-1}$ but also the covariance of $\hat{D}_{n-1}$ and $\hat{D}_n$. It is shown in Section 12.4 that this covariance is

$$\mathcal{E}\{(\hat{D}_{n-1} - D_{n-1})(\hat{D}_n - D_n)\} = \sigma^2_{\hat{D}_n} \tag{12.35}$$

Equations (12.6) and (12.30) now yield

$$\mathcal{E}\{|\,z^{(c)}_{n+1}\,|\} = \sqrt{\frac{2}{\pi}}\,\frac{\sqrt{\sigma^2_{\hat{D}_{n-1}} - \sigma^2_{\hat{D}}}}{1 - t_{n+1}} \tag{12.36}$$

To carry out the minimization of

$$S_N = \sum_{n=1}^{N} \mathcal{E}\{|\,\dot{z}^{(c)}_n\,|\}$$

we shall make a further approximation to Eq. (12.34), valid near $t_n = 1$:

$$\sigma^2_{\hat{D}_{n-1}} \cong \frac{\kappa^2}{\lambda_0}(1 - t_n) \tag{12.37}$$

Substitution of Eqs. (12.37) into (12.36) leads to a total velocity correction:

$$S_N = \sum_{n=1}^{N} \mathcal{E}\{|\,z^{(c)}_n\,|\} = \frac{\kappa}{\sqrt{\lambda_0}}\sqrt{\frac{2}{\pi}}\sum_{n=1}^{N}\frac{\sqrt{t_n - t_{n-1}}}{1 - t_n} \tag{12.38}$$

To carry out the minimization of S_N in Eq. (12.38) we find by differentiation, first of all, that for fixed t_{n-1} and t_{n+1} the optimum t_n must satisfy

$$\frac{2\rho_n - 1}{\sqrt{\rho_n - 1}} = \frac{\rho^{3/2}_{n+1}}{\sqrt{\rho_{n+1} - 1}} \tag{12.39}$$

where ρ_n and ρ_{n+1} denote $(1 - t_{n-1})/(1 - t_n)$ and $(1 - t_n)/(1 - t_{n+1})$, respectively, so that the product $\rho_n\rho_{n+1}$ is temporarily fixed. We obtain in this way, from Eq. (12.39), two values for ρ_n and hence of $\rho_n\rho_{n+1}$, corresponding to any $\rho_{n+1} > 2$ and to any ρ_{n+1} between 1 and $\sqrt{5} - 1$. However, the

$$\frac{\sqrt{t_{n+1} - t_n}}{1 - t_{n+1}} + \frac{\sqrt{t_n - t_{n-1}}}{1 - t_n}$$

is actually smaller when t_n coincides with either t_{n-1} or t_{n+1} than when t_n is defined by Eq. (12.39), unless $\rho_{n+1} > 2.10$ and the larger ρ_n is chosen, leading to $\rho_n \rho_{n+1} > 3.76$. It follows that, given $1/(1 - t_N) > 3.76$, the optimum factorization of $1/(1 - t_N)$ into a product $\rho_1 \rho_2 \cdots \rho_N$, with N unspecified, must be such that no single ρ_n exceeds 3.76 (or else this ρ_n would be factored into a pair to reduce S_N) and no single ρ_n is less than 2.10. Finally, Eq. (12.39) is regarded as a recurrence relation for ρ_n, and

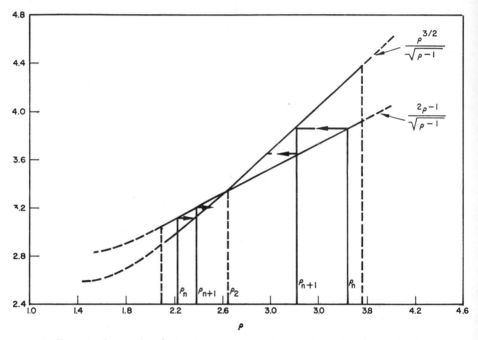

FIG. 7.   Optimum relation between successive spacing-ratios (example 2).

is illustrated in Fig. 7 whence it is apparent that the sequence $\{\rho_n\}$ converges rapidly toward the limit:

$$\rho_2 = \frac{3 + \sqrt{5}}{2} = 2.62 \qquad (12.40)$$

We next consider how S_N varies as a function of a constant spacing-ratio ρ differing in general from ρ_2. We are now interested in the function

$$\frac{1}{\kappa} \sqrt{\frac{\pi \lambda_0}{2}}\, S_N = \sum_{n=1}^{N} \rho^n \sqrt{\left(\frac{1}{\rho}\right)^{n-1} - \left(\frac{1}{\rho}\right)^n} = \frac{\sqrt{\rho(\rho - 1)}}{\sqrt{\rho} - 1}\,(\rho^{N/2} - 1)$$

$$\cong \rho^{N/2}\, \frac{\sqrt{\rho(\rho - 1)}}{\sqrt{\rho} - 1}$$

where ρ^N, assumed $\gg 1$, is fixed by the requirement that $\sigma_{DN} = \sigma_{\dot{D}N-1}$ shall be sufficiently small, as follows from Eq. (12.37)

$$\rho^{-N} = \frac{\lambda_0}{\kappa^2} \sigma_{DN}^2 \qquad (12.41)$$

Thus S_N may be expressed in the form

$$S_N = \sqrt{\frac{2}{\pi}} \frac{\kappa^2}{\lambda_0 \sigma_{DN}} F_2(\rho) \qquad (12.42)$$

where

$$F_2(\rho) = \frac{\sqrt{\rho(\rho-1)}}{\sqrt{\rho}-1} \qquad (12.43)$$

The function $F_2(\rho)/F_2(\rho_2)$ is plotted in Fig. 6.

12.4 The Covariance of D_n and D_{n+1} in the Case of Frequent Observations Since Launch; One-Dimensional Model

If we introduce the notation q_n for the column-vector

$$\left\| \begin{array}{c} z_n \\ \dot{z}_n \end{array} \right\|$$

the minimization of Eq. (12.27) leads to the following matrix equation for the estimate $\hat{q}_n$ of q_n:

$$\| M^{(n)} \| \, \| \hat{q}_n \| = \sum_{t<t_n} \frac{\bar{z}(t) - b_n(t)}{\sigma_{\bar{z}(t)}^2} \left\| \frac{\partial z(t)}{\partial q_n} \right\| \qquad (12.44)$$

Using Eq. (12.24), we now have

$$\hat{D}_{n-1} = \left\| \frac{\partial D}{\partial q_n} \right\|^T \| \hat{q}_n \| = \sum_{t<t_n} a_n(t) \{ \bar{z}(t) - b_n(t) \} \qquad (12.45)$$

where

$$a_n(t) = \frac{1}{\sigma_{\bar{z}(t)}^2} \left\| \frac{\partial D}{\partial q_n} \right\|^T \| M^{(n)} \|^{-1} \left\| \frac{\partial z(t)}{\partial q_n} \right\|$$

$$= \frac{1}{\sigma_{\bar{z}(t)}^2} \left\| \frac{\partial z(t)}{\partial q_n} \right\|^T \| M^{(n)} \|^{-1} \left\| \frac{\partial D}{\partial q_n} \right\| \qquad (12.46)$$

the last equality following from the symmetry of the matrix $\| M^{(n)} \|$.

From Eq. (12.45) and the assumption of independent observation errors with variance $\sigma_{\bar{z}(t)}^2$, we obtain

$$\mathcal{E}\{(\hat{D}_{n-1} - D_{n-1})^2\} = \sigma_{\hat{D}_{n-1}}^2 = \sum_{t<t_n} a_n{}^2(t)\,\sigma_{\bar{z}(t)}^2 \qquad (12.47)$$

Expressing $a_n{}^2(t)$ in Eq. (12.47) as the product of the two expressions in Eq. (12.46), we obtain

$$\sigma_{\hat{D}_{n-1}}^2 = \left\|\frac{\partial D}{\partial q_n}\right\|^T \| M^{(n)} \|^{-1} \left(\sum_{t<t_n} \frac{1}{\sigma_{\bar{z}(t)}^2} \left\|\frac{\partial z(t)}{\partial q_n}\right\| \left\|\frac{\partial z(t)}{\partial q_n}\right\|^T\right)$$

$$\cdot \| M^{(n)} \|^{-1} \left\|\frac{\partial D}{\partial q_n}\right\| \qquad (12.48)$$

But

$$\sum_{t<t_n} \frac{1}{\sigma_{\bar{z}(t)}^2} \left\|\frac{\partial z(t)}{\partial q_n}\right\| \left\|\frac{\partial z(t)}{\partial q_n}\right\|^T$$

is just the matrix $\| M^{(n)} \|$ itself. Equation (12.48) thus simplifies to

$$\sigma_{\hat{D}_{n-1}}^2 = \left\|\frac{\partial D}{\partial q_n}\right\|^T \| M^{(n)} \|^{-1} \left\|\frac{\partial D}{\partial q_n}\right\| \qquad (12.49)$$

This justifies our earlier equation (12.29).

Next, the covariance of $\hat{D}_{n-1}$ and $\hat{D}_n$ is

$$\mathcal{E}\{(\hat{D}_{n-1} - D_{n-1})(\hat{D}_n - D_n)\} = \sum_{t<t_n} a_n(t)\,a_{n+1}(t)\,\sigma_{\bar{z}(t)}^2$$

$$= \left\|\frac{\partial D}{\partial q_n}\right\|^T \| M^{(n)} \|^{-1} \sum_{t<t_n} \frac{1}{\sigma_{\bar{z}(t)}^2} \left\|\frac{\partial z(t)}{\partial q_n}\right\| \left\|\frac{\partial z(t)}{\partial q_{n+1}}\right\|^T \| M^{(n+1)} \|^{-1} \left\|\frac{\partial D}{\partial q_{n+1}}\right\|$$

$$(12.50)$$

But

$$\left\|\frac{\partial D}{\partial q_n}\right\|^T = \left\|\frac{\partial D}{\partial q_{n+1}}\right\|^T \left\|\frac{\partial q_{n+1}}{\partial q_n}\right\|$$

$$(12.51)$$

$$\left\|\frac{\partial z(t)}{\partial q_{n+1}}\right\|^T = \left\|\frac{\partial z(t)}{\partial q_n}\right\|^T \left\|\frac{\partial q_n}{\partial q_{n+1}}\right\|$$

where $\| \partial q_{n+1}/\partial q_n \|$ and $\| \partial q_n/\partial q_{n+1} \|$ are inverse matrices.

The last expression in Eq. (12.50) may thus be written

$$\left\|\frac{\partial D}{\partial q_{n+1}}\right\|^{T}\left\|\frac{\partial q_{n+1}}{\partial q_n}\right\| \; \|\, M^{(n)}\,\|^{-1}\; \|\, M^{(n)}\,\| \; \left\|\frac{\partial q_n}{\partial q_{n+1}}\right\| \; \|\, M^{(n+1)}\,\|^{-1}\left\|\frac{\partial D}{\partial q_{n+1}}\right\|$$

which reduces to

$$\mathcal{E}\{(\hat{D}_{n-1} - D_{n-1})(\hat{D}_n - D_n)\} = \left\|\frac{\partial D}{\partial q_{n+1}}\right\|^{T} \|\, M^{(n+1)}\,\|^{-1}\left\|\frac{\partial D}{\partial q_{n+1}}\right\| = \sigma^2_{\hat{D}_n}$$

$$(12.52)$$

which is our earlier equation (12.35).

12.5 Estimation of D from Frequent Position Measurements since the Last Correction; One-Dimensional Model

If we consider a model in which D_{n-1} is estimated only on the basis of measurements subsequent to t_{n-1}, $\hat{D}_{n-1}$ and $\hat{D}_n$ now have statistically independent errors, their variances being given by Eq. (12.30), where the information matrix $\|\, M^{(n)}\,\|$ involves summation only over observation times between t_{n-1} and t_n. In place of Eq. (12.32) we now have

$$\|\, M^{(n)}\,\|$$

$$= \frac{\lambda_0}{\kappa^2} \left\| \begin{array}{cc} \dfrac{t_{n-1}' - t_n'}{t_{n-1}'t_n'} & 1 - \dfrac{t_n'}{t_{n-1}'} - \ln\dfrac{t_{n-1}'}{t_n'} \\[3ex] 1 - \dfrac{t_n'}{t_{n-1}'} - \ln\dfrac{t_{n-1}'}{t_n'} & \left(1 + \dfrac{t_n'}{t_{n-1}'}\right)(t_{n-1}' - t_n') - 2t_n'\ln\dfrac{t_{n-1}'}{t_n'} \end{array} \right\|$$

$$(12.53)$$

where t_n' denotes $1 - t_n$.

The variance of $\hat{D}_{n-1}$ is now

$$\sigma^2_{\hat{D}n-1} = \frac{\kappa^2}{\lambda_0} \frac{t_{n-1}' - t_n'}{\dfrac{(t_{n-1}' - t_n')^2}{t_{n-1}'t_n'} - \ln^2\dfrac{t_{n-1}'}{t_n'}}$$

$$(12.54)$$

Equation (12.6) and the independence of the errors in D_{n-1} and D_n now lead to

$$S_N = \sqrt{\frac{2}{\pi}} \frac{\kappa}{\sqrt{\lambda_0}} \left\{ \frac{1}{t_1'} \sqrt{\frac{1 - t_1'}{\frac{(1 - t_1')^2}{t_1'} - \ln^2 \frac{1}{t_1'}}} \right.$$

$$\left. + \sum_{n=2}^{N} \frac{1}{t_n'} \sqrt{\frac{t_{n-2}' - t_{n-1}'}{\frac{(t_{n-2}' - t_{n-1}')^2}{t_{n-2}' t_{n-1}'} - \ln^2 \frac{t_{n-2}'}{t_{n-1}'}} + \frac{t_{n-1}' - t_n'}{\frac{(t_{n-1}' - t_n')^2}{t_{n-1}' t_n'} - \ln^2 \frac{t_{n-1}'}{t_n'}}} \right\}$$

$$(12.55)$$

Without attempting a general optimization of the times $\{t_n\}$ so as to minimize S_N in Eq. (12.55), we may again consider S_N for the case of a constant spacing ratio $t_{n-1}'/t_n' = \rho$ (all n). For large values of ρ^N we have

$$S_N \cong \kappa \sqrt{\frac{2}{\pi \lambda_0}} \rho^{N/2} \frac{\sqrt{\rho} \sqrt{\rho^2 - 1}}{(\sqrt{\rho} - 1) \sqrt{\frac{(\rho - 1)^2}{\rho} - \ln^2 \rho}} \qquad (12.56)$$

and, from Eq. (12.54),

$$\sigma_{\hat{D}_N}^2 = \sigma_{\hat{D}_{N-1}}^2 = \frac{\kappa^2}{\lambda_0} \frac{(\rho - 1)\rho^{-N}}{\frac{(\rho - 1)^2}{\rho} - \ln^2 \rho} \qquad (12.57)$$

Thus in place of Eq. (12.42) we have

$$S_N = \sqrt{\frac{2}{\pi} \frac{\kappa^2}{\lambda_0 \sigma_{\hat{D}_N}} F_3(\rho)} \qquad (12.58)$$

where

$$F_3(\rho) = \frac{\sqrt{\rho + 1} (\sqrt{\rho} + 1)}{\frac{(\rho - 1)^2}{\rho} - \ln^2 \rho} \qquad (12.59)$$

For comparison, the function $F_3(\rho)/F_2(\rho_2)$ is plotted in Fig. 6 together with $F_2(\rho)/F_2(\rho_2)$.

Nomenclature

a_1	Semitransverse axis of hyperbola around planet
$a_n(t)$	Coefficient in expression for $\hat{D}_{n-1}$
A	Starting point in example 2
$b_n(t)$	$\displaystyle\sum_{\substack{i \\ t_i < t < t_n}} v_i^{(c)}(t_i - t)$
B	Terminal point in example 2
D_0	In-plane terminal error after launch
D_n	In-plane terminal error after nth correction
$D_n{}'$	Out-of-plane error after nth correction
$\hat{D}_n$	Estimate of D_n
$\hat{D}_n{}'$	Estimate of $D_n{}'$
$\partial D(t)/\partial v$	Magnitude of $\partial D(t)/\partial\mathbf{v}$
$\partial D(t_n)/\partial\mathbf{v}$	2-vector $(\partial D/\partial\dot{x},\ \partial D/\partial\dot{y})$ evaluated at t_n
$\left\Vert \dfrac{\partial D}{\partial q_n} \right\Vert$	Column-vector $\left\Vert \begin{array}{c} \partial D/\partial z_n \\ \partial D/\partial\dot{z}_n \end{array} \right\Vert$
$\varepsilon\{\ \}$	Expected value of random variable inside $\{\ \ \}$
F_1	Dimensionless expected sum of velocity corrections, example 1
$F_2(\rho)$	Dimensionless expected sum of velocity corrections, example 2
$F_3(\rho)$	Dimensionless expected sum of velocity corrections, example 2, based on information only since last correction
G	Universal gravitational constant
K	Dimensionless rms initial miss
l	Semi-latus-rectum of transfer ellipse
m	Mass of planet
$\Vert M^{(n)} \Vert$	Information matrix after $(n-1)$ corrections
$\Vert M^{(n)} \Vert^{-1}$	Inverse of $\Vert M^{(n)} \Vert$
$\Vert M^{(n)} \Vert^{-1}_{ij}$	ij element of $\Vert M^{(n)} \Vert^{-1}$
N	Number of corrections
P_n	Position at nth correction
q_n	Column-vector $\left\Vert \begin{array}{c} z_n \\ \dot{z}_n \end{array} \right\Vert$
$\hat{q}_n$	Estimate of q_n
$\left\Vert \dfrac{\partial q_{n+1}}{\partial q_n} \right\Vert$	Matrix of partial derivatives of elements of vector q_{n+1} with respect to elements of vector q_n
$\left\Vert \dfrac{\partial q_n}{\partial q_{n+1}} \right\Vert$	Matrix of partial derivatives of elements of vector q_n with respect to elements of vector q_{n+1}.

Nomenclature (continued)

R	Distance of nearest approach to target planet
S_N	Sum of expected velocity corrections
t_f	Time of arrival at target planet
t_n	Time of nth correction
t_n'	$t_f - t_n$ (with t_f scaled to equal 1)
T	Total transfer time
$\mathbf{v}_n^{(c)}$	Computed nth velocity correction
$\mathbf{v}_n'$	Error in mechanizing $\mathbf{v}_n^{(c)}$
v_R	Velocity of approach relative to planet
V	Velocity
w_n'	Component of $\mathbf{v}_n'$ in direction of $\partial D(t_n)/\partial \mathbf{v}$
$\dot{x}_n^{(c)}$	x-component of nth intended velocity correction
$\dot{y}_n^{(c)}$	y-component of nth intended velocity correction
$\tilde{z}$	Measured value of z
z_n	Lateral position (example 2) at time t_n
$\dot{z}_n^-$	Time derivative of lateral position immediately prior to t_n
$\dot{z}_n^{(c)}$	z-component of nth intended velocity correction
$\dot{z}_n'$	Error in mechanizing $\dot{z}_n^{(c)}$
$\hat{z}_n$	Estimate of z_n
$\hat{\dot{z}}_n$	Estimate of $\dot{z}_n^-$
$\left\lVert \dfrac{\partial z(t)}{\partial q_n} \right\rVert$	Column-vector $\left\lVert \begin{matrix} \partial z(t)/\partial z_n \\ \partial z(t)/\partial \dot{z}_n \end{matrix} \right\rVert$
$\lVert \ \ \rVert^T$	Transpose of $\lVert \ \ \rVert$
ϵ	Eccentricity of transfer ellipse
ϵ_1	Eccentricity of hyperbola around target planet
θ	Supplement of subtended angle (Fig. 5)
κ	$V\sigma_\theta$
λ	Lagrange multiplier
λ_0	Observation rate
μ	Gravitational constant times the sun's mass
ρ	Spacing ratio
ρ_2	Optimum ρ in example 2
ρ_n	τ_{n-1}/τ_n
σ'	rms error in w'
σ_v	rms velocity measurement error
σ_z	rms error in measuring z
σ_θ	rms error in measuring θ
$\sigma_{\hat{D}_n}$	rms error in estimate $\hat{D}_n$

$\sigma_{\tilde{z}(t)}$	rms error in measurement $\tilde{z}(t)$
τ_n	$\dfrac{\partial D}{\partial v}(t_n) \Big/ \dfrac{\partial D}{\partial v}(0)$
ψ	Angle between asymptotes of hyperbola
ω	Mean heliocentric angular velocity
Σ_n	Weighted sum of squares of position residuals

GENERAL REFERENCES

1. A. Rosenbloom, Final-value systems with total effort constraints, presented at First International Congress of the International Federation on Automatic Control, Moscow, June, 1960.
2. J. V. Breakwell, Fuel requirements for crude interplanetary guidance, presented at Second Western National Meeting of the American Astronautical Society, Los Angeles, California, August 1959; *Advances in Astronaut. Sci.* **5,** (1960).
3. D. F. Lawden, Optimal programme for correctional manoeuvres, *Astronaut. Acta* **6,** 195–205 (1960).

—13—

Propulsive Efficiency of Rockets*

G. LEITMANN
University of California, Berkeley, California

13.0 Introduction

The subject of propulsive efficiency of aircraft and rockets is one treated in all texts on propulsion and might not be expected to present any new problems at this late date. However, that this is not so is evident from the continuing controversy regarding even so basic a question as the proper definition of propulsive efficiency.[1] More recently, all of the definitions in common use have come under scrutiny.[2-8] Here the meaning and properties of rocket propulsive efficiency, for both constant and variable exhaust speed, will be examined. Particular attention will be paid to the requirement of invariance under coordinate transformations, and propulsive efficiency will be defined in accord with that requirement. Finally, optimum conditions will be derived yielding maximum propulsive efficiency. The invariance property mentioned previously will be utilized to obtain optimum conditions by means of a direct argument.

* This chapter is based on a paper read before the Third International Symposium on Rockets and Astronautics, Tokyo, Japan, 1961.

377

13.1 Propulsive Efficiency—Point Function

Two definitions of propulsive efficiency in common use may be found in standard texts.[9,10] These are, respectively,

$$\eta = \frac{\text{rate of increase of rocket kinetic energy}}{\text{rate of increase of rocket and jet kinetic energy}}$$

$$= \frac{-\dot{m}cv}{-\dot{m}cv - \frac{1}{2}\dot{m}(c - v)^2} \tag{13.1}$$

$$= \frac{2R}{1 + R^2}$$

where

$$R = \frac{v}{c} \tag{13.2}$$

and

$$\eta = \frac{\text{rate of change of rocket kinetic energy}}{\text{rate of change of rocket and jet kinetic energy}}$$

$$= \frac{-\dot{m}cv + \frac{1}{2}\dot{m}v^2}{-\frac{1}{2}\dot{m}c^2} \tag{13.3}$$

$$= 2R - R^2$$

Propulsive efficiency so defined is a point function, i.e., it depends on the instantaneous operating conditions.

One notes that in both cases the maximum value of η is unity and occurs when $c = v$, i.e.,

$$\eta = \eta_{max} = 1$$

when

$$R = 1 \tag{13.4}$$

Two situations can arise: The exhaust speed c is constant, in which case maximum propulsive efficiency can occur at most once during flight (with increasing speed), and the exhaust speed c is variable and so can be made to satisfy condition (13.4) throughout flight. We shall examine these possibilities separately.

But before doing so it is instructive to look at condition (13.4) more closely. Two points are certainly in its favor: First, that the maximum efficiency equals unity is in accord with our previous experience with efficiency, say, in the field of machine design, and hence is a fact that makes us comfortable. Second, that maximum propulsive efficiency, as defined in Eqs. (13.1) and (13.3), occurs when $c = v$, i.e., when the jet speed relative to the chosen coordinate system, $c - v$, vanishes, is in accord with our intuition. For it seems to mean that the jet is at rest in the inertial coordinate system in which the motion is described, and hence, it seems, all the propulsive energy is converted into kinetic energy of the rocket, "clearly" the most efficient manner of operation.

Now, however, a second look is indicated. Condition (13.4) is equivalent to

$$v = c \qquad (13.5)$$

i.e., a quantity, namely, the speed v, which is *not invariant* (whose value depends on the choice of inertial coordinate system) is required to equal an *invariant* quantity, namely, the exhaust speed c. In other words, propulsive efficiency, as defined in (13.1) and (13.3), does not have a unique value at any particular instant of flight, but rather its value depends on the motion of the observer. Thus, if the rocket seems to operate at maximum efficiency, as seen by one observer, it will operate below maximum efficiency, as seen by all other observers moving relative to the first one. That circumstance is certainly disturbing.

In the case of constant exhaust speed c, one can circumvent the difficulty of the noninvariance of η by simply restricting the observer to a particular coordinate system, e.g., the one in which the initial rocket speed $v_0 = 0$.[10] However, then condition (13.4) cannot be satisfied throughout flight.

13.11 Constant Exhaust Speed

Recognizing that $c = v$ cannot be met throughout flight, one may ask for that value of c which results in the greatest mean value, η_m, of propulsive efficienty.[10] Letting

$$R_1 = \frac{v_1}{c} \qquad (13.6)$$

the mean value of propulsive efficiency is

$$\eta_m = \frac{1}{R_1} \int_0^{R_1} \frac{2R}{1 + R^2} \, dR = \frac{\ln(1 + R_1^2)}{R_1} \qquad (13.7)$$

for η as given in (13.1), and

$$\eta_m = \frac{1}{R_1} \int_0^{R_1} (2R - R^2) \, dR = R_1 - \tfrac{1}{3} R_1^2 \qquad (13.8)$$

for η as given in (13.3). Upon setting $d\eta_m/dR_1 = 0$ one finds that η_m is maximum when

$$R_1 = 1.98 \quad \text{or} \quad \frac{m_0}{m_1} = 7.17 \quad \text{for (13.1)}$$

and $\qquad\qquad\qquad\qquad\qquad\qquad\qquad\qquad\qquad\qquad$ (13.9)

$$R_1 = 1.50 \quad \text{or} \quad \frac{m_0}{m_1} = 4.48 \quad \text{for (13.3)}$$

13.12 Variable Exhaust Speed

If the exhaust speed c is permitted to vary (ideally without restriction), then one should be able to optimize propulsive efficiency in two ways. One should be able to find that exhaust speed program $c(v)$ as well as that mass ratio m_0/m_1 which maximize propulsive efficiency. For expressions (13.1) and (13.3) this cannot be done.[5] If η is to be maximum throughout flight, then condition (13.4) substituted in the equation of motion

$$m \, dv = -c \, dm \qquad (13.10)$$

yields

$$d(mv) = 0 \qquad (13.11)$$

so that

$$\frac{m_0}{m_1} = \frac{v_1}{v_0} \qquad (13.12)$$

Thus, operation at maximum propulsive efficiency, as defined in (13.1) or (13.3), in going from initial speed v_0 to final speed v_1, is possible only if the mass ratio satisfies Eq. (13.12). Two other difficulties arise. Again, η is not invariant to choice of inertial coordinate system. Also, the motion cannot be described in a coordinate system in which the initial speed $v_0 = 0$.

It will be shown later that the mode of operation discussed here is a special case of the general optimum mode of operation.

13.2 Propulsive Efficiency—Interval Function

One way of defining propulsive efficiency is to say that a propulsion system operates in the most efficient manner when the least amount of energy need be converted to increase the speed of the burnout mass by a specified amount. That is this a meaningful definition is apparent, for not only may the total available energy be limited (see Chapter 14), but perhaps more often the energy to be converted, i.e., $\int_0^{t_1} P\,dt$, will be limited because of the limitation on power P and operating time t_1.

The rate of converting energy into kinetic energy of rocket and jet, i.e., the propulsive power, is invariant. For rectilinear motion, subject to the equation of motion (13.10)

$$dT_R = d(\tfrac{1}{2}mv^2) = (\tfrac{1}{2}v^2 - cv)\,dm \qquad (13.13)$$

and

$$dT_J = \tfrac{1}{2}(c - v)^2\,d\mu = -\tfrac{1}{2}(c - v)^2\,dm \qquad (13.14)$$

so that

$$dE = dT_R + dT_J = -\tfrac{1}{2}c^2\,dm \qquad (13.15)$$

Thus,

$$P = -\tfrac{1}{2}c^2\dot{m} \qquad (13.16)$$

which is independent of the choice of (inertial) coordinate system.

13.21 Constant Exhaust Speed

One may now inquire after that value of c, and hence of m_0/m_1, which leads to the minimum expenditure of energy ΔE for specified values of m_1, v_0, and v_1.

From Eq. (13.10)

$$v_1 - v_0 = c \ln \frac{m_0}{m_1} \qquad (13.17)$$

and from Eq. (13.15)

$$\Delta E = \tfrac{1}{2}c^2(m_0 - m_1) \qquad (13.18)$$

Letting

$$v_c = v_1 - v_0 \qquad (13.19)$$

one may define an "invariant kinetic energy change" of m_1

$$\Delta T_1 = \tfrac{1}{2}m_1 v_c^2 \qquad (13.20)$$

and a propulsive efficiency[3]

$$\eta = \frac{\Delta T_1}{\Delta E} \qquad (13.21)$$

So defined, propulsive efficiency is an interval function in that its value depends on the trajectory as a whole rather than on conditions at a point. One may then define a specific energy

$$\epsilon = \frac{\Delta E}{\Delta T_1} \qquad (13.22)$$

In view of Eqs. (13.17)–(13.19)

$$\eta = \epsilon^{-1} = \frac{\ln^2 m_0/m_1}{m_0/m_1 - 1} \qquad (13.23)$$

Propulsive efficiency, as expressed by Eq. (13.23), is invariant and, for given values of m_1 and v_c, ΔE is minimum when η is maximum. The propulsive efficiency is maximum when

$$\frac{v_c}{c} = 1.59 \quad \text{and} \quad \frac{m_0}{m_1} = 4.9 \qquad (13.24)$$

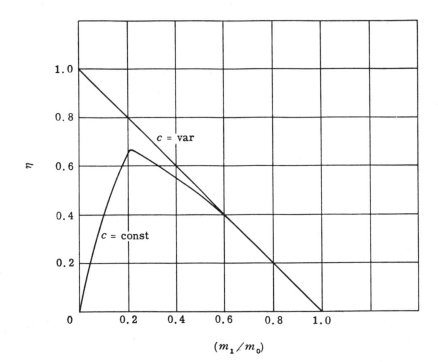

FIG. 1.

By means of the specific energy one may now compare energy expenditure for the optimized values of v_e/c (or m_0/m_1) according to the three definitions of η discussed:

Definition	v_e/c	m_0/m_1	ϵ	
(13.1)	1.98	7.17	1.574	
(13.3)	1.50	4.48	1.547	(13.25)
(13.23)	1.59	4.9	1.543	

It is of interest to note that the energy converted is quite insensitive to choice of the optimized conditions. On the other hand, operation at non-optimized conditions is very wasteful of energy as can be seen in Fig. 1.

13.22 Variable Exhaust Speed

Using the definition of maximum efficiency stated in the previous section, one may now inquire after the optimum mode of operation when the exhaust speed is allowed to vary. That is, given v_0, v_1, m_0, m_1, i.e., ΔT_R, what is $c(v)$ in order that ΔE be minimum? And then, for the optimum exhaust speed program, what is the value of m_0/m_1 with respect to which ΔE becomes minimum?

From Eq. (13.15)

$$\Delta E = \tfrac{1}{2}m_1v_1^2 - \tfrac{1}{2}m_0v_0^2 + \tfrac{1}{2}\int_0^{m_0-m_1} (c - v)^2 \, d\mu \qquad (13.26)$$

Since ΔT_R is specified as regards solution for the optimum exhaust speed program $c(v)$, one seeks a minimum of

$$\Delta T_J = -\tfrac{1}{2}\int_{m_0}^{m_1} (c - v)^2 \, dm \qquad (13.27)$$

subject to the equation of motion (13.10) and boundary conditions

$$m = m_0 : v = v_0$$

$$\qquad (13.28)$$

$$m = m_1 : v = v_1$$

Two methods of solution are possible, one by variational means,[3,4,11] the other by direct invariance argument.[7]

13.23 Variational Solution

Perhaps the simplest variational solution is the following. From Eq. (13.10)

$$c = -m \frac{dv}{dm} \tag{13.29}$$

so that the integral to be minimized is

$$\Delta T_J = -\tfrac{1}{2} \int_{m_0}^{m_1} \left(m \frac{dv}{dm} + v \right)^2 dm \tag{13.30}$$

The corresponding Euler-Lagrange equation (see Chapter 4) is

$$m \frac{d^2v}{dm^2} + 2 \frac{dv}{dm} = 0 \tag{13.31}$$

which, together with Eq. (13.12), yields

$$dv = dc \tag{13.32}$$

i.e., the optimum exhaust speed program is

$$c - c_0 = v - v_0 \tag{13.33}$$

The value of c_0 is found by integrating Eq. (13.10), whence

$$c_0 = \frac{v_1 - v_0}{m_0/m_1 - 1} \tag{13.34}$$

Equations (13.33) and (13.34) constitute the optimal solution. A solution exists for every choice of speed increase $v_e = v_1 - v_0$ and mass ratio m_0/m_1, and furthermore it is invariant. It is seen now that the solution based on definition (13.1) or (13.3), namely, $c = v$, is but a special case, the one for which $c_0 = v_0$. In that case, Eq. (13.12) is automatically satisfied.

13.24 Direct Solution

For the direct solution it is again required that ΔT_J be minimum. If the motion is described in any one inertial coordinate system and the exhaust speed program is found, which results in a minimum value of ΔT_J, then this program will be optimum for the description of the motion in any other inertial coordinate system.

If this were not so, i.e., if one could find an optimum exhaust speed program $c(v)$ for one choice of inertial coordinate system, which yields a smaller value of ΔE than that due to the optimum program for second choice of coordinate system, then one could use it for the second choice of coordinate system and obtain a smaller value of ΔE than the one resulting from its optimum exhaust speed program. This is clearly a contradiction.

The minimum value of ΔT_J is zero, a value it can have in but one of the infinity of possible inertial coordinate systems. In that special coordinate system the condition for

$$\Delta T_J = 0 \tag{13.35}$$

is, of course,

$$c = \bar{v} \tag{13.36}$$

where $\bar{v}$ denotes the speed in that particular coordinate system. Then, from Eqs. (13.10) and (13.29) it follows that

$$d(m\bar{v}) = 0 \tag{13.37}$$

$$\frac{m_0}{m_1} \bar{v}_0 = \bar{v}_1 \tag{13.38}$$

and

$$\left(\frac{m_0}{m_1} - 1\right) \bar{v}_0 = \bar{v}_1 - \bar{v}_0 \tag{13.39}$$

But

$$\bar{v}_0 = c_0 \tag{13.40}$$

and for rectilinear motion

$$\bar{v} - \bar{v}_0 = v - v_0 \tag{13.41}$$

so that

$$c_0 = \frac{v_1 - v_0}{m_0/m_1 - 1} \tag{13.42}$$

Also, in view of Eqs. (13.36) and (13.41)

$$c - c_0 = v - v_0 \tag{13.43}$$

Thus, one has the same result as that of the variational solution.

Finally, in terms of propulsive efficiency, as defined in Eq. (13.21)

$$\eta = \frac{m_0/m_1 - 1}{m_0/m_1} \tag{13.44}$$

Comparison of Eqs. (13.23) and (13.44) shows that the propulsive efficiency for constant exhaust speed is always, i.e., for every value of m_0/m_1, less than that for the optimum variable exhaust speed program, see Fig. 1.

For the same value of ΔT_1, the ratio of energy expended in the case of constant and variable exhaust speed, respectively, is

$$\frac{\Delta E_{\text{const}}}{\Delta E_{\text{var}}} = \frac{(m_0/m_1 - 1)^2}{(m_0/m_1)\ \ln^2 m_0/m_1} > 1 \tag{13.45}$$

as shown in Fig. 2.

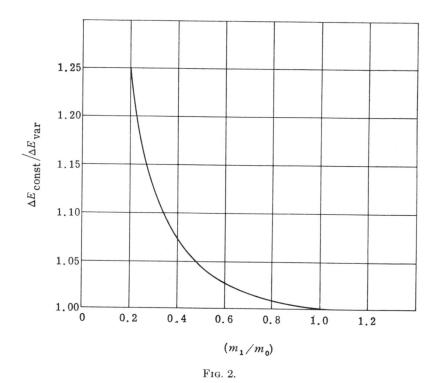

Fig. 2.

Finally, one notes that the propulsive efficiency possesses a maximum (less than unity) with respect to mass ratio m_0/m_1 for constant exhaust speed, whereas, for variable exhaust speed, the propulsive efficiency increases monotonically (to unity) with increasing mass ratio m_0/m_1. Thus, the advantage of using optimum variable exhaust speed as opposed to constant exhaust speed becomes the more pronounced the higher the mass ratio.

Nomenclature

P	Propulsive power
R	v/c
c	Exhaust speed
m	Mass of rocket
v	Speed of rocket
v_c	$v_1 - v_0$
t	Time
t_1	Operating time
ΔE	Energy converted into kinetic energy
ΔT_R	Change in kinetic energy of rocket
ΔT_J	Change in kinetic energy of jet
ΔT_1	Invariant change in kinetic energy of burnout mass
η	Propulsive efficiency
μ	Mass of jet
0	Initial
1	Final
	Dot denotes differentiation with respect to time

REFERENCES

1. A. V. Cleaver, Power-plant efficiencies, *Aircraft Eng.* **17,** 156 (1945).
2. R. R. Newton, On the optimization of physical propulsion systems, *Jet Propulsion* **28,** 752 (1958).
3. R. H. Fox, Optimum exhaust velocity programming and propulsion efficiency, *J. Astronaut. Sci.* **6,** 13 (1959).
4. G. Leitmann, Some remarks on the optimum operation of a nuclear rocket, *Proc. 10th Intern. Astronaut. Congr., London, 1959,* p. 85 (1960).
5. G. Zebel, Vergleich des Energiebedarfes von Raketen mit konstanter bzw. variabler Strahlgeschwindigkeit, *Raketentech. Raumfahrtforsch.* **3,** 81 (1959).
6. G. Leitmann and G. Zebel, Ueber Energiebedarf von Raketen, *Raketentech. Raumfahrtforsch.* **3,** 117 (1959).
7. G. Leitmann, Weiteres ueber Energiebedarf von Raketen, *Raketentech. Raumfahrtforsch.* **4,** 58 (1960).
8. W. R. Corliss, "Propulsion Systems for Spaceflight." McGraw-Hill, New York, 1960.
9. G. P. Sutton, "Rocket Propulsion Elements." Wiley, New York, 1956.
10. J. M. J. Kooy and J. W. H. Uytenbogaart, "Ballistics of the Future." McGraw-Hill, New York, 1946.
11. J. Ulam, L'Ecoulement a vitesse variable dans la propulsion des fusees, *Rev. fran. astronaut.* **1,** 23 (1958).

—14—

Some Topics in Nuclear Rocket Optimization

R. W. BUSSARD

Los Alamos Scientific Laboratory of the University of California,
Los Alamos, New Mexico

14.1 Introduction and Definition

14.11 Nuclear Rocket Vehicles

Before we can discuss the optimization of nuclear propulsion systems for rocket vehicle flight we must first examine why and how nuclear energy offers an advantage over chemical energy for propulsion and define what constitutes a nuclear rocket vehicle. In carrying out such an assessment it is not necessary initially to consider the details of specific designs proposed for the nuclear power plant.

Present address: Space Technology Laboratories, Redondo Beach, California.

The basic difference between chemical and nuclear powered rockets is in the method of obtaining the energy required for vehicle propulsion. The chemical rocket fills its energy needs from the combustion or decomposition of its propellants; the working fluid of a nuclear rocket need not provide any such intrinsic energy since this is supplied by the kinetic energy of nuclear fragments released in the controlled reactions taking place within the nuclear energy source, the reactor. This is equally true whether we are considering rocket vehicles of the sort sketched in Fig. 1*A*, using

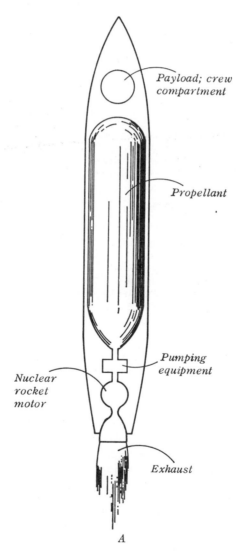

Payload; crew compartment

Propellant

Pumping equipment

Nuclear rocket motor

Exhaust

A

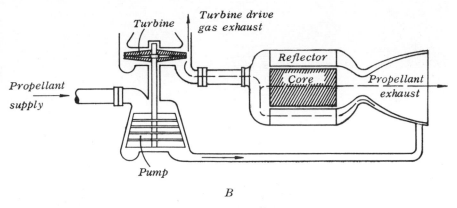

Fig. 1. *A*, Vehicle using "direct" nuclear propulsion (typically a high-acceleration vehicle). *B*, Direct heat-exchanger propulsion system.

direct heat exchanger systems as in Fig. 1*B*, in which the working fluid is heated by contact with regions containing hot nuclear fuel, or vehicles of the type shown in Fig. 2*A*, with indirect (electrical) propulsion systems as in Fig. 2*B*, in which nuclear energy is first converted to electrical form and then used for heating or acceleration of propellant gases. The potential energy content of fusionable and fissionable fuels is nearly 10^7 times that of the best chemical combustible mixtures, and nuclear fuel mass consumption will be essentially negligible for most missions of interest in the solar system, although certain long duration flights may be limited in this respect (see Section 14.33).

Since rockets are propelled by virtue of momentum conservation it is generally desirable that the working fluid heated or accelerated by use of nuclear energy be expelled rearward at as high a velocity as possible, in order to minimize the working fluid mass required.* At a given equilibrium gas temperature the energy content per atom is roughly independent of the atomic mass and is set principally by the number of degrees of freedom of excitation available to each atom. The energy content per unit mass then is evidently inversely proportional to the atomic mass of the working fluid used. Since we are free to choose propellant without regard to considerations of combustion characteristics, it is clear that propellants of the lowest possible atomic or molecular weight are preferred for use in temperature-limited rocket motors, which are supplied with energy from sources independent of the propellant supply. For a given propellant the

---

* This is strictly true only for operation without constraints imposed on the total flight characteristics or on system power levels. Some cases in which variable exhaust velocity yields "optimum" results are discussed later and in Chapter 5, previously.

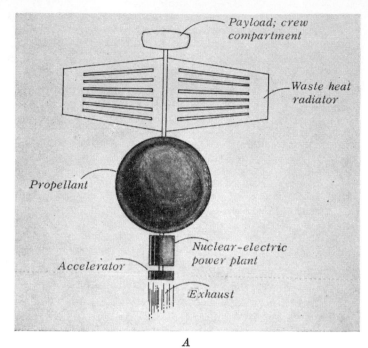

A

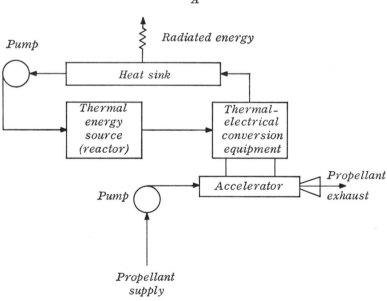

B

FIG. 2.   *A*, Vehicle using "indirect" nuclear propulsion (typically a low acceleration vehicle). *B*, Nuclear/electric propulsion system.

exhaust velocity increases with increasing maximum gas temperature, thus nuclear reactors which operate at high temperature are of interest, assuming other features of the power plant operation (e.g., conversion efficiency) remain constant. In indirect systems, high reactor temperature may be desirable for reasons of high cycle efficiency, but working fluid molecular weight may give way to other parameters such as charge/mass ratio as a criterion of desirability.

14.12 System Analysis and Optimization

The two most special features of nuclear propulsion systems, the independence of energy source and working fluid and the nearly unlimited availability of energy, are the two keystones to system optimization. It is because of these two features that nuclear propulsion systems offer such great opportunities for the determination of optimal conditions; conditions which are beyond the capabilities of chemically powered rocket systems, where the energy source and its sink—the working fluid—are generally wedded indissolubly. The vast field opened up by this separation of essential functions raises a difficult problem. This is simply the problem of defining optimal conditions. What is one analyst's optimum may be another's poison.

Probably the oldest criterion (historically) of *optimum* in rocket vehicle performance is the vehicle gross mass at launching, an optimum vehicle traditionally being considered as one of minimum gross mass for given mission capabilities. In part this was chosen as a useful optimization parameter because it is relatively easy to calculate, but another reason was the generally held conviction that minimum mass also somehow implies minimum size, tends to yield minimum dry mass, and therefore indicates minimum cost as well. All of these auxiliary items which have contributed to past acceptance of gross takeoff mass as a useful optimization parameter actually depend strongly upon the kind of propellant to be used in the rocket vehicle. If all propellants have about the same liquid density and roughly the same performance capability, then the above remarks hold fairly well. However, if propellant density and specific impulse can vary over extreme limits, the above considerations do not hold at all. The simplest example is that of comparison of a nuclear rocket vehicle using hydrogen propellant, as compared with a chemical rocket using an oxygen/jet-fuel combination, for a rather modest mission such as carrying a payload of 1000 lb a distance of 2500 miles. Here calculations can be made which will show that the nuclear rocket vehicle will have a considerably lower gross mass than its chemical competitor, but it will be much larger in size, and may or may not have a larger dry mass, depending upon assumptions about tankage construction and other characteristics of vehicle design. Which vehicle is "best"? There is no truly rational way to answer this question, at least from a technical standpoint. Dilemmas similar to this one arise in many paper exercises in comparison of chemical vs. nuclear rocket vehicle performance, but the only answers yet obtained have been as the result of the progress of time and continued developmental construction. For instance, it can be demonstrated analytically that nuclear rocket vehicles offer certain real technical advantages for some long-range, military bombardment missions, yet it is extremely unlikely that they will supplant the chemical rocket vehicles which now exist for this job, just because these latter vehicles do exist. We have working chemical rockets; we do not now (1961) have flying nuclear rockets. A unanimously acceptable, clear, and convincing demonstration of the superiority of nuclear rocket vehicles seems possible only when missions are considered which are sufficiently ambitious that the nuclear systems are not only lighter, but are smaller, and sturdier as well.

Of course, the point at which this sort of result emerges from analysis is itself difficult to define, because the results of system analysis generally reflect the assumptions used in the input so strongly that questions about the assumptions become questions about the correctness or applicability of the results. If the analyst is optimistic, and chooses to use lightweight structures, or very high reactor temperature in his basic data, the results he obtains will be optimistic as well. Conversely, if heavy tankage is assumed, or low specific impulse is chosen, the vehicle performance will appear poor; perhaps considerably poorer than it should. This latter point is the most pertinent one; that the output of a study is often a very sensitive function of the input assumptions about operating conditions, and small changes in these will often cause rather large changes in the study results. The relative size of such fluctuations depends upon the error in knowledge of input data. The better these are known, the more correct will be the performance prediction. If we are considering parameters describing rocket reactor performance there is no way to learn about the proper input data except by experimental testing of rocket reactors. This, alone, is a strong argument for as rapid an experimental program as possible, so as to dispel some of the mystery and uncertainty which is a natural result of an absence of knowledge about real capabilities.

One field of system optimization in which assumption plays a strong role is that of economic analysis. Here again the difficulties stem chiefly from lack of accurate facts, and only time, coupled with close cost-accounting of development expenses, can provide a remedy. This situation is actually quite unfortunate, because people who plan long-term programs generally desire to base their planning upon some prognostication of ultimate cost, or ultimate capability, when in fact it is often not possible to make such predictions correctly within a factor of 10 or so. As an example of this, let us consider briefly some difficulties of predicting the cost of putting mass into orbit by launching from the surface of the earth. Basic costs are the cost of developing the rocket vehicles to carry the payload(s) to orbit, the cost of flight operations, the financial charges on capital investment, and the depreciation of ground quipment. If we ignore the development cost by reason of assuming an "infinite" use of vehicles, we will get a very different result than that obtained by inclusion of these costs and restriction to a limited number of flights for each vehicle. Propellant costs can be made large relative to other operational considerations if vehicles are assumed re-usable many times at small cost in recovery and in between-flight cleanup, and we consider only chemical rocket systems, or choose low values for the cost penalty associated with handling of radioactive nuclear rocket systems. Conversely, if between-flight refurbishment is chosen to be sufficiently expensive it can be "proven" that no advantage accures from vehicle re-use. Similarly, by appropriate assumption, nuclear systems can be demonstrated to cost more to develop than chemical systems, or less to fly, or recover and re-use, etc. If aircraft construction planning had been made on such a basis, we would still be flying in fabric-covered, bamboo-structured vehicles, for aluminum was estimated as far too expensive in 1910 to warrant its general use.

In many cases, we may find that the parameter under study does not have strict extrema, but varies between asymptotic limits; yet we desire to arrive at some criteria to set up as design goals. In such cases it is possible to define functions which do possess extrema, chosen with respect to the other features of the problem not yet included (sometimes because of the nonanalyticity of these), to use as synthetic optimizing functions. The utility of these obviously depends upon the cleverness of the choice made, and in every case of their use careful investigation should be made of the dependence of the results upon the normalizing factors used or upon the functional form chosen.

The discussion above is not meant to discourage us from carrying out and making use of a variety of system analyses when attempting to assess the potential role of a new system, or to define "best" areas for operation of new or old systems. Rather it should serve to emphasize that the results of a system analysis are not always ends in themselves, and that the most useful function of such a study may be to disclose trends of behavior to guide the system designer, and to define margins for error and performance penalties associated with these.

Let us turn now to consideration of some of the more interesting problems of optimization of vehicle performance. We consider first the optimization of nuclear powered vehicles moving in the field of a massive, gravitating body such as the earth, and second the optimization of some low acceleration vehicles moving in field-free space, and conclude in the last two sections with discussion of some optimization problems of the propulsion systems of most interest for each type of vehicle.

14.2 High Acceleration Flight

14.21 Basic Vehicle Performance*

We have indicated earlier that large exhaust velocity is desirable from the propellant used.† This is a well-known consequence of the basic rocket performance equation, the mass-ratio equation

$$\frac{m_0}{m_b} = \exp\left(\frac{v_c}{v_e}\right) = \exp\left(\frac{v_c}{g_0 I_{sp}}\right) \tag{14.1}$$

where m_0 and m_b are full and "burnt" masses, respectively, and the exhaust velocity v_e has been replaced by $g_0 I_{sp}$, where g_0 is the earth-gravitational force-to-mass conversion factor ($g_0 = 980$ cm/sec^2 = 980 dynes/gm) and I_{sp} is the effective specific impulse, defined as "thrust per unit weight flow rate of propellant." The velocity v_c is the vehicle's "characteristic velocity," i.e., the velocity it would attain at burnout in the absence of all losses, and in field-free space. This velocity will serve as a measure of comparative vehicle performance.

Also of prime importance with regard to vehicle performance is the nuclear power plant mass per unit power output. It is intuitively obvious that power plants of large specific mass will not yield vehicle performance as good as those of small specific mass. The specific mass λ_{pr} is defined by

$$m_{pr} = \lambda_{pr} P_r = \lambda_{pr} P_j/\eta_j \tag{14.2}$$

where m_{pr} is nuclear power plant mass, P_r is reactor thermal power, P_j is exhaust jet kinetic power, and η_j is over-all conversion efficiency from thermal (fission fragment) energy to exhaust jet kinetic energy. The jet power is related to the propellant performance by

$$P_j = -(\tfrac{1}{2})\dot{m}_p (g_0 I_{sp})^2 \tag{14.3}$$

where m_p is propellant mass, the dot indicates the time derivative, the negative sign is a result of our choice of sign convention such that vehicle

---

* Also see Bussard.[1]

† See discussion of footnote in Section 14.11.

mass loss is negative, and other symbols are as previously defined. For direct heat exchanger power plants of the type sketched in Fig. 1B it is often convenient to break the power plant up into its two principal components, the reactor itself, m_r, and the pumping plant m_{pe}, and use an equation of the form (14.2) for the reactor only, thus

$$m_r = \lambda_r P_r \qquad (14.4)$$

For indirect (electric) systems as in Fig. 2B we will use λ_{pr} as defined by Eq. (14.2).

To lay the ground work for vehicle performance analysis let us consider the two rocket vehicles sketched in outline in Figs. 1A and 2A. Figure 1A shows a vehicle using a direct power plant, essentially a reactor and turbopump, while Fig. 2A shows use of an indirect system, with all of its associated equipment. Vehicles of the type shown in Fig. 1A are customarily thought of as "high-acceleration" vehicles and those of the type shown in Fig. 2A as "low-acceleration," but this identification may not always be correct. Aside from the power plant (m_{pr}) discussed above, the components of chief interest here are the propellant m_p, its tank structure m_t, and the dead load m_L, defined to include all remaining items (e.g., useful payload, guidance equipment, instrumentation, food, water, crew compartment, etc.).

We consider first vehicles of the type shown in Fig. 1A employing direct heat exchanger nuclear reactors. Here the gross mass of the vehicle is just

$$m_0 = m_t + m_p + m_L + m_r + m_{pe} \qquad (14.5)$$

For given stress limitation and design pressure, the mass of the tanks is obviously roughly proportional to their volume. Consideration of practical problems (e.g., hydrostatic head changes with changes in propellant density) shows that the dependence on density is in fact weaker than linear. A useful approximate formula relating tank and propellant masses is

$$m_t = A_t(m_p/\rho_p^{2/3}) \qquad (14.6)$$

where ρ_p is propellant density, and A_t is a numerical factor determined by the properties of the tank material and the operating pressure. This coefficient is typically the order of $(1/14)$ $(gm/cm^3)^{2/3}$ for large rocket vehicles using balloon tank construction.

For a given discharge pressure, P_d, the turbopump mass is roughly proportional to the volumetric flow rate, $\dot{m}_p/\rho_p$, thus to the rocket motor thrust, $F/g_0 = a_0 m_0 = -\dot{m}_p I_{sp}$, propellant density, and specific impulse. Experience in turbopump development shows that the dependence on discharge pressure is considerably weaker than linear and that the formula

$$m_{\text{pe}} = -A_{\text{pe}}(\dot{m}_{\text{p}}/\rho_{\text{p}}) P_{\text{d}}^{2/3} = A_{\text{pe}}(a_0 m_0/\rho_{\text{p}} I_{\text{sp}}) P_{\text{d}}^{2/3} \qquad (14.7)$$

holds fairly well over a wide range of flow rates, pressure, and fluid densities. Here a_0 is force acceleration at launching, in units of earth-gravity, and A_{pe} is a numerical factor analogous in use to A_t and has a value the order of $(1/17)$ gm/$(\text{cm}^3/\text{sec})(\text{atm}^{2/3})$ for typical modern turbopumps.

The nuclear rocket reactor mass is defined by Eq. (14.4) in terms of reactor power and specific mass. Since the power output of a direct system goes entirely into the exhaust jet, and thus is proportional to the product of thrust and theoretical exhaust velocity we can write Eq. (14.4) as

$$m_{\text{r}} = A_{\text{r}}(a_0 m_0 I_{\text{sp}} \lambda_{\text{r}}/\eta_{\text{e}}) \qquad (14.8)$$

where η_{e} is the nozzle expansion (energy conversion) efficiency

$$[1 - (p_{\text{e}}/p_{\text{e}})^{\gamma - 1/\gamma}]$$

and A_{r} is a conversion factor to permit use of power in the units of megawatts (Mw) conventionally in use in the nuclear rocket field; $A_{\text{r}} = 4.8 \times 10^{-5}$ Mw/kg-sec.

If we combine Eqs. (14.5)–(14.8) and use the result to eliminate the propellant mass from the mass-ratio Eq. (14.1) (by use of $m_{\text{b}} = m_0 - m_{\text{p}}$), we obtain a relation between (type in Fig. 1A) vehicle performance as measured by the characteristic velocity v_{c} or the mass-ratio exponent, $v_{\text{c}}/v_{\text{e}}$, and internal parameters characterizing the nuclear powerplant performance. This is

$$\frac{v_{\text{c}}}{v_{\text{e}}} = -\ln \left[\left(\frac{\rho_{\text{p}}^{2/3}}{\rho_{\text{p}}^{2/3} + A_t} \right) \left(A_{\text{r}} \frac{a_0 I_{\text{sp}} \lambda_{\text{r}}}{\eta_{\text{e}}} + A_{\text{pe}} \frac{a_0 P_{\text{d}}^{2/3}}{\rho_{\text{p}} I_{\text{sp}}} + \frac{m_{\text{L}}}{m_0} + \frac{A_t}{\rho_{\text{p}}^{2/3}} \right) \right] \qquad (14.9)$$

We will return to this equation in Sections 14.3 and 14.4.

In analyzing rocket vehicle flight performance it is often necessary to determine the *actual* burnout velocity v_{b}, rather than the characteristic velocity v_{c}. To a first approximation, including the effect of finite burning time and other losses, these are related by

$$v_{\text{b}} = \chi v_{\text{c}} - (g_0 I_{\text{sp}}/a_0)(m_{\text{p}}/m_0) \overline{\sin \theta} \qquad (14.10)$$

for flight in an atmosphere in a gravitational field. Here we have allowed a fraction $(1 - \chi)$ of the propellant to account for atmospheric drag, changing nozzle back pressure, and turbopump drive gas requirements, and $\overline{\sin \theta}$ is the time-averaged sine of the flight velocity vector angle with the local gravitational equipotential surfaces.

14.22 Effect of Specific Impulse

As a first step in the study of optimal conditions we look at the influence of propellant specific impulse on the ballistic range of ground-launched nuclear rocket vehicles. For first estimation let us assume a reactor specific power of $\lambda_r = 1$ kg/Mw, and make the approximations that the term $\rho_p^{2/3}/(\rho_p^{2/3} + A_t)$ in Eq. (14.9) may be regarded as unity, and that the term $A_{pe}(a_0/I_{sp}\rho_p)(P_d^{2/3})$ may be neglected relative to $A_t/\rho_p^{2/3}$. In effect we are neglecting the pumping plant mass relative to that of the propellant tankage. Using these approximations, choosing $\eta_e = 0.8$ (typical for large nozzles) and introducing the new variable $(m_D/m_0) = (A_t/\rho_p^{2/3}) + (m_L/m_0)$, Eq. (14.9) becomes

$$v_c/v_e = -\ln\left[(m_D/m_0) + 6.0 \times 10^{-5} a_0 I_{sp}\right] \qquad (14.11)$$

To compute vehicle range, S, we must find the true burnout velocity, in order to make use of a standard equation,[2]

$$S = 2R_e \cot^{-1}\left[\frac{2g_0 R_e}{v_b^2}\left(1 - \frac{v_b^2}{g_0 R_e}\right)\right] + h_b\left(1 - \frac{v_b^2}{g_0 R_e}\right)^{1/2} \qquad (14.12)$$

for the maximum ballistic range of a mass point projected over an airless, nonrotating, spherical body of radius R_e from a burnout height h_b. We choose h_b as of the order of 100 miles, to facilitate calculation, and take the values $a_0 = 1.3$, $\overline{\sin\theta} = 0.75$, and $\chi = 0.95$ as representative of probable usage. Results of range calculations made under these assumptions are shown in Fig. 3 which plots the ground range (nonrotating earth) of single-stage vehicles as a function of the parameter m_0/m_D for various values of specific impulse. Two features of these curves are of particular interest. First, note how relatively flat are the curves for $I_{sp} < 400$ sec as compared to $I_{sp} > 600$ sec. It is just this difference which makes nuclear rocket propulsion, even of the ordinary solid core heat exchanger reactor variety, interesting as compared to chemical rockets today. Of course, chemical rockets which can achieve long range are being built even though attainable I_{sp}'s are not high ($I_{sp} \leq 350$ sec), but this has been done only by multiple-staging and/or use of extreme limit-design in system components. The relative weakness of the chemical bond forever excludes chemical rocket propulsion from the interesting region of high specific impulse attainable energetically in nuclear rockets. The second point of interest to be drawn is that the ratio of gross mass to dead load mass decreases only slowly with increasing specific impulse for $I_{sp} > 1000$ sec or so, even for the maximum range shown, 12,000 miles. In practical terms, we see that a great increase in gross mass is required for low I_{sp} vehicles for the same increase in range achieved by only a small increase in gross mass with high I_{sp}. This situa-

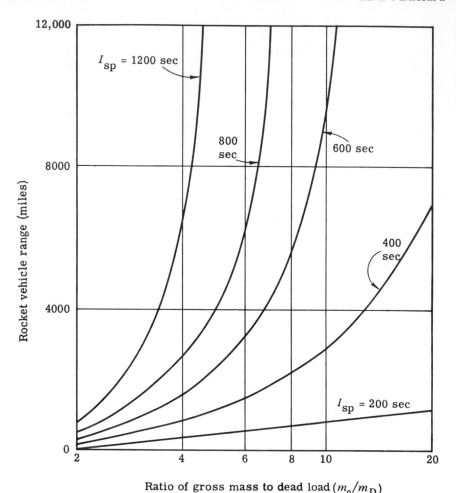

Fig. 3. Performance of single-stage nuclear rocket vehicles.

tion relieves the necessity for stress-limit minimum-mass design in the construction of high I_{sp} vehicles, allows use of large safety factors, and consequently permits much greater freedom to the vehicle designer. Of course, this is precisely the kind of qualitative advantage discussed in Section 14.1 for which it is very difficult to define an "optimum" condition. In this circumstance it may be instructive to generate an optimum by the introduction of an arbitrary optimizing function. Consider systems designed for some given flight range. The two parametric variables left in the curves of Fig. 3, once range is fixed, are the gross to dead-load ratio, m_0/m_D, and the propellant specific impulse. It is an empirical fact that rocket vehicle construction becomes progressively more difficult as the ratio m_0/m_D is made larger, and that the attainment of specific impulse in direct heat-exchanger systems is limited by various limitations of reactor materials and design.[*] Neither limitation is linear in terms of its controlling variables, thus any synthetic optimizing function devised for purposes of fixing attention upon some region of system behavior should in fact reflect the kinds of nonlinearity observed from empirical data. However, for illustration here of the use of such a function we assume the simple form

$$\varphi = \left(\frac{m_0/m_D}{7}\right)^n + \left(\frac{I_{sp}}{800}\right)^m \tag{14.13}$$

where we have arbitrarily chosen to normalize the two variables to 800 (sec) and 7, respectively. We now define an "optimum" vehicle as one which fulfills its range mission with a minimum value of the function φ, above. Such a vehicle would be the easiest one to develop or construct, and therefore to obtain for actual use, if we had been able to choose φ to reflect exactly the real (nonanalytic, complicated, and generally difficult to express) functional dependence of constructability on output performance. Even though probably incorrect, we may draw some interesting qualitative conclusions by a numerical examination of this function. Values of φ for several different sets of exponents n, m are listed in Table I, at various values of propellant specific impulse, and for two different vehicle ranges, 8000 and 4000 miles, based upon the curves of Fig. 3. The italicized entries are minimum tabular values.

TABLE I

PERFORMANCE OPTIMIZATION WITH SYNTHETIC OPTIMIZING FUNCTION OF EQ. (14.13)

I_{sp} (sec)	$n = 1$ $m = 1$	$n = 2$ $m = 2$	$n = 1$ $m = 2$	$n = 2$ $m = 1$	Range (miles)
1200	2.11	2.62	2.86	1.87	
800	*1.93*	*1.86*	1.93	*1.86*	
600	2.08	2.33	*1.89*	2.52	$S = 8000$
400	3.57	9.68	3.32	9.93	
1200	1.99	2.49	2.74	1.74	
800	*1.70*	*1.49*	1.70	*1.49*	
600	1.74	1.54	*1.55*	1.73	$S = 4000$
400	2.42	3.93	2.17	4.18	

---

[*] A detailed discussion of such limitations is given by Bussard and DeLauer,[2] Bussard,[1,3] and Orndoff and Durham.[4]

Inspection of the table shows that the optimum specific impulse is close to 800 sec for the 8000-mile mission, so long as the difficulty of construction remains about the same with respect to both mass-ratio and specific impulse, but is close to 700 sec for the 4000-mile mission. Thus we conclude that more difficult missions favor high specific impulse. Furthermore, we observe that the optimum specific impulse for either mission decreases as we make the vehicle development relatively less difficult than that of the reactor ($n < m$), thus the easier it is to build low-I_{sp} vehicles, the less is the incentive to strive for high-I_{sp} propulsion systems. This is in fact the situation which has confronted the nuclear propulsion field relative to its chemical rocket competition ever since the large expansion of chemical rocket development which followed the opening of the space age by Sputnik I of the U.S.S.R. Conversely, if vehicle development is assumed to be relatively more difficult than reactor development ($n > m$), the optimum specific impulse falls above the values for the "equal-difficulty" case ($n = m$).

In the general case we are interested in a wider class of missions than those described by Fig. 3; we wish to extend our study to interplanetary journeys within the solar system. Here we can simplify the analysis by dealing with vehicle performance in terms of the characteristic velocity v_c, and incor-

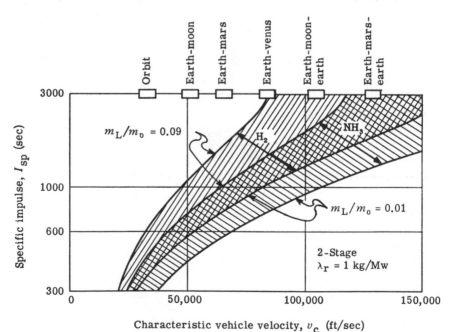

FIG. 4.   Performance of two-stage nuclear rocket vehicles.

porating the gravitational and other correction factors directly into the velocity requirements for the various missions. We again use $a_0 = 1.3$, $\lambda_r = 1$ kg/Mw, but now compute v_c as a function of I_{sp} for a range of values of the actual dead load to gross mass ratio, m_L/m_0, for the two propellants H$_2$ ($\rho_p = 0.071$ gm/cm^3) and NH$_3$ ($\rho_p = 0.71$ gm/cm^3). Results of the calculations are shown in Fig. 4 which applies to two-stage nuclear-powered vehicles for the m_L/m_0 values shown. Also marked on the figure are the approximate characteristic velocities required for several trips of interest within the solar system; each one including powered takeoff and landing at departure, terminus, and all intermediate points. From Fig. 4 we conclude that nearly all of these missions can be accomplished with ground-launched two-stage rocket vehicles if specific impulse of 500 to 1200 sec

TABLE II

PERFORMANCE OPTIMIZATION WITH SYNTHETIC FUNCTIONS FOR HYDROGEN
AND AMMONIA PROPELLANTS

m_L/m_0	$n = 1, m = 1$		$n = 1, m = 2$		$n = 2, m = 1$		Characteristic velocity, v_c(ft/sec)
	NH$_3$	H$_2$	NH$_3$	H$_2$	NH$_3$	H$_2$	
0.09	3.22	2.82	3.82	2.84	4.66	4.26	40,000
0.01	1.03	0.76	0.89	0.51	0.87	0.60	
0.09	5.8	5.3	17.8	14.1	7.24	6.74	80,000
0.01	2.15	1.55	4.0	2.02	1.99	1.39	

can be attained with ammonia, or 800 to 2400 sec with hydrogen. Here again it is instructive to attempt to draw some conclusions by numerical examination of an arbitrary optimizing function. We again assume the form used previously, but now normalize to 400-sec I_{sp} for ammonia propellant, and to 20 for the ratio m_0/m_L. Results of calculations are listed in Table II for two characteristic vehicle velocities, two values of m_L/m_0, and for both hydrogen and ammonia as propellants.

We see from inspection of the table that hydrogen propellant systems are better than ammonia for all entries in the table, and that ammonia vehicles become relatively worse as increasing importance is attached to the difficulty of achieving larger specific impulse from either system. However, we see that ammonia vehicles deteriorate less rapidly than hydrogen vehicles as the payload fraction is increased; a trend which is more pronounced at high burnout velocity.

14.23 Ballistic Trajectory Optimization

Let us now turn to an example of direct optimization in which it is not necessary to introduce synthetic optimizing functions. The example of interest is the question of optimum conditions for maximizing the payload delivered to a given range, per unit of impact area. We will consider this as a problem in bound flight over a nonrotating earth, but the results will be illustrative of the qualitative character of other missions, such as the delivery of payloads to fixed points along orbits in space missions. To study this we must make use of the standard ballistic trajectory equation giving range as a function both of burnout velocity magnitude and velocity vector angle φ_i relative to the local horizon plane. Without derivation this is

$$S = 2R_e \cot^{-1}\left[\left(\frac{g_0 R_e}{v_b^2 \cos^2 \varphi_i} - 1\right) \cot \varphi_i\right] \qquad (14.14)$$

where we are now neglecting the vehicle height at burnout.* By examination of this equation we see that as φ_i approaches zero or $(\pi/2)$ the range S approaches zero, and that there must therefore be an optimum choice of burnout launch angle φ_i which will yield maximum range for a given burnout velocity. To find this optimum angle we differentiate Eq. (14.14) and solve for φ, setting $dS/d\varphi = 0$. Substitution of the result into Eq. (14.14) above and addition of a term to account for finite burnout height leads to Eq. (14.12) used previously for flight range at optimum burnout angle. Graphical display of the optimum-angle range equation shows that the range is very sensitive to small changes in burnout velocity when the range is itself numerically comparable to the diameter of the earth. Because of this, extremely accurate control of the burnout velocity magnitude must be maintained for long range missiles flying on optimum launch angle trajectories. However, numerical examination of the more general range equation (14.14) shows that range/velocity sensitivity can be reduced greatly by use of other than optimum launch angles, but only at the cost of increased required burnout velocity. Increased burnout velocity in turn means a reduction in vehicle payload, if gross mass at takeoff is to be kept fixed, thus the possibility arises of determining an optimum launch angle *and* burnout velocity, for a given range, which will maximize the payload delivered per unit impact area with a given dispersion in control of burnout velocity vector. To find this we first solve Eq. (14.14) for the burnout velocity in terms of angle and range as

$$v_b = \frac{1}{\cos \varphi_i} \sqrt{\frac{g_0 R_e}{1 + (\tan \varphi_i) \cot (S/2R_e)}} \qquad (14.15)$$

_____

* This is valid only for $v_b^2 \leq g_0 R_e$. For the special case of $v_b^2 = g_0 R_e$, optimum φ_i is $0°$ and range is πR_e.

From this we can calculate the incremental change in v_b with change in φ_i for fixed S, and find that it is proportional to the cube of the burnout velocity, according to

$$\left.\frac{\partial v_b}{\partial \varphi_i}\right)_S = -\frac{v_b^3 \left[\sin 2\varphi_i + (\cos 2\varphi_i) \cot (S/2R_e)\right]}{2g_0 R_e} \tag{14.16}$$

Similarly, for fixed φ_i the change in S with v_b is inversely proportional to the cube of the burnout velocity, by

$$\left.\frac{\partial S}{\partial v_b}\right)_{\varphi_i} = \frac{4g_0 R_e^2 \sin^2 (S/2R_e)}{v_b^3 \cos \varphi_i \sin \varphi_i} \tag{14.17}$$

In using these equations we note that the term v_b^3 on the right-hand side of Eq. (14.16) must be that calculated from Eq. (14.15) to satisfy the chosen values of φ_i and S, and that S on the right-hand side of Eq. (14.17) must match the assumed values of φ_i and v_b. These two equations together with the mass-ratio equation (14.1) corrected for real losses according to Eq. (14.10) can be used to find optimum flight conditions (as described above) by numerical calculations.

To illustrate the behavior expected we consider a numerical example. Suppose we desire to deliver a payload to a distance of 9000 statute miles on a nonrotating earth, and that an equivalent 4000 ft/sec of vehicle characteristic velocity will be used up in various losses. From the foregoing range equations we find that the over-all mass ratio required for a launch angle of 45° must be 31.2, while that for flight at the optimum angle of 13.5° is only 18.8, if a typical chemical rocket exhaust velocity of 10,000 ft/sec is used. The corresponding mass ratios for a typical nuclear rocket exhaust velocity of 30,000 ft/sec are 3.14 and 2.66, respectively. For a payload of 3000 lb delivered on an optimum-angle trajectory to the impact point, the chemical vehicle must weigh 227,000 lb at takeoff if its dry weight less payload is 4% of the fully loaded weight. For a nuclear rocket vehicle whose dry weight less payload is 30% of fully loaded weight (due to relatively heavier tankage, and equipment than for the chemical system), the corresponding figure is 40,000 lb. For flight at $\varphi_i = 45°$ we find from the gross mass equation (14.5) that the chemical system cannot do the mission at all if the dry weight fraction is held at 4%. Instead consider increased staging such that the over-all average dry weight fraction is reduced to 3%. Then the chemical rocket must be 6.42 times as heavy per unit payload carried on the 45° trajectory as the 4% dry weight vehicle was at optimum launch angle. However, by use of the range/velocity sensitivity equation (14.16) we find that the error in range due to error in burnout velocity is 3.17 times as great at optimum launch angle flight as for 45° flight. This means that impact point area dispersion in 45° flight is about 0.10 times that at optimum angle, hence that the chemical rocket vehicle to deliver the same payload mass per unit impact area need be only 0.642 as heavy at takeoff as that for use in optimum angle flight. Allowing reduction in dry weight fraction similar to that assumed for the larger chemical rocket, and following out the arguments and analysis above, we find that the nuclear rocket to do the same impact point coverage task with launch at 45° need weigh only 0.081 as much as the vehicle required for optimum angle launching. From comparison of these numerical results it is obvious that greater exploitation of this characteristic feature of vehicle dynamics is possible for high I_{sp} (nuclear) systems than for those with low I_{sp} (chemical) propellants.

We have so far considered only aspects of vehicle dynamics on a non-rotating, spherical, gravitating body. In the true case of the earth the situation is of course quite different, since the effects of rotation and of finite time-of-flight must be included in any impact error analysis and in comparison of the merits and demerits of large-angle vs. optimum-angle launching. A detailed discussion of these and other features of the range and accuracy of earth-bound missiles has been given by Henry.[5] However, the results discussed above do in fact apply fairly correctly to a qualitative picture for interorbital missions, of the kind of improvement in accuracy which may be expected by increased burnout velocity and the general trend of changes in over-all initial vehicle mass required to achieve this. For detailed comparisons numerical computations must be made for each case of interest, following the methods developed by Ehricke[6] or Baker[7] and Baker and Makemson[8] (also see the survey article by Baker[9]).

14.24 Miscellaneous Topics

Two other areas of interest in optimization of nuclear rocket vehicles which merit some discussion are those of maximizing range or payload capability with fixed vehicle mass by variation of propellant exhaust velocity during flight, and minimization of vehicle weight for given mission parameters for manned missions by appropriate choice of shield mass and reactor power level.

Unlike chemical rocket engines, which must operate at relatively fixed gas enthalpy conditions at nozzle entrance, it is possible in nuclear rocket motors to change the specific energy content of the propellant gas over a considerable range during operation by wide variation in reactor core operating pressure. For reactors whose thrust output is limited by core exit Mach number considerations, decreasing pressure means concurrently decreasing total thrust. However, decreased operating pressure allows greater dissociation of the propellant gas at fixed gas temperature, and slightly higher exit gas temperature for fixed structure temperature, thus yielding higher specific impulse, principally from recombination processes taking place in the nozzle flow. Since thrust is lower at higher I_{sp} under these conditions, it may be that the vehicle acceleration becomes insufficient for pure thrust-lifting flight. It is then obvious that there must be some combination of flight trajectory (in a gravitational field) and reactor system pressure (and hence rocket motor thrust output) which will achieve a maximum burnout velocity for fixed payload over a specified range. It is not possible to determine in a simple way the complicated set or program of conditions which produce this result, and optimization of this sort must be done for each case of interest by numerical methods and use of computing machines. However, an approximate indication of the effect of interest has been demonstrated by Wang *et al.*[10] who studied the burnout velocity attainable with various reactor thrust and pressure programs, for single stage vehicles in vertical flight. They found that gains up to the order of 30% increase in burnout velocity for the same mass ratio could be achieved with optimum pressure programming.

The problem of optimization with respect to shield mass and reactor power choice is similar to that above in that no general solutions are possible. Rather, specific solutions must be obtained by numerical calculation in each case. The problem here is to minimize the vehicle mass required for a given payload/range mission, for manned payloads, by optimum choice of reactor power level, hence vehicle acceleration, and shield mass. An increase in shield mass reduces the useful payload capacity of a given vehicle for a fixed burnout velocity, if all other parameters appearing in the vehicle performance equation are held constant. However, larger shield mass means that larger reactor power may be allowed for the same dose rate in the payload or crew (shielded) compartment. Larger reactor power means larger thrust thus larger acceleration for fixed gross weight of vehicle. Larger acceleration in turn yields shorter reactor operating time, thus a reduction in the "gravity losses" due to lifting mass in flight within a gravitational field. This gives a smaller exponent in the vehicle mass-ratio equation, for the same desired burnout velocity, and tends to counteract the increased vehicle component masses resulting from operation at higher power with more shielding. It is clear that there must be an optimum shield-mass/reactor-power combination which will minimize the vehicle gross weight for any given mission with dose-rate-limited payloads, but equally clear that determination of this combination can only be done numerically for specific systems and missions. Results of studies made on specific single stage vehicles show that, in general, the optimum depends very much more strongly on reactor power than on shield mass, and that minimum power (capable of accomplishing the mission specified) is most desirable.

14.3 Low Acceleration Flight*

A wealth of optimization problems confront us when we turn to low acceleration flight in field-free space, both with regard to vehicle trajectory extremization and to specification of optimal relations between internal parameters characterizing the propulsion system alone, as they may influence vehicle performance. First we take up some general considerations of vehicle flight, independent of internal mass distributions, and later extend our optimization analysis to cover the more important features of nuclear/electric propulsion systems for use in low acceleration flight.

14.31 General Considerations

Since the mass of power plant of a low acceleration vehicle is in general fixed by the maximum power output expected during flight, it is intuitively obvious that the propulsion system will be used most efficiently, with regard to employment of mass (e.g., radiators, turbines, generators, etc.), if the power is held constant at its maximum value throughout flight.† It is therefore convenient in the analysis to introduce system power P_r as a primary variable. Returning to Eqs. (14.2) and (14.3) and combining these, we find the total power as

$$P_r = -\frac{1}{2\eta_j}\left(\frac{dm}{dt}\right)v_e^2 = -\frac{1}{2\eta_j}\left(\frac{dm}{dt}\right)(g_0 I_{sp})^2 \qquad (14.18)$$

where we have written dm/dt in place of $\dot{m}_p$ used previously. If we now allow the exhaust velocity to be variable in time and specify that the total power output remain constant, which in turn requires that dm/dt be variable also, we can obtain the time variation of vehicle mass by integration of Eq. (14.18) to yield

$$m(t) = m_0 - 2\eta_j P_r \int_0^t \frac{dt}{v_e^2(t)} \qquad (14.19)$$

For constant power operation over a given time interval t_b with a consequent fixed energy expenditure $P_r t_b$, Eq. (14.19) shows that minimum change in vehicle mass, thus maximum final mass $m_b = m(t_b)$ will be achieved by making v_e as large as possible. This conclusion is of little physical significance, however, since it says nothing about the burnout

---

* The material in this section is taken largely from the manuscript of the author's forthcoming book on "Fundamentals of Nuclear Flight" by permission of McGraw-Hill.

† This point is considered in some detail in Chapter 5, Section 5.3.

velocity attained by the vehicle. This is determined by the momentum rather than the total energy expended in the exhaust. We wish, therefore, to obtain a maximum $m(t)$ by minimization of the integral term in Eq. (14.19), subject to the further condition that the velocity change of the vehicle be the same for all cases considered. For one-dimensional motion this requires that

$$\int_0^{t_b} a(t)\, dt = \text{const} = v_b - v_0 \tag{14.20}$$

For simplicity we first discuss the case of flight in a field-free space. Here the acceleration $a(t)$ is just that due to thrust and can be written in terms of $v_e(t)$ from Newton's law of motion of the form $F = ma$ by use of the fact that the effective thrust is $F = -(dm/dt)v_e$. This yields

$$a(t) = -\frac{v_e(t)}{m(t)}\left(\frac{dm}{dt}\right) \tag{14.21}$$

where the functional dependence on time of each parameter has been indicated formally. We must also make use of Eq. (14.19) to eliminate the mass m itself from the force balance equation. These manipulations reduce Eq. (14.20) to the form

$$v_b - v_0 = 2P_r\eta_j \int_0^{t_b} \frac{dt}{v_e\left[m_0 - 2P_r\eta_j \int_0^t (dt'/v_e^2)\right]} \tag{14.22}$$

The problem of optimization is now a variational one in which we wish to find the time dependence of v_e which will make the integral term of Eq. (14.22) stationary (an extremum) subject to the constraint expressed by Eq. (14.20). However, this direct approach is mathematically cumbersome and it is simpler to investigate the condition for optimum variation of the vehicle acceleration, $a(t) = F(t)/m(t)$, rather than the propellant exhaust velocity directly. We will later see that we can find the optimum variation of $v_e(t)$ only in terms of the variation of vehicle mass $m(t)$. Algebraic substitutions similar to those used in obtaining Eq. (14.22) may be applied to Eq. (14.18) to eliminate the exhaust velocity and obtain a new differential equation relating the vehicle mass to the acceleration by

$$\frac{dm}{m^2(t)} = -\frac{a^2(t)}{2P_r\eta_j}\, dt \tag{14.23}$$

The left-hand side is an exact differential, and Eq. (14.23) can therefore be integrated to yield

$$\frac{1}{m(t)} = \frac{1}{m_0} + \frac{1}{2P_r\eta_j} \int_0^t a^2(t)\ dt \tag{14.24}$$

Here we see that to maximize $m(t)$, P_r should be as large as possible, in agreement with our previous conclusion that v_e should be as large as possible. For a fixed power it is clear that maximum $m(t)$ for any type of motion will be achieved by minimizing the integral term in Eq. (14.24). If we wish, as above, to study rectilinear vehicle motion to a fixed final velocity in field-free space we must again apply the restriction of Eq. (14.20). Now the variable in *both* integrands, (14.20) and (14.24), is $a(t)$ and we can apply directly the variational principles developed in earlier chapters. We recall that a function Q which will extremize an integral of the form $\int Q\ dt$ [as in Eq. (14.24)] must satisfy the Euler-Lagrange equations. To include the single constraint of form $\int P\ dt = \text{constant}$ [as in Eq. (14.20)] we make use of a Lagrangian multiplier λ to form the new function $M = Q + \lambda P$ which must also satisfy the variational principle. Our function M is

$$M = a(t)^2 + \lambda a(t) \tag{14.25}$$

where we are treating a as a generalized coordinate. We note that M is a function only of a, not of $\dot{a}$ (λ is a constant), thus only the first-order derivatives of the Euler-Lagrange equation contribute and give us

$$2a(t) + \lambda = 0 \tag{14.26}$$

from which we see that a must be constant throughout the motion; a result obtained by Irving[10a] by similar methods of analysis. For this to be so, Eqs. (14.18) and (14.19) tell us that the exhaust velocity must be adjusted continually in order that the product $m(t)v_e(t)$ also remain constant. For this special case of motion with constant propulsive system power, in a field-free space the final velocity is given by the classical formula*

$$v_b - v_0 = at_b \tag{14.27}$$

and the final mass by Eq. (14.24) as

$$\frac{1}{m_b} - \frac{1}{m_0} = \frac{a^2 t_b}{2P_r\eta_j} \quad \text{or} \quad \frac{m_0}{m_b} = 1 + \frac{a^2 t_b m_0}{2P_r\eta_j} \tag{14.28}$$

---

* Special relativistic effects are ignored consistently throughout this chapter.

From Eqs. (14.27) and (14.28) we can eliminate t_b and find the magnitude of the acceleration as

$$a = \left(\frac{m_0}{m_b} - 1\right) \frac{2P_r \eta_j}{(v_b - v_0)m_0} \tag{14.29}$$

The variation of exhaust velocity relative to the vehicle required to achieve this constant acceleration is readily found by use of Eqs. (14.18) and (14.21) to eliminate P_r and a from Eq. (14.29) and thus find $v_e(t)$ as a function of $m(t)$ and the design flight conditions. The result is

$$v_e(t) = \frac{2\eta_j P_r}{am(t)} = \frac{(v_b - v_0)m_0}{m(t)[(m_0/m_b) - 1]} \tag{14.30}$$

The time variation of vehicle mass may be found directly from Eq. (14.24) integrated for constant acceleration. Using this we solve Eq. (14.30) to obtain v_e as an explicit function of time:

$$v_e(t) = at + \frac{v_b - v_0}{(m_0/m_b) - 1)} = v(t) + \frac{m_b v_b - m_0 v_0}{m_0 - m_b} \tag{14.31}$$

In closing this section we note that the use of constant acceleration may not be optimum for sets of flight constraints other than those used here (see, e.g., Leitmann[11]).

14.32 Component Mass and Flight Optimization

Having explored vehicle performance without recourse to internal constitution of the vehicle itself, let us turn now to consideration of the interrelation between internal variables describing the component masses and external variables related to the flight mechanics of the vehicle. Subdivision of the complete vehicle into components is logically somewhat different here than for the case of high-acceleration, direct propulsion vehicles just considered. We still have component masses of propellant, tankage and structure, and dead load, as previously, as well as a nuclear powered propulsion system. For high-acceleration vehicles we found it profitable to split the propulsion system mass into two components, the nuclear energy source m_r and the pumping plant m_{pe}. This was done for two main reasons: (1) we were interested in studying the role of specific power output of the energy source alone in determining vehicle performance; and (2) the large thrusts required to provide force acceleration sufficient to lift the full vehicle in turn require relatively large propellant flow rates, and the mass of pumping plant equipment may be a significant fraction of that of the complete propulsion system. Here, however, we will not attempt to divide the nuclear propulsion system m_{pr} into subcomponents. First, because we do not wish to get into detailed engineering considerations of the great variety of systems, methods, and devices which can be considered for use in "free-fall" propulsion, and second, because it is more instructive to carry out the performance analysis on a generalized basis, which, of course, may be specialized at the end to specific systems, if so desired.

Thus we have only four component masses to consider: The propellant m_p; dead load (as previously defined) m_L; propellant tankage and structure m_{st}; and nuclear propulsion system m_{pr}; so that the gross mass is just

$$m_0 = m_{pr} + m_{st} + m_p + m_L \tag{14.32}$$

As previously, general performance analysis can be carried out only because we can relate some of these masses to the power or energy requirements for vehicle flight. The energy expenditure is uniquely fixed by the exhaust velocity and the total propellant mass only so long as the exhaust velocity is held constant throughout powered flight. However, as we have seen from Eq. (14.30) a time-varying exhaust velocity may in some circumstances give better over-all vehicle performance than a constant exhaust velocity. For such a case the energy expenditure is the time integral of the instantaneous power, as given by Eq. (14.18), over the system operating time, and is thus not simply related to the total propellant mass. To avoid the mathematical complications which arise in determining the relation between total propellant mass and total energy expenditure, which is fixed by the desired flight conditions, we return instead to use of the propellant mass itself as a primary variable. This amounts to assuming that the energy supply for propulsion is essentially unlimited and does not constitute a restriction on the vehicle dynamics; we will discuss this point in greater detail later. Since we do not now have available an equation for m_p in terms of m_0 such as the mass-ratio equation for constant I_{sp} rockets (where energy is proportional to m_p) we must retain m_p as a parameter in the performance equation.

We take the tank and structure mass to be as before, in Eq. (14.6),

$$m_{st} = A_{st}(m_p/\rho_p{}^{2/3}) \tag{14.33}$$

and assume that the complete propulsion system mass is linearly related to its power output, and characterized by a specific mass per unit power output λ_{pr}, as defined in Eq. (14.2). Thus

$$m_{pr} = \lambda_{pr}P_r \tag{14.34}$$

Here, since the propulsion system might include items such as rotatory electrical generators, waste heat radiators, etc., and since we have previously been able to determine the optimum exhaust velocity without considering propulsion system structures, we will not attempt to relate m_{pr} to I_{sp}, as was done for Eq. (14.8) describing the nuclear rocket motor.

The gross mass is given by combination with Eq. (14.32) to yield

$$m_0 = P_r \lambda_{pr} + A_{st}(m_p/\rho_p{}^{2/3}) + m_p + m_L \qquad (14.35)$$

This may be solved to find the power required per unit initial mass of vehicle as

$$\frac{P_r}{m_0} = \frac{1}{\lambda_{pr}} \left[1 - \left(\frac{m_p}{m_0}\right)\left(1 + \frac{A_{st}}{\rho_p{}^{2/3}}\right) - \left(\frac{m_L}{m_0}\right) \right] \qquad (14.36)$$

which we use to eliminate P_r/m_0 from Eq. (14.28), and manipulate to find the relation between vehicle acceleration in field-free space and component mass fraction to be

$$a = \frac{2\eta_j[1 - p(m_p/m_0) - (m_L/m_0)][m_p/m_0]}{\lambda_{pr}(v_b - v_0)[1 - (m_p/m_0)]}$$

or   (14.37)

$$a = \frac{2\eta_j(m_{pr}/m_0)(m_p/m_0)}{\lambda_{pr}(v_b - v_0)[1 - (m_p/m_0)]}$$

where we have introduced the symbol $p = 1 + (A_{st}/\rho_p{}^{2/3})$. Now let us consider flight conditions optimized to yield minimum flight *time* for a given velocity change, independent of the distance traversed during flight. For constant acceleration flight, which we have previously seen yields maximum final mass, minimum flight time is here equivalent to maximum acceleration. Thus we are interested in the mass distribution and other conditions which will yield maximum vehicle acceleration. Before proceeding further we wish to recall that our interest lies in motion in field-free space; a case investigated extensively by Preston-Thomas,[12,13] Fox,[14] and others. Results obtained for this category of low-acceleration flights may not be optimally correct for flight in gravitational fields. Optimization of flight in gravitational fields is generally considerably more complicated than that for field-free space (see, e.g., Faulders,[15] Schindler,[16] Michielsen,[17] Leitmann,[17a] and Fox[18]), but offers nothing in the way of optimal phenomena essentially different from those features we will see arising from a study of flight in field-free space.*

---

* In fact, as is demonstrated in Chapter 5 (and earlier by Leitmann[11]), constant acceleration is also optimum for flight in constant-field space, if only v_b but not S_0 is fixed.

From Eqs. (14.37) we see that maximum acceleration will occur when the propulsion system specific power is infinite or when $\lambda_{pr} = 0$. It is thus obviously desirable to strive for propulsion systems of high specific power output. To find a condition on m_p/m_0 for maximum acceleration with given propulsion system and dead load fractions, we differentiate the first of Eqs. (14.37) with respect to m_p/m_0, set equal to zero, and solve for m_p/m_0. The result is further reduced by use of Eq. (14.32) to eliminate m_L/m_0 and obtain

$$\frac{m_p}{m_0}\left(1 - \frac{m_p}{m_0}\right) p = \frac{m_{pr}}{m_0} \tag{14.38}$$

for which the maximum acceleration is found from the second of Eqs. (14.37) as

$$a_{max} = \frac{2\eta_j}{\lambda_{pr}(v_b - v_0)}\left(\frac{m_p}{m_0}\right)^2 p \tag{14.39}$$

Here the value of m_p/m_0 used must be that found by solution of Eq. (14.38) for a given ratio m_{pr}/m_0.

If we use an average acceleration $\bar{a}$, defined by

$$\bar{a}t_b = (v_b - v_0) = \int_0^{t_b} a(t)\, dt \tag{14.40}$$

we can study the conditions for optimum minimum-time flight of vehicles which operate with other than constant acceleration. In particular, for the energetically less favorable, but more immediately practical case of constant exhaust velocity the average acceleration defined by Eq. (14.40) is found by use of the mass-ratio equation (14.1) to be

$$\bar{a} = \frac{v_b - v_0}{t_b} = -\left(\frac{v_e}{t_b}\right)\ln\left(1 - \frac{m_p}{m_0}\right) \tag{14.41}$$

The powered flight time t_b can be replaced in this expression by a function of m_p, P_r, and v_e, by use of Eq. (14.18) for constant exhaust velocity and the identity $- t_b(dm/dt) = m_p$. This yields

$$\bar{a} = -\frac{2\eta_j(P_r/m_0)}{(m_p/m_0)v_e}\ln\left(1 - \frac{m_p}{m_0}\right) \tag{14.42}$$

which can be reduced still further by substitution for v_e from the mass-ratio equation (14.1) again, and by use of Eq. (14.36) for P_r/m_0. The final result is

$$\bar{a} = \frac{2\eta_j}{\lambda_{pr}(v_b - v_0)} \frac{[1 - p(m_p/m_0) - (m_L/m_0)] \ln^2 [1 - (m_p/m_0)]}{m_p/m_0}$$

$$(14.43)$$

or

$$\bar{a} = \frac{2\eta_j}{\lambda_{pr}(v_b - v_0)} \frac{(m_{pr}/m_0) \ln^2 [1 - (m_p/m_0)]}{m_p/m_0}$$

To find the condition on m_p/m_0 which will provide minimum time of flight (maximum $\bar{a}$) we follow the method used to derive Eq. (14.38) for the constant acceleration case. Application of this method to Eq. (14.43) gives the restrictive relation

$$\frac{(m_{pr}/m_0) + p(m_p/m_0)}{m_p/m_0} \ln \left(1 - \frac{m_p}{m_0} \right) + \frac{2(m_{pr}/m_0)}{1 - (m_p/m_0)} = 0 \quad (14.44)$$

Using this to eliminate the propulsion system mass fraction m_{pr}/m_0 from the second of Eqs. (14.43), the maximum average acceleration is found to be

$$\bar{a}_{max} = \frac{-2\eta_j}{\lambda_{pr}(v_b - v_0)} \frac{p[1 - (m_p/m_0)] \ln^3 [1 - (m_p/m_0)]}{2(m_p/m_0) + [1 - (m_p/m_0)] \ln [1 - (m_p/m_0)]}$$

$$(14.45)$$

where, of course, m_p/m_0 must satisfy Eq. (14.44). A numerical comparison of the two types of operation described by Eqs. (14.39) and (14.45) is shown in Table III. Here are listed the results of calculation of the relative vehicle accelerations and flight times for a variety of propellant mass fractions, [equivalent to a variety of propulsion system mass fractions, from Eq. (14.44)], and for the typical conditions: $A_{st} = \frac{1}{6}$ (gm/cm^3)$^{2/3}$: $\rho_p =$

TABLE III

PERFORMANCE OF LOW-ACCELERATION VEHICLES IN FIELD-FREE SPACE

Condition	m_p/m_0	0.25	0.50	0.75	0.90	Units
Constant	$a(v_b - v_0)$	131.3	525	1182	1701	cm/sec
a	$t/(v_b - v_0)^2$	7.79×10^{-6}	1.95×10^{-6}	8.61×10^{-7}	6.00×10^{-7}	sec^3/cm^2
Constant	$\bar{a}(v_b - v_0)$	131.6	536	1204	1635	cm/sec
v_e	$t/(v_b - v_0)^2$	7.77×10^{-6}	1.91×10^{-6}	8.47×10^{-7}	6.25×10^{-7}	sec^3/cm^2

13.6 gm/cm³ (Hg assumed as propellant); $\eta_j = 0.25$; and $\lambda_{pr} = 2500$ kg/Mw. To keep the units straight, λ_{pr} as given must be multiplied by the conversion factor 0.98×10^{-7} Mw-sec/kg-cm, for $\bar{a}$ in units of earth surface gravity ($g_0 = 980$ cm/sec²). Actual numerical values of a and t_b can be calculated from the table for any desired vehicle velocity change $v_b - v_0$ during powered flight in field-free space.

Let us now consider the optimum use of a vehicle with fixed distribution of mass among its components. Of most interest to us is the determination of optimum relations between the range and burnout velocity capability of any given vehicle. In the flight of a rocket vehicle capable of attaining a burnout velocity v_b in field-free space it is obvious that the minimum transit time between states of zero velocity at any two given points will be achieved by an initial instantaneous acceleration to $v_b/2$ followed by coasting flight over the desired distance S_0, terminated by an instantaneous deceleration through a velocity change of $v_b/2$. The velocity vs. time diagram for this process is indicated in Fig. 5A. The integral of this curve (shaded area) is the distance S_0 traversed during flight. However, for a finite exhaust velocity, Eqs. (14.18) and (14.21) show that the propulsion system would require infinite power during the acceleration and deceleration periods, and the propulsion system mass would therefore also be infinite. To achieve minimum transit time with a propulsion system of minimum mass and thus of minimum power, thrust would be applied continuously, accelerating the vehicle to $\frac{1}{2}(v_b - v_0)$ during one-half of the flight time and decelerating through the same velocity change during the remaining half. In order to cover the same distance S_0 during flight, from assumed zero initial velocity ($v_0 = 0$), the constant-thrust rocket must operate for twice the flight time of the infinite-acceleration rocket above. The velocity vs. time diagram is then as shown in Fig. 5B. Since an increase in the propulsion system power will permit the use of greater accelerations and thus yield shorter flight times, while at the same time reducing the load capacity of the vehicle, it is clear than an optimum distribution of time between acceleration and coasting can be found, which will yield minimum transit time t_0, for a given payload or dead load fraction, m_L/m_0. For this more general case the velocity vs. time diagram is like that shown in Fig. 5C.

For the case of constant acceleration, which yields maximum final total mass at end of powered operation, optimum flight time and optimum acceleration implies an optimum vehicle burnout velocity.* In terms of

---

* In contrast to the situation indicated in the footnote on page 413, constant acceleration is no longer optimum in constant-field space for minimization of flight time over a specified distance and to fixed velocity. Rather Leitmann[11] has shown that a small (about 4%) reduction in flight time under such circumstances can be obtained by use of a linearly varying acceleration.

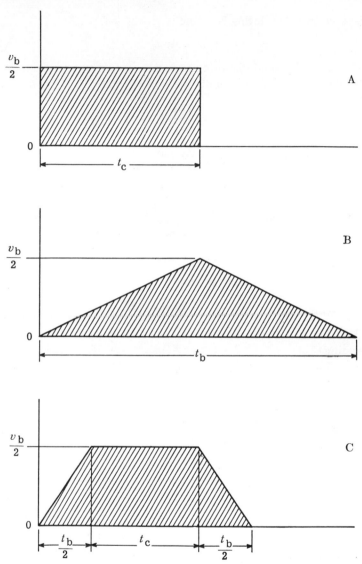

Fig. 5. Extremes and optimal flight performance of low-acceleration vehicles. *A*, Infinite acceleration and power plant; minimum theoretical transit time. *B*, Minimum acceleration and power plant; maximum transit time. *C*, Optimum acceleration and power plant; minimum practical transit time.

the burnout velocity capability the total distance traversed during the powered portions of flight shown in Fig. 5*C* is just the integral of the triangular sections of the graph and is

$$S_b = \tfrac{1}{4}at_b{}^2 = \tfrac{1}{4}v_bt_b \qquad (14.46)$$

The distance traveled during coasting is

$$S_c = \tfrac{1}{2}v_b t_c \tag{14.47}$$

The total flight time and distance are just $t_0 = t_b + t_c$ and $S_0 = S_b + S_c$ and are related by combination of Eqs. (14.46) and (14.47) as

$$t_0 = \frac{2S_0}{v_b} + \frac{t_b}{2} \tag{14.48}$$

To find the vehicle burnout velocity capability for zero initial velocity, which will produce the minimum total transit time t_0, we differentiate Eq. (14.48) with respect to v_b, set equal to zero, and solve for v_b, using the identity $v_b = at_b$ and the second of Eqs. (14.37) to write t_b in terms of the burnout velocity and the vehicle component mass fractions. The result is that the optimum burnout velocity is

$$v_{b \text{ opt}} = 2S_0/t_b \tag{14.49}$$

for which the total flight time becomes

$$t_{0 \text{ min}} = \tfrac{3}{2}t_b = 3S_0/v_b \qquad \text{(acceleration and coasting)} \tag{14.50}$$

From Eq. (14.46) we have, for constant acceleration throughout flight (no coasting)

$$t_b = t_{0 \text{ min}} = 4S_0/v_b \qquad \text{(constant acceleration)} \tag{14.51}$$

These two results are not directly comparable because the burnout velocity v_b for the constant acceleration flight is different, for the same vehicle mass distribution, from that for the accelerate-coast-decelerate flight. By use of Eqs. (14.37) we can combine Eqs. (14.50) and (14.51) for the same mass distribution and show that the total transit times for the cases considered are related by

$$t_{0(c)} = \tfrac{3}{8}t_{0(a)} \tag{14.52}$$

where subscripts (c) and (a) refer to the coasting and constant acceleration types of flight.

A similar analysis may be carried out for vehicles operating with constant exhaust velocity. Here we must start with the range equation in field-free space (not given here) rather than the simple form of Eq. (14.46). Because of the logarithmic terms appearing in this equation the analysis is more tedious and will not be carried out here. The results are of the same form as Eqs. (14.49) and (14.50) for optimum burnout velocity and minimum transit time (for given vehicle masses) but multiplied by a correction factor arising from the change of acceleration during powered flight. As for constant acceleration flight, transit times for constant exhaust velocity systems can be greatly reduced by intermediate coasting from those attainable under constant application of thrust.

Although not a direct result of the foregoing analyses it is readily seen that specification of vehicle flight requirements leads, through Eqs. (14.38) and (14.44) for optimum propellant mass fraction, to an optimum exhaust velocity for any given vehicle. For example, for the constant exhaust velocity vehicle Eq. (14.44) shows that the optimum propellant mass fraction is determined only by the fraction of vehicle mass allotted to the power plant, other things (such as payload fraction) being equal. The maximum time-average acceleration $\bar{a}$ is then found from Eq. (14.45). The mass-ratio equation (14.1) gives the ratio of vehicle burnout velocity to exhaust velocity for this propellant mass fraction. For flight over a given distance S_0 the equation relating powered flight time t_b to flight distance and burnout velocity v_b, analogous to Eq. (14.50) for the case of constant acceleration, can then be used together with the defining Eq. (14.40) for $\bar{a}$ to eliminate $\bar{a}$ from Eq. (14.45) and t_b from the resulting combination with the constant-exhaust-velocity equivalent of Eq. (14.50). The mass-ratio equation (14.1) can then be used to write v_b in terms of v_e, and thus to find the optimum exhaust velocity corresponding to the given vehicle internal design parameters and external operating conditions.

For the constant exhaust velocity vehicle we can show the qualitative dependence of optimum v_e on these variables in another way than that described above. To do so it is convenient to use the gross specific impulse of the vehicle as an optimization parameter. This is defined by

$$I_{0a} = \frac{F t_b}{m_0} = \frac{v_e}{g_0}\left(\frac{m_p}{m_0}\right) \qquad (14.53)$$

for constant exhaust velocity and constant propellant flow rate. By use of Eq. (14.35) for m_0 in terms of component masses, and of Eq. (14.18) for P_r, the gross specific impulse can be written as

$$I_{0a} = \frac{v_e/g_0}{(v_e^2 \lambda_{pr}/2\eta_j t_b g_0) + p + (m_L/m_p)} \qquad (14.54)$$

From the identity $m_L/m_p = (m_L/m_0)(m_0/m_p)$ and Eq. (14.53) we eliminate m_L/m_p from Eq. (14.54) and solve the result for I_{0a}. This is found to be given only in terms of internal design parameters and the exhaust velocity as

$$I_{0a} = \left[\frac{[1 - (m_L/m_0)]\,(v_e/g_0)}{(\lambda_{pr}v_e^2/2\eta_j t_b g_0) + p}\right] \qquad (14.55)$$

Differentiating with respect to v_e, equating to zero, and solving for v_e yield the condition for an extremum (here a maximum) on I_{0a}. This gives

$$v_{e \text{ opt}} = \sqrt{\frac{2\eta_j t_b g_0 p}{\lambda_{pr}}} \tag{14.56}$$

The increase with increasing t_b exhibited here is a reflection of the increasing vehicle flight requirements (i.e., burnout velocity) for continuously powered flight. We see that $v_{e \text{ opt}}$ approaches infinity, according to Eq. (14.56), as t_b increases indefinitely. Substitution of Eq. (14.56) into Eq. (14.55) and manipulation with Eq. (14.53) yield the initial force acceleration for this sort of optimum flight as

$$a_0 = \left(1 - \frac{m_L}{m_0}\right)\left(\frac{\eta_j}{v_e \lambda_{pr}}\right) = \left(1 - \frac{m_L}{m_0}\right)\sqrt{\frac{\eta_j}{2\lambda_{pr} t_b g_0 p}} \tag{14.57}$$

which is the constant v_e equivalent of Eq. (14.39) for constant a.

For the case of constant acceleration the optimum exhaust velocity is a function of time, increasing continuously throughout powered flight so long as the operating power is held constant. This result is seen immediately by combination of Eqs. (14.30) and (14.39) to eliminate a and thus find $v_e(t)_{\text{opt}}$ as a function of time, burnout velocity, and the vehicle internal design parameters. Alternatively, the powered operating time may be eliminated by use of Eq. (14.50), yielding an equation involving the flight distance as well as the vehicle velocity change capability. Carrying this out with the substitution $v_b - v_0 = a t_b$ from Eq. (14.27) we find the optimum time-varying exhaust velocity to be

$$v_e(t)_{\text{opt}} = \sqrt{\frac{2\eta_j g_0 p}{\lambda_{pr}}\left[\frac{m_p}{m_0}\left(\frac{t - t_b}{\sqrt{t_b}}\right) + \sqrt{t_b}\right]} \tag{14.58}$$

which is identical at $t = t_b$ with the optimum condition of Eq. (14.56) for constant exhaust velocity. Some quantitative aspects of these optimal conditions can be shown by a numerical example. For the internal design parameters previously used; $\eta_j = 0.25$, $\lambda_{pr} = 2500$ kg/Mw, $A_{st} = \frac{1}{6}$ (gm/cm³)$^{2/3}$, and $\rho_p = 13.6$ gm/cm³, Eq. (14.56) gives the optimum exhaust velocity as $v_e = \sqrt{2.06 \times 10^6 \, t_b}$ cm/sec. For an operating time of 10^7 sec (116 days), for example, we require an exhaust velocity of $v_e = 4.54 \times 10^6$ cm/sec, or a specific impulse of $I_{sp} = 4630$ sec, about 15 times as large as that produced by the best conventional chemical rocket propulsion systems today.

The existence of an optimum propellant exhaust velocity is of more than pedagogical interest because the exhaust velocity which can be produced by any type of propulsion system is determined by the internal design and operating conditions of the particular system, thus the optimum exhaust velocity can serve as a variable connecting propulsion system design parameters with desired vehicle flight conditions (see, e.g., Bussard,[19] Langmuir[20]). In particular, if the propulsion system derives its thrust from the acceleration of charged particles or ions by electrostatic fields the exhaust velocity is found approximately by a simple energy balance as

$$v_e = \sqrt{\frac{2e^-}{m_+} \frac{Q}{M} V_a} \qquad (14.59)$$

where e^- is the magnitude of the charge on an electron, m_+ is the proton mass, Q is the charge on the particle in units of electronic charge, M is its mass in proton masses, and V_a is the electric potential through which the charged particles are accelerated before leaving the system. Using handbook values for the mass of the proton and the electronic charge, Eq. (14.59) becomes

$$v_e = 1.38 \times 10^6 \sqrt{QV_a/M} \qquad (14.60)$$

for v_e in centimeters per second with V_a in practical volts. Q and M are dimensionless. We can find $V_a(Q/M)$ in terms of t_b by combination of Eqs. (14.56) or (14.58) with (14.59). The constant exhaust velocity case yields

$$V_a\left(\frac{Q}{M}\right) = \frac{\eta_i}{\lambda_{pr}} p \frac{t_b g_0}{e^-/m_+} \qquad (14.61)$$

For our previous assumptions this becomes $V_a(Q/M) = 1.08 \times 10^{-6} t_b$. For $t_b = 10^7$ sec once again this is $V_a(Q/M) = 10.8$ and we see that the dimensionless ratio of mass to charge must be $M/Q = 93$ for $V_a = 1000$ volts. This is nearly the ratio of mass to charge for singly ionized atoms of Rb, often proposed for use as the propellant of ion propulsion systems.

The thrust produced per unit cross-sectional area in the accelerated beam is proportional to the square of the accelerating voltage gradient. Since dimensional problems in construction of an accelerating grid assembly are less severe for smaller grids and larger grid spacing, a very practical incentive exists to increase the accelerating voltage as far as possible, consistent with the natural limitations imposed by arcing in the generating or accelerating equipment. However, higher accelerating voltages require greater mass to charge ratios in the exhaust beam, for optimum operation; for example, if we wish to use $V_a = 50,000$ volts our "ions" must have $M/Q = 4650$ for the mission previously cited. This is equivalent, from a macroscopic point of view, to the single ionization of only 2% of all atoms if Rb is employed as propellant.

14.33 Effect of Energy Limitation

In all of the foregoing we have tacitly assumed that the available energy supply is infinite, or rather that differences in energy consumption are of no consequence in terms of vehicle masses, thus allowing us to consider propulsion system power output P_r and powered operating time t_b as independent parameters. This assumption is good only so long as the mass of nuclear fuel required to supply the energy requirements of flight remain small relative to the mass required to maintain reactor criticality. For reactors with a fixed investment of fissionable material it is generally not possible to "burn" or cause to fission more than about 10 to 20% of the fuel available. Thus if the critical mass is 50 kg, for example, our energy supply for any round-trip journey would be limited to that available from fission of about 5 to 10 kg of nuclear fuel However, it is possible to conceive of reactors which are continually supplied with fissionable material as this is used up. For such systems an upper limit on fuel use may be someting like 500 kg per trip, based upon economic considerations alone (highly enriched U^{235} costs about \$12,000/kg). Since about 1 Mwday of thermal energy is produced by the fission of 1 gm of nuclear fuel,* we can consider use of an upper limit of some 10^7 Mwhour worth of energy per flight, before invalidating our assumption of an infinite energy source. The limit would be only 0.01 of this figure if we could not employ continuously refuelable reactors in the propulsion system. This amount of energy (10^7 Mwhour) is equal to the total electrical energy output of all power plants in the United States for about 200 hours of operation. If high acceleration can be achieved with high exhaust velocity by the attainment of relatively very low specific mass λ_{pr} of the electrical generating equipment, the energy consumption desired for vehicle flight could well exceed this large value. Therefore, as first pointed out by Leitmann[21] (see also Leitmann[17a]) it is of interest to see how some of our earlier conclusions may be modified, and what new features appear, if we include a limitation on available energy as part of our algebraic description of system interrelations.

---

* Actually, about 1.3 gm of U^{235} are used up per Mwday of fission energy liberated. The additional use of 0.3 gm/Mwday is due to nonfission capture of neutrons.

The first modification we must make is to include a term for mass of fuel m_f, in the expression (14.32) for vehicle gross mass. Thus

$$m_0 = m_{pr} + m_{st} + m_p + m_f + m_L \qquad (14.62)$$

For nuclear fuels the total energy expenditure E_b during powered flight is linearly proportional to the fuel mass, thus we can write

$$m_f = \lambda_f E_b = \lambda_f P_r t_b \qquad (14.63)$$

where λ_f is about $(1/24,000)$ kg/Mwhour for fissionable fuels. By comparison with Eq. (14.34) for m_{pr} we see that $\lambda_f t_b$ and λ_{pr} both appear multiplied by P_r in the equation for m_0, thus the new coefficient of P_r may be written as $1 + (\lambda_f t_b/\lambda_{pr})$ times the old one. This factor carries through the previous analysis for optimum exhaust velocity [Eqs. (14.56) and (14.58)] to yield the modified result

$$v_{e \text{ opt}} = \sqrt{\frac{2\eta_j t_b g_0 p}{\lambda_{pr} + \lambda_f t_b}} \qquad (14.64)$$

for the case of constant exhaust velocity. Here the optimum exhaust velocity does not become infinite with increasing t_b, as did Eq. (14.56), derived without regard to limitations on system energy expenditure, but approaches the asymptotic value $v_e^\infty{}_{\text{opt}} = \sqrt{2\eta_j g_0 p/\lambda_f}$. For the values of η_j, A_{st}, and ρ_p used previously, the limiting optimum exhaust velocity and specific impulse are found to be $v_e^\infty{}_{\text{opt}} = 6.70 \times 10^8$ cm/sec and 685,000 sec for use of fissionable nuclear fuels. These values are far beyond the propellant performance levels required for efficient exploration of the solar system, and in fact for all practical solar system missions the influence of limited fuel mass can be neglected, so long as λ_{pr} is the order of 10 kg/Mw or greater.

Another characteristic difference is found in the study of conditions to yield maximum acceleration and thus minimum transit time in flight. If we specify the allowable fuel mass m_f, then the total energy E_b available for any given flight is also fixed. For this situation the burning time t_b is no longer an independent variable, being related to the power by Eq. (14.63), hence we can eliminate it and the burnout velocity v_b from the acceleration equations (14.37) by use of Eqs. (14.27) and (14.63) and obtain an expression for the acceleration as

$$a = \sqrt{\frac{2\eta_j \lambda_f (m_{pr}/m_0)^2 (m_p/m_0)}{\lambda_{pr}^2 [1 + (m_f/m_0)][1 - (m_p/m_0)](m_f/m_0)}} \qquad (14.65)$$

where we have used Eq. (14.62) including the m_f term in place of Eq. (14.32) in the derivation. For a fixed mass of fuel we find the condition on m_p/m_0 for maximum acceleration by differentiation of Eq. (14.65) after substituting from Eq. (14.63) for the terms in m_{pr}. The result of this operation is

$$\left(\frac{m_p}{m_0}\right)\left(1 - \frac{m_p}{m_0}\right) p\left(2 + \frac{m_f}{m_f + m_{pr}}\right) = \frac{m_{pr}}{m_0} \qquad (14.66)$$

which differs from its non-energy-limited counterpart Eq. (14.38) by the factor[21] $(2 + [(m_{pr}/m_f) + 1]^{-1})$. The maximum acceleration is then

$$a_{max} = \sqrt{\frac{2\eta_j\lambda_f}{\lambda_{pr}^2}\frac{2 + 3(m_f/m_{pr})}{[1 + (m_f/m_{pr}]^2}\left(\frac{m_{pr}}{m_f}\right)\left(\frac{m_p}{m_0}\right)^2 p} \qquad (14.67)$$

For given values of λ_f and λ_{pr} the ratio m_{pr}/m_f is uniquely fixed by the powered flight time, through Eqs. (14.34) and (14.63). The relation is

$$\frac{m_{pr}}{m_f} = \frac{\lambda_{pr}}{\lambda_f t_b} = \frac{\lambda_{pr}}{\lambda_f}\left(\frac{a}{v_b - v_0}\right) \qquad (14.68)$$

We can use this to eliminate the fuel and propulsion system masses from Eq. (14.67) and obtain the acceleration in terms of internal design parameters and the burnout velocity. For the case where m_f/m_{pr} is small compared to unity, we have

$$a_{max} = \frac{4\eta_j}{\lambda_{pr}(v_b - v_0)}\left(\frac{m_p}{m_0}\right)^2 p \qquad (14.69)$$

This is to be compared with the non-energy-limited expression (14.39) from which we see that the optimum maximum acceleration for the present case is just twice that obtained earlier without consideration of energy limitations. Of course, in restricting energy usage we have introduced another constraint in the problem, and we therefore must have one less free parameter available for adjustment by the astronaut making use of our propulsion system.[22] In this case we have lost the freedom to specify vehicle burnout velocity, as can be seen by inspection of the equation for burnout velocity obtained by use of Eq. (14.27) to eliminate the acceleration from Eq. (14.69). This is

$$(v_b - v_0)^2 = \frac{4\eta_j}{\lambda_f}\left(\frac{m_f}{m_{pr}}\right)\left(\frac{m_p}{m_0}\right)^2 p \qquad (14.70)$$

for m_f/m_{pr} small compared to unity. Thus the $(v_b - v_0)$ which can be achieved by operation at optimum conditions for energy-limited flight is uniquely fixed by the value of m_f or of $E_b = m_f/\lambda_f$ allowed for the system, as expected from elementary considerations. Conversely, Eq. (14.70) defines the fuel mass required for any given vehicle burnout velocity and propellant mass fraction.

For a quantitative understanding of the situation let us consider a vehicle with $m_p/m_0 = 0.5$, $\eta_j = 0.25$, $A_{st} = \frac{1}{6}(gm/cm^3)^{2/3}$, $\rho_p = 13.6$ gm/cm^3, and powered by fission energy. With these values, Eq. (14.70) yields the relation $m_f/m_{pr} = 4.48 \times 10^{-18}v_b^2$ for zero initial velocity and v_b in centimeters per second. Similarly, Eq. (14.69) gives the acceleration in units of earth surface gravity as $a_{max} = 1.05 \times 10^7/\lambda_{pr} v_b$ for λ_{pr} in kilograms per megawatt. Suppose we wish a burnout velocity capability of $v_b = 5 \times 10^6$ cm/sec (31.1 miles/sec), then the ratio of "burnable" fuel to propulsion system mass must be 1.12×10^{-4}. If the propulsion system mass is chosen as 20,000 kg, the fissionable fuel consumption per flight must be 2.24 kg. Even though small, only about 4 flights of this vehicle could be accomplished before replacing the reactor core energy source, assuming a critical mass of 100 kg and allowing 10% burnup of the fuel investment. If the propulsion system specific mass can be made as low as $\lambda_{pr} = 250$ kg/Mw, one-tenth of the value used earlier, the system would operate at 80 Mw for a period of 2.42×10^6 sec or 28 days [from Eq. (14.68)], and produce a vehicle acceleration of $2.10 \times 10^{-3} g_0$. Other choices of parameters would yield different results; however, rather than pick further arbitrary values for illustrative purposes we leave such numerical exercises to the reader.

14.34 Radiation Shielding

One other subject is of interest to us in connection with optimization of low acceleration vehicles flying in vacuum. This is the investigation of shield mass distributions which yield maximum vehicle performance. In a low acceleration system it is possible to consider the reactor/crew-compartment separation distance as an independent variable, and thus to make use of the inverse-square reduction of radiation flux to help with crew or payload shielding. Of course, some penalty must be paid in terms of mass of structure required to establish the desired separation distance. If propulsion is via traction, with the thrust unit located forward of the crew and payload compartment, separation may be by means of a long cable, as proposed by Spitzer,[23] and the mass involved (which is essentially just the mass of cable required) will increase roughly linearly with separation distance. On the other hand, if the thrust unit is located behind the crew and payload compartment, separation will require the use of some stiffened structure, loaded in compression, and the mass will vary more nearly as the square of the separation distance.

In addition to separation mass, shielding will in general require the use of absorbing material placed between the radiation source and the region to be shielded. Shadow shielding suffices for protection against radiation in vacuum. To first approximation, the attenuation caused by interposition of material as described is an exponential function of the shield thickness,* thus the mass of shadow shielding will depend logarithmically on the ratio of unattenuated radiation dose rate at the crew compartment to the total dose rate allowable at that position over the whole compartment. Following these general considerations we may write the total shield mass as

$$m_{\text{sh}} = \frac{A_{\text{s}}\rho_{\text{s}}}{\mu_{\text{s}}} \ln\left(\frac{KP_{\gamma}}{4\pi s^2 D}\right) + \lambda_{\text{s}} s^n \tag{14.71}$$

where the first term represents the shadow shielding, and the second is the mass of separation structure, here taken as a general exponential function of the separation distance s. The coefficient λ_{s} is fixed by limitations of material strength, allowable safety factors in design, etc. In the shadow shielding term, KP_{γ} is the radiation source strength (radiation leakage from the reactor) in the same units as D, the allowable dose rate at the crew compartment. The shadow shield cross-sectional area is A_{s}, and the density and attenuation coefficient of its material are ρ_{s} and μ_{s}, respectively. To find the minimum shield mass for any given reactor power we differentiate Eq. (14.71) with respect to s, set equal to zero and solve for the separation distance which yields this minimum. The result is

$$s = \left[\frac{1}{n}\frac{2A_{\text{s}}\rho_{\text{s}}}{\mu_{\text{s}}\lambda_{\text{s}}}\right]^{1/n} \tag{14.72}$$

and the corresponding total shield mass is

$$m_{\text{sh min}} = \frac{A_{\text{s}}\rho_{\text{s}}}{\mu_{\text{s}}}\left[\frac{2}{n}\left(1 + \ln\left(\frac{n\mu_{\text{s}}\lambda_{\text{s}}}{2A_{\text{s}}\rho_{\text{s}}}\right)\right) + \ln\left(\frac{KP_{\gamma}}{4\pi D}\right)\right] \tag{14.73}$$

For calculation in cgs units, with source strength in megawatts, the coefficient K is $K = 1.11 \times 10^{13}$ (rad/hour)/(Mw/cm^2).

Let us consider two numerical examples. First take a system with linear dependence of mass upon separation distance, so that $n = 1$, and assume that the mass coefficient is $\lambda_{\text{s}} = 10$ gm/cm. The ratio $\mu_{\text{s}}/\rho_{\text{s}}$ is about the

---

* We restrict attention here to shielding against gamma photons, as shielding against fast neutrons is generally less difficult and therefore not controlling in the shield design, for low acceleration vehicles in vacuum flight.

same for all typical shielding materials, and has the value 0.03 cm²/gm. Using this we find from Eq. (14.72) that the optimum separation distance for a shadow shield of 10^4 cm² cross section is $s = 6.67 \times 10^4$ cm (about 2200 ft). Then assuming that about 1/80 of the total power of our previous example of a low acceleration power plant leaks out of the reactor in gamma radiation we have a source strength of $P_\gamma = 1$ Mw. Allowing a continuous dose rate of $D = 0.01$ rad/hour, we compute the minimum shield mass from Eq. (14.73) as $m_{sh} = 3960$ kg. Next, suppose we are interested in a different type of separation structure, with $n = 2$ and $\lambda_s = 0.01$ gm/cm². Now the optimum separation distance for the above shadow shield area is $s = 5.77 \times 10^3$ cm (about 190 ft), and the minimum shield mass for 1-Mw gamma leakage power is found to be $m_{sh} = 5250$ kg.

So far we have considered shield optimization only for the case of fixed power. To be strictly correct from the standpoint of vehicle performance we should return to Eq. (14.62) for gross vehicle mass and include another term therein to account for shield mass; a term of the form of Eq. (14.71) above showing the functional dependence of shield mass on reactor power. From our previous discussion we know that there is an optimum power, other things being equal, and neglecting the shield mass variation, which will minimize the transit time of a low acceleration vehicle in flight over any given distance while yielding maximum payload capacity for a given propellant mass fraction. The variation of shield mass with reactor power will act to shift the above optimum slightly in the direction of smaller power, since lower reactor power allows smaller shield mass. However, the dependence is only logarithmic, and thus a very good approximation to optimum conditions may be obtained by neglecting the shield-mass/reactor-power relation when optimizing vehicle performance, followed by minimization of shield mass for fixed power, as above.

With this we end our discussion of some optimization problems of nuclear powered vehicles, and turn to consideration of optimal conditions between internal variables which characterize the propulsion unit performance alone. This is not to say that we have exhausted the range of problems of interest in vehicle flight; far from it, we have only barely scratched the surface. However, for many kinds of problems beyond those we have discussed, and for a thorough treatment even of these, it is often necessary to resort to numerical calculations using large automatic computing machines. This is especially true in problems of trajectory optimization, for these are traditionally "soluble" only in terms of perturbation theory or by numerical methods whenever three or more gravitating bodies appear in the problem. The other fact of nature which makes analytical solution difficult in real problems is that nearly all real systems exhibit considerable nonlinearity in functional relationships between the various internal and external parameters which characterize performance of the vehicle and its propulsion system. The value of linear or other simplified analysis is not that it may or may not provide the "correct" answer, rather it is in the display of qualitative trends which may be of great interest and importance to the system designer.

14.4 Heat Exchanger Propulsion Systems

Having considered some problems of optimization and optimal conditions for flight of nuclear-powered vehicles, let us now turn to the optimization of nuclear propulsion systems. As a first step in this examination we investigate the characteristics of direct heat-exchanger type propulsion systems (Figs. 1*A* and 1*B*), and later (next section) take up study of features of indirect power plants (Figs. 2*A* and 2*B*).

From the discussion of Section 14.11 it is evident that a rocket reactor of the direct type is nothing more than a heat-exchanger in which propellant gas is vaporized and heated to as high a temperature as possible before expulsion through an exhaust nozzle. For these, one central problem of development is that of achieving high temperature in the reactor core structure. For solid-core reactors the peak gas temperature is limited chiefly by the limiting strength and corrosion characteristics of the fissioning fuel elements, and use of proper materials is essential to successful reactor operation. Unfortunately, it is not possible to choose fuel element materials on the basis of their physical properties alone, for the reactor must first of all be capable of nuclear criticality. In assessing the worth of one material as compared with another we must take the nuclear properties into account. Furthermore, there is some degree of interaction between nuclear and heat transfer features of any given reactor design, and while it is true that almost any heat exchanger can be made critical with sufficient nuclear fuel the temperature capability of the fuel-loaded material may change with changing fuel loading, and thus change the heat exchanger performance.

For reactors using liquid or gaseous fuel, the temperature limits do not depend upon the fuel material strength, but rather upon various thermodynamic and other properties of the fuel and fuel/propellant mixtures. Since little is known about the probable performance characteristics of liquid and gaseous reactors, while four tests have been made to date (1961) of solid core rocket reactors, we will concentrate our attention on this latter type with but brief excursion into the gaseous reactor world.

The other central problem of reactor development is that of achieving low specific mass, discussed previously. The specific mass is just the ratio of total reactor mass per unit core volume to core power density. In solid core reactors the latter parameter is determined by the heat exchanger geometry and core operating temperature and pressure, while the former is fixed by the over-all reactor geometry and density of materials used. Choice of geometry and materials is strongly influenced by the neutronic character of the reactor since fast neutron reactors best use different materials and geometries than do thermal or intermediate reactors. Here again we see interaction effects between nuclear and heat transfer facets of design.

14.41 Specific Mass and Impulse as Free Variables

To study the effect of varying reactor specific mass, and to determine if optimal conditions exist with respect to this parameter, we return to Eq. (14.9) from which we see that decreasing the specific mass λ_r, with fixed values for other parameters, will yield improved vehicle performance. How far is it worthwhile to go in seeking reduction of λ_r? A strict optimum will occur for $\lambda_r = 0$; i.e., when the rocket reactor is massless. However, it is ever more difficult to construct reactors as the design value of λ_r is lowered. We are thus interested in determining if there is a region in which vehicle performance is sensitive to changes in λ_r and, if so, to examine it quantitatively for help in establishing reactor design goals.

To simplify the analysis we again make the approximations leading to Eq. (14.11), but leave λ_r as a variable in the equation. Thus

$$\frac{v_c}{v_e} = -\ln \left[\frac{m_D}{m_0} + 6.0 \times 10^{-5}(a_0 I_{sp}\lambda_r) \right] \tag{14.74}$$

for λ_r in units of kilograms per megawatt.

The effect of reactor specific mass is displayed graphically in Fig. 6 which plots v_c/v_e as a function of the specific power $1/\lambda_r$ for a wide range of the product $a_0 I_{sp}$, for an assumed value of $m_D/m_0 = 0.2$. The significant feature of these curves is that the mass-ratio exponent is insensitive to reactor specific power for $\lambda_r < \frac{1}{2}$ kg/Mw, but varies rapidly with λ_r for $\lambda_r > 1$ to 8 kg/Mw, depending upon the value of $a_0 I_{sp}$ for the mission. It seems unreasonable to strive for low specific mass for only small gain in performance and equally unsound to consider operation on the near vertical portion of the curves. For ground launching the range of $a_0 I_{sp}$ is roughly from 300 to 1000 sec, thus we conclude that nuclear reactor design for such use should aim for $\frac{1}{2} < \lambda_r < 2$ kg/Mw. To test how other choices of a_0, m_D/m_0, and of I_{sp} will change this result, we may sharpen our conclusion by postulating that the desirable region is that just beyond the "knee" of

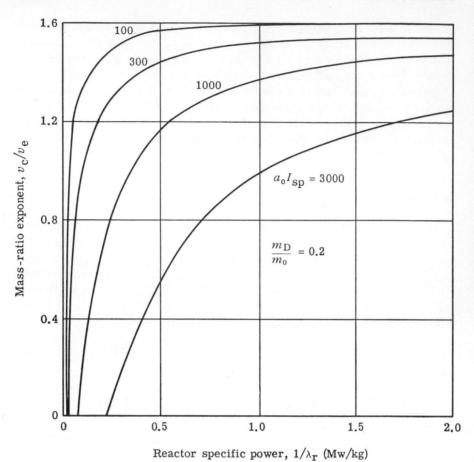

FIG. 6. Rocket vehicle performance as a function of reactor specific power.

the curves in Fig. 6, where the mass-ratio exponent is relatively insensitive
to the reactor specific mass. To find the conditions which restrict us to this
region, say to a given slope $L = d(v_c/v_e)/d(1/\lambda_r)$, we differentiate Eq.
(14.74), set the result equal to the desired slope L, and solve for the
reactor specific mass. If we restrict consideration to $a_0 I_{sp} \ll 10^5 \ (m_D/m_0)$,
which covers all cases of practical interest, the resulting expression reduces
approximately to

$$\lambda_r \simeq \sqrt{\frac{10^5 L (m_D/m_0)}{6 a_0 I_{sp}}} \tag{14.75}$$

For $m_D/m_0 = \frac{1}{3}$ and $L = \frac{1}{6}$, for example, this yields $\lambda_r \simeq 30.4/\sqrt{a_0 I_{sp}}$.
If $I_{sp} = 800$ sec and $a_0 = 1.3$, we find $\lambda_r \simeq 0.94$ kg/Mw as a design goal;

a value within the range previously determined. However, if we allow $a_0 = 0.1$, as for launching from an earth orbit, and postulate $I_{sp} = 1000$ sec, the reactor specific mass need not be made less than about $\lambda_r \simeq 5.3$ kg/Mw. Ground launching, when $a_0 > 1$, thus poses a somewhat more difficult reactor design and development problem than does launching from free fall, when useful vehicle accelerations may be as small as $a_0 \simeq 10^{-1}$ to 10^{-2}, for example.

Another way in which we may sharpen our conclusions is by the introduction of a synthetic optimizing function, designed to include in an approximate way the fact that reactor construction becomes more difficult as λ_r is made smaller. Such a function, convenient for our purposes, is

$$\varphi = \frac{(v_c/v_e)^m}{\lambda_r} \tag{14.76}$$

where the exponent m is left as a parameter whose effect we desire to study. The function defined in Eq. (14.76) becomes smaller directly as λ_r is made larger, thus as reactor construction is made easier, and larger as the ratio v_e/v_c becomes larger (an indirect result of increasing λ_r) if we allow only negative values for m. Thus we can define an optimum system as one which yields a minimum value of φ. To find this minimum we differentiate Eq. (14.76) [using Eq. (14.74)], set equal to zero, and solve for the optimal relation between λ_r and the parameter a_0I_{sp}. The resulting equation is displayed graphically in Fig. 7, for a range of values of m, for an assumed value of $m_D/m_0 = 0.2$. From the graph the trend discussed earlier is evident, namely, that the lower the product a_0I_{sp}, the higher is the optimum (allowable) value of reactor specific mass. A numerical calculation discloses that the optimum reactor specific mass varies almost as the square root of the a_0I_{sp} product, as written in Eq. (14.75), over the mid-range of Fig. 7.

Suppose we wish to find the optimum value of specific impulse which will yield the best vehicle performance, assuming specific impulse is a controllable independent variable and other parameters in the problem remain fixed. Then it is not sufficient to consider the mass-ratio exponent also as an independent variable, as was done above, since the effective exhaust velocity is just $v_e = g_0I_{sp}$. To be exact, in fact, we must include the additional dependence on I_{sp} in the term accounting for gravitational losses [see Eq. (14.10)] if our vehicle is to fly in gravitational fields. However, for purposes of illustration we neglect this term, and maximize v_c with respect to I_{sp}, yielding a result which applies strictly only to flight in field-free space. The form of the performance equation of interest here is

$$v_c = -g_0I_{sp} \ln \left[(m_D/m_0) + 6.0 \times 10^{-5} (a_0\lambda_rI_{sp}) \right] \tag{14.77}$$

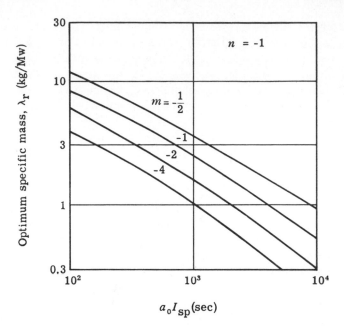

Fig. 7. Optimum reactor specific mass as a function of vehicle acceleration and propellant specific impulse.

Following the usual differentiation procedure we find that there is an optimum product $(a_0\lambda_r I_{sp})$ which is given by solution of the implicit equation

$$-6 \times 10^{-5}(a_0\lambda_r I_{sp}) = [(m_D/m_0) + 6 \times 10^{-5}(a_0\lambda_r I_{sp})]$$

$$\times \ln [(m_D/m_0) + 6 \times 10^{-5} (a_0\lambda_r I_{sp})] \quad (14.78)$$

This result is in contrast to that of Eq. (14.75) and of Fig. 7, where there appeared an optimum product $\lambda_r\sqrt{a_0 I_{sp}}$. For the previous value of dead-load fraction, we find the optimum product from Eq. (14.78) to be $(a_0\lambda_r I_{sp}) = 5573$ kg-sec/Mw. Thus, for $a_0 = 1.3$ (units of earth surface gravity) and $I_{sp} = 800$ sec, the optimum reactor specific mass is now $\lambda_r = 5.36$ kg/Mw; a result considerably larger than before for the same parameters, thus illustrating that different optimization criteria can yield quite different results, even when the same parameters are being considered. The characteristic velocity corresponding to the optimum of Eq. (14.78) is readily found to be $v_c = 0.63 \, g_0 I_{sp}$ for the parameter values given previously. This is just $(1 - e^{-1})$ of the effective propellant exhaust velocity.

14.42 Pressure, Specific Mass, and Impulse Related

Another feature of interest in connection with nuclear rocket motor propulsion systems arises in consideration of the interrelation of reactor specific mass and propellant specific impulse. In all of the foregoing work we have ignored any possible connection between these two parameters, however results of reactor design studies indicate that a connection exists if increased gas temperature (and hence I_{sp}) is to be achieved by varying the choice of fuel element materials, since the materials which offer highest melting point seem to be denser than some of those preferred for operation at lower temperature. Because of this fact, reactors which are capable of operating at high gas temperature may have higher specific mass than those which yield gas at lower temperature, thus a question arises as to the desirability of striving for the highest possible gas temperature and the highest possible specific impulse. To study this situation let us assume that the reactor specific mass is related to the propellant specific impulse by the simple exponential formula

$$\lambda_r = \lambda_{r0} \left(\frac{I_{sp}}{800}\right)^n \tag{14.79}$$

Using this in Eq. (14.77), and following the differentiation procedure above, we obtain the implicit equation

$$(n+1)\left[6 \times 10^{-5} \frac{a_0 \lambda_{r0} I_{sp}^{n+1}}{(800)^n}\right] = -\left[\frac{m_D}{m_0} + 6 \times 10^{-5} \frac{a_0 \lambda_{r0} I_{sp}^{n+1}}{(800)^n}\right] \tag{14.80}$$

$$\times \ln\left[\frac{m_D}{m_0} + 6 \times 10^{-5} \frac{a_0 \lambda_{r0} I_{sp}^{n+1}}{(800)^n}\right]$$

whose solution yields the optimum values of the product $(a_0 \lambda_{r0} I_{sp}^{n+1}/800^n)$ for given values of the exponent n. Approximate results are listed in Table IV for several values of n. Using these numbers we can display the per-

TABLE IV

Optimum Values of $(a_0 \lambda_{r0}^{n+1})/(800)^n$

Exponent n	$(a_0 \lambda_{r0} I_{sp}^{n+1})/(800)^n$
0	5573
1	3000
2	2000
3	1500
5	1000

tinent behavior by plotting the optimum specific impulse as a function of the exponent n, for given values of $(a_0\lambda_{r0})$. Such a plot is shown in Fig. 8. From the figure we see that increased functional dependence of reactor specific mass upon propellant specific impulse gives rise to drastic reductions in the optimum specific impulse which will maximize the vehicle characteristic velocity for a given dead-load fraction. Thus, as n increases there is less and less incentive to strive for reactors capable of yielding high specific impulse [relative to the 800 sec chosen as the normalizing value in Eq. (14.79)] when its achievement involves use of denser materials and consequent greater specific mass. In particular, if n is $\frac{3}{2}$ or greater there is little reason to strive for I_{sp} much higher than the normalization value of 800 sec, for high acceleration vehicles, unless the value of λ_{r0}

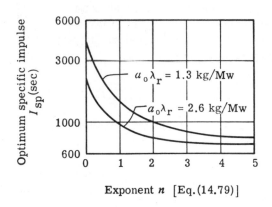

FIG. 8.   Optimum specific impulse as a function of reactor specific mass exponent.

(which corresponds to I_{sp} of 800 sec) can be made less than about $\frac{3}{2}$ kg/Mw. For example, for $a_0\lambda_{r0} = 2.6$ kg/Mw and $n = 3$, operation at $I_{sp} = 850$ sec will yield a *smaller* vehicle burnout velocity (with fixed payload) than that attained with the optimum value of $I_{sp} = 740$ sec.

The results just obtained have been described so as to relate them to the possibility of increasing specific impulse by virtue of use of reactor fuel element materials whose temperature capability is somehow proportional to material density. The proportionality envisioned is purely empirical, and does not imply any true physical dependence of one parameter on the other. However, such is actually the case if we are comparing the performance capabilities of graphite (density of 1.7 gm/cm³) with various metallic carbides (density of 5 to 10 gm/cm³) which have been discussed[1] for use in rocket reactors. However, it is possible to provide another interpretation to the optimal conditions just derived. Suppose the reactor materials are fixed; then the gas temperature at core exit will depend upon the fineness of heat transfer geometry, system pressure, and upon the total area available for heat transfer to the gas. For a limiting material temperature, the exit gas temperature will approach this limit ever more closely as the reactor is made larger in extent, thus we see again here that the reactor specific mass and propellant specific impulse may be related in such a way that higher I_{sp} means heavier reactors. This situation differs from that previously, however, in that now there is an upper limit to the gas temperature from the reactor core, whereas before we allowed gas temperature (and I_{sp}) to increase generally with increasing λ_r. For detailed analysis of the present case we must have available information from reactor design calculations relating heat transfer, gas temperature, and reactor core size. The resulting equivalent of Eq. (14.79) might be written in the simple form

$$\frac{\lambda_r}{\lambda_{r0}} = \exp\left(\frac{I_{sp} - I_{sp}^0}{I_{sp}^u - I_{sp}}\right)$$

where I_{sp}^0 corresponds to λ_{r0} and I_{sp}^u is the upper limit on specific impulse, set by the limiting core material temperature. It is evident that the dependence of λ_r on I_{sp} is much stronger here than in the examples previously considered, and that the resulting optimum I_{sp} will likely fall much closer than before to the chosen normalization value, I_{sp}^0.

One other optimum condition will concern us here. This is the question of choice of optimum system pressure to yield maximum vehicle performance for fixed gas temperature and choice of propellant. Analyses of reactor core heat transfer processes (Bussard and DeLauer,[2] p. 80 ff) show that the average core power density for fixed geometry and structure temperatures varies roughly inversely as the 0.8 power of the system pressure, higher pressure giving larger power density. If the reactor core mass was the sole mass in determining over-all reactor mass, then this too would vary as $(P_c)^{-0.8}$. However, two other elements of the complete reactor are important; these are the external neutron reflector and the containing pressure shell. The reflector mass generally will not be large relative to core mass in most designs of interest, and since it is independent of pressure it cannot make any significant change in the exponential behavior outlined above. On the other hand, the mass of the pressure shell is roughly directly proportional to the system pressure, and thus inclusion of this mass in an expression for the total reactor mass will change the functional dependence from that of the core mass alone. However, calculations show that this change can be incorporated, to fair approximation, in the exponential dependence on pressure which characterizes the core, simply by adjustment of the value of the exponent. For our immediate purposes we will take the reactor specific mass to depend on pressure by the general formula

$$\lambda_r = \lambda_{r0} \left(\frac{P_{c0}}{P_c}\right)^n \tag{14.81}$$

where λ_{r0} is the specific mass at the normalization pressure P_{c0}. Substitution of this into the vehicle performance equation (14.9) shows that maximum vehicle performance will occur when the function

$$\varphi(P_c) = \left(\frac{A_r \lambda_{r0} a_0 I_{sp}}{\eta_e}\right) \left(\frac{P_{c0}}{P_c}\right)^n + \left(\frac{A_{pe} a_0}{\rho_p I_{sp}}\right) (P_c)^{2/3} \tag{14.82}$$

is a minimum with respect to choice of pressure. Differentiating to find the simple minimum, we obtain the optimum pressure as

$$P_{c\ opt} = \left(\frac{3\rho_p A_r \lambda_{r0} (P_{c0})^n n I_{sp}^2}{2\eta_e A_{pe}}\right)^{3/(3n+2)} \tag{14.83}$$

As a numerical example let us assume the following values: $\rho_p = 0.07$ gm/cm^3 (liquid H_2), $P_{c0} = 50$ atm, $\lambda_{r0} = 1$ kg/Mw, $I_{sp} = 800$ sec, and $n = \frac{2}{3}$. With these, and using values of A_r and A_{pe} given previously [see Eqs. (14.7) and (14.8)] we compute the optimum system pressure to be 123 atm. Choice of NH_3 propellant would have given a larger result because the product $(\rho_p I_{sp}^2)$ is larger for dissociated NH_3 than for H_2 propellant at the same temperature. While interesting, this result does not tell the whole story, for we have neglected another pressure-dependence of considerable importance on over-all vehicle performance. This is the dependence of *effective* average propellant exhaust velocity or specific impulse on system pressure by virtue of the fact that increased pressure means increased propellant consumption for turbopump drive requirements, hence decreased utilization of propellant for direct thrust production. This has been found (Bussard and Delauer,[2] pp. 55–56) to be relatively unimportant for system pressure the order of 10 or a few tens of atmospheres, but certainly is not negligible for pressures the order of 100 atm, as computed above. We can include this dependence in a satisfactory way by writing v_e and I_{sp} in Eq. (14.9) in the form $v_e/g_0 = I_{sp} = I_{sp}^0(1 - fP_c)$ where f depends upon the conditions of turbine and drive gas operation and typically has a value between 2 and 6 $\times$ 10^{-4}/atm for propellants ranging from NH_3 to H_2. We leave the determination of optimum conditions, including this effect, to the interested reader.

14.43 Gaseous Vortex Reactor

We have so far investigated only the conditions for optimum operation of solid-core reactor power plants. Before leaving the field of direct propulsion systems let us consider briefly the gaseous heat-exchanger rocket reactor, so often discussed in the literature as a possibility for increased performance. The basic concept of this reactor is simple. A mixture of fissionable fuel in gaseous form and of propellant is supplied to a large cavity or void space within a thick shell of moderating material such as heavy water or graphite; neutrons from fissions occurring in the cavity are thermalized by the external moderator shell and are returned to the gas-mixture region, where they cause further fissions, thus heating the gas directly in the gas phase without the intermediate step of heat transfer from a fuel element structure. In principle the gas temperature may therefore be made much higher than that allowed by the limits of solid fuel elements, and thus higher propellant exhaust velocity might be achieved. A wide variation in conceptual detail has been discussed, but all concepts in the end embody the principle of the simple system outlined above.

This would be a very satisfactory way of achieving increased performance except for the fact that unfissioned atoms of fissionable fuel will be swept out of the mixture region by the heated propellant as it moves toward and through the nozzle orifice which must penetrate the moderator shell to allow propellant exhaust. Analysis of the basic problems involved[3,24] has shown that fuel losses will be intolerable unless some method of separating unfissioned fuel atoms from propellant atoms can be found such that only about 1/1000 of all such atoms which would escape without separation will actually leave with the propellant. Most often proposed for the achievement of this separation is the use of a centrifugal force field acting on the difference in mass of hydrogen and uranium atoms. However, calculations indicate that the velocity which can be achieved by tangential injection of heated propellant into a cavity vortex is not large enough to allow significant diffusional throughflow of propellant if we consider only the single large cavity discussed above, and the thrust output of such a system must be very small. Larger throughflow can be attained only with increased tangential velocity, which itself requires gas rotation by other than hydrodynamic means. In particular, rotation by interaction of external and induced magnetic fields (such as drive "squirrel-cage" motors) has been proposed as one method of achieving large tangential gas velocity. While feasible, in principle, this method requires the use of considerable electrical generating equipment aboard the vehicle, and thus tends to increase the mass of the system while allowing larger thrust output. As the tangential velocity is made ever larger, the electrical equipment mass must become larger, and it is evident that the ratio of thrust to system mass must eventually decrease. There must be an optimum choice of system parameters somewhere between the limits above, which will yield maximum system acceleration capability for any given gas temperature or specific impulse. In attempting to assess this optimum it is important to know how much electrical power must be supplied for gas rotation at any given tangential velocity. At first thought we might say that all of the $\frac{1}{2}\rho v_{\tan}^2$ rotational energy must be supplied by the generating equipment, but closer consideration of the vortex flow process indicates that this need not be the case. In flow through the vortex, the propellant tends to conserve angular momentum, thus it tends to increase in tangential velocity as it moves to smaller radii and towards the central nozzle exit radius. However, if the system is driven by squirrel-cage magnetic fields, the field vector rotates with a constant angular velocity, thus the speeding-up propellant tries to outrun the field. This in turn induces a "bucking" field which extracts kinetic energy of directed motion from the propellant and returns it to the field system which is driving the peripheral gas at high tangential velocity. In the limit of perfect coupling between gas and field (i.e., no "slip" allowed) the gas will rotate as a rigid body, and the rotational energy lost from the system, and therefore that which must be supplied by the generating equipment, will be just that which the gas still contains when it reaches the nozzle inlet radius.

The reactor mass can be expressed crudely by the formula

$$m_r \simeq 2.5 t_r \rho_r A \tag{14.84}$$

where t_r and ρ_r are thickness and density of the reflector-moderator shell, and A is the propellant inlet flow area, assumed equal here to the surface area of the core void cavity. The factor 2.5 represents an allowance for necessary structure, cooling channels, field coils, etc. The mass of electrical generating equipment can be written as earlier [Eq. (14.34)] by

$$m_{el} = \lambda_{pr} P_{el} / \eta_g \tag{14.85}$$

where P_{el} is the electrical power requirement, η_g is the efficiency of conversion of thermal power to electrical power, and λ_{pr} is the specific mass of equipment per unit thermal power in the electrical power plant. The thrust from our system is given by

$$F = \dot{m}_p I_{sp} = \rho_i A v_h I_{sp} \tag{14.86}$$

where ρ_i is the propellant gas density at inlet to the core region, and v_h is the purely radial drift velocity of the incoming propellant. The electrical power requirements are

$$P_{el} = \tfrac{1}{2} f \dot{m}_p v_{\tan}^2 = \tfrac{1}{2} f \rho_i A v_h I_{sp} v_{\tan}^2 \tag{14.87}$$

as previously discussed, where f is the fraction of tangential rotational kinetic energy which actually is lost from the system. In order to write the over-all thrust/mass ratio of this system we must yet find a relation between the tangential gas velocity and the radial drift velocity to allow the elimination of one or the other parameter. Such a relation can be derived by consideration of the centrifugal separation process, since the tangential velocity required for establishment of a properly separating centrifugal field must depend upon the radial throughflow of propellant through fissionable fuel gas. Analysis of this process is beyond the scope of the present discussion, but the functional relation of interest has been obtained elsewhere[1] as

$$v_{\text{tan}}^2 = 10^{11}(1 + v_{\text{h}}) \tag{14.88}$$

for velocity in centimeters per second. Diffusion forces and the effects of turbulence (at typical flow and pressure levels of interest) have been taken into account crudely in the derivation of this formula. Combining Eqs. (14.84)–(14.88) we find the dimensionless ratio of thrust to total mass as

$$\frac{F}{m_{\text{tot}}} = a_{\text{p}} = \frac{I_{\text{sp}}}{5(\lambda_{\text{pr}}/\eta_{\text{g}})(1 + v_{\text{h}})f + 100(t_{\text{r}}\rho_{\text{r}}T_{\text{i}}/v_{\text{h}}P_{\text{i}})} \tag{14.89}$$

for temperature in degrees Kelvin, pressure in atmospheres, specific impulse in seconds, λ_{pr} in kilograms per megawatt (thermal), density in grams per cubic centimeter, and velocity in centimeters per second. From this it is evident that maximum propulsion system acceleration will occur when $v_{\text{h}}^2 = 20(t_{\text{r}}\rho_{\text{r}}T_{\text{i}}\eta_{\text{g}})/(\lambda_{\text{pr}}P_{\text{i}}f)$ and is just

$$a_{\text{p max}} = \frac{I_{\text{sp}}}{5f(\lambda_{\text{pr}}/\eta_{\text{g}}) + 10\sqrt{20t_{\text{r}}\rho_{\text{r}}T_{\text{i}}\lambda_{\text{pr}}f/\eta_{\text{g}}P_{\text{i}}}} \tag{14.90}$$

As a numerical example suppose we choose the following values: $t_{\text{r}} = 100$ cm, $\lambda_{\text{pr}} = 3000$ kg/Mw, $\eta_{\text{g}} = 0.25$, $P_{\text{i}} = 100$ atm, $\rho_{\text{r}} = 1$ gm/cm³, $T_{\text{i}} = 3000°$K (corresponds to about 10% of the energy required to achieve assumed I_{sp}), $I_{\text{sp}} = 3000$ sec, and $f = 0.1$. With these, the optimum drift velocity is found to be $v_{\text{h}}^2 = 50$ (cm/sec)², and the maximum acceleration is $a_{\text{p max}} = 0.03\ g_0$. If the propulsion system is 0.1 of the total mass of its vehicle, the vehicle initial acceleration can be only $3 \times 10^{-3}\ g_0$, about comparable to that attainable by use of various indirect cycle propulsion systems (see Sections 14.3 and 14.5).

Other types of gaseous reactor concepts differ in detail, but all seem to be limited by simple physical processes to theoretical maximum accelerations the order of that obtained above for the single cavity vortex reactor, if high performance is demanded of the propellant.

14.5 Nuclear/Electric Propulsion Systems

The indirect propulsion systems of interest here involve the basic components sketched in Fig. 2B, namely, an energy source, energy conversion equipment, equipment for the disposal of unusable energy from the "bottom" of the engine cycle, and equipment to transform the converted energy into directed energy of motion of the exiting propellant. Each of these basic component groups is connected to others in the system, and thus choice of optimum operating level of any one group can not be made in general without consideration of the overall propulsion system optimization.

14.51 Cycle Temperature Optimization

First let us investigate some optimum conditions of cycle temperature choice. Consider the simple system outlined in Fig. 9. Here the engine cycle operates between a maximum temperature T_m and minimum temperature T_s, and for convenience we have specified that all waste heat in the engine cycle is rejected at a constant temperature T_s. The output of the conversion equipment is supplied to a propellant accelerator of unspecified type, which accelerates the working fluid with an efficiency η_{accel} and rejects its waste heat through a separate radiator at a temperature which may be chosen independently of the temperatures in the engine cycle. The engine cycle converts the source energy into electrical energy with an efficiency η_{conv} which is always less than the Carnot cycle efficiency $\eta_{Carnot} = (T_m - T_s)/T_m$ but is related to it by the defined relation $\eta_{conv} = f_c \eta_{Carnot}$. The masses of the four principal system components can be written as

$$m_{reac} = \lambda_r P_r \tag{14.91}$$

$$m_{rad_1} = s_{r_1} P_{rad_1}/\sigma \epsilon_{r_1} T_{r_1}^4 \qquad (T_{r_1} \equiv T_s) \tag{14.92}$$

$$m_{rad_2} = s_{r_2} P_{rad_2}/\sigma \epsilon_{r_2} T_{r_2}^4 \tag{14.93}$$

$$m_{elec} = \lambda_{elec} P_{elec} \tag{14.94}$$

$$m_{accel} = \lambda_{accel} P_j \tag{14.95}$$

where s is the radiator surface area mass density, σ is the Stefan-Boltzmann constant, ϵ denotes emissivity, and other subscripts are self-explanatory.

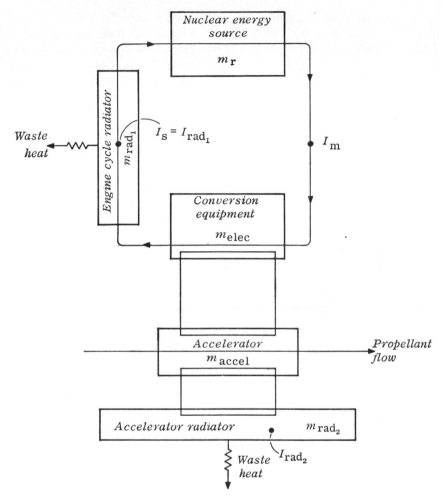

FIG. 9. Typical nuclear/electric reactor-engine/cycle-accelerator propulsion system.

The various different powers used in the above defining equations are themselves related through the various component efficiencies by

$$P_{\text{elec}} = P_{\text{r}}\eta_{\text{conv}} \tag{14.96}$$

$$P_{\text{rad}_1} = P_{\text{r}}(1 - \eta_{\text{conv}}) \tag{14.97}$$

$$P_{\text{rad}_2} = P_{\text{elec}}(1 - \eta_{\text{accel}}) \tag{14.98}$$

$$P_{\text{j}} = P_{\text{elec}}\eta_{\text{accel}} \tag{14.99}$$

Using these, we can combine Eqs. (14.91)–(14.95) to find an expression for total power plant mass in terms of one power variable. If we write this relation so that the remaining power variable is the total thermal power generated by the source, P_r, then the resulting coefficient of P_r will be just the powerplant specific mass λ_{pr} used previously (Section 14.32). However, we prefer here to write the powerplant mass as proportional to the power contained in the propulsive jet, P_j [e.g., as in Eq. (14.2)], thus

$$m_{pr} = \left[\left(\frac{\lambda_r}{\eta_{accel}\eta_{conv}} \right) + \left(\frac{s_{r_1}(1 - \eta_{conv})}{\sigma\epsilon_{r_1}T_s^4\eta_{accel}\eta_{conv}} \right) \right.$$

$$\left. + \left(\frac{s_{r_2}(1 - \eta_{accel})}{\sigma\epsilon_{r_2}T_{r_2}^4\eta_{accel}} \right) + \left(\frac{\lambda_{elec}}{\eta_{accel}} \right) + \lambda_{accel} \right] P_j \quad (14.100)$$

Optimum performance of the propulsion system will occur when the power-plant mass per unit power delivered to the jet is a minimum, for then the mass is being used to maximum capacity for propulsive purposes. We desire to find the conditions on cycle temperature which will give this optimum condition. To do so we substitute our previously written expression for the cycle conversion efficiency in terms of the system temperatures, and differentiate Eq. (14.100) with respect to the ratio of maximum to mini-mum temperature, $\bar{T} = T_m/T_s$, holding constant the parameters T_m, T_{r_2}, η_{accel}, λ_{elec}, λ_{accel}, ϵ, s, λ_r, and f_c. The resulting condition on $\bar{T}$ is

$$4\bar{T}^5(1 - f_c) - \bar{T}^4(5 - 8f_c) - 4\bar{T}^3 f_c = \frac{\lambda_r\sigma\epsilon_{r_1}T_m^4}{s_{r_1}} \quad (14.101)$$

A similar equation, for a somewhat simpler system, has been obtained by Pitkin.[25] Solution of this fifth-order equation, for given f_c and other param-eters, gives the optimum value of the cycle temperature ratio which will maximize the jet power per unit power plant mass. Fifth-order equations are difficult to solve in general, however we can gain an understanding of the behavior expected by restriction to the case when the reactor source mass is negligibly small relative to the primary radiator mass. Present-day systems (where usually $T_m \ll 1000°C$) fit this restriction rather well, since the predominant mass in most nuclear/electric power plants for space application is that of the principal waste heat radiator. With this assump-tion we neglect the right-hand side of Eq. (14.101), thus reducing this to a quadratic equation, which has the general solution (for positive root only)

$$\bar{T} = \frac{(5 - 8f_c) + \sqrt{25 - 16f_c}}{8(1 - f_c)} \quad (14.102)$$

Table V shows the trend of $\bar{T}$ with varying degrees of relative efficiency in the engine cycle.

If the right-hand side term of Eq. (14.101) is not negligible we must solve the fifth-order equation for $\bar{T}$. In general we find that a nonzero right-hand term will yield larger ratios of maximum to minimum cycle temperature, for a given f_c, than those listed in Table V. For example, suppose that the maximum temperature is $T_m = 2000°K$, that $\lambda_r = 10$ kg/Mw, $\epsilon_{r_1} = 1.0$, and the radiator surface area density is $s_{r_1} = 0.25$ gm/cm². Then the right-hand side term has the value 3.63 and we find the optimum

TABLE V

Optimum Cycle Temperature Ratio as a Function of Cycle Relative Efficiency

f_c	$\bar{T} = T_m/T_s$	$\bar{T}^{-1} = T_s/T_m$
1.0	4/3 = 1.33	3/4 = 0.75
0.8	1.31	0.762
0.625	1.29	0.775
0.3	1.27	0.789
0	5/4 = 1.25	4/5 = 0.8

$\bar{T}$ as $\bar{T} = 1.57$ for $f_c = 0.75$; considerably larger than the tabular value of about 1.30. In general we conclude that the optimum temperature ratio is greater for higher source temperature, for larger source specific mass, and for lower radiator surface area density.

14.52 Direct Conversion Reactors

It is not possible, at the present state of engineering technology, to construct reliable, conventional, turbogenerator systems which operate at maximum cycle temperatures much above 1000°C. To achieve higher temperatures we must find some way to replace the highly stressed pieces of rotating machinery in such systems by other equipment which is inherently less highly stressed. One method is by abandoning the use of rotating machinery entirely, and adopting some means of direct conversion of nuclear-heat-energy to electrical energy, such as via use of the direct-conversion, plasma-filled thermionic diode recently under study.[26] With such a direct system the potential gain in performance is twofold: first, because the absence of rotating machinery may allow cycle operation at high source and sink temperatures, thus allowing considerable reduction in primary radiator mass [Eq. (14.92)]; and, second, because the conversion equipment mass [Eq. (14.94)] is now absent entirely from the total powerplant mass as given in Eq. (14.100). This latter amounts to a saving of typically 500 kg/Mw (electrical), while the former would give a reduction of similar order if radiator temperature could be raised about 200°K from present levels.

If we are willing to consider gaseous core reactors once again, the maximum cycle temperature can be considerably greater (conceptually) than for solid-core reactors, and we are attracted by the possibility of achieving conditions for high Carnot cycle efficiency, thus minimizing the mass of the reactor source part of the power-plant. Of course, there is little incentive to do this unless the other power plant components are already small in mass relative to the source, but this is exactly the case in the gaseous/electrical reactor concept.[27] Here we think of a gaseous core region, completely enclosed, and pulsing under the action of an externally generated magnetic field coupled with a pulsed neutronic control system. We assume (falsely, at the present state of the art of plasma physics) that the oscillations can be maintained stably. The gaseous core alternately expands by virtue of fission heating, and is compressed by a rising external magnetic field. The hot, ionized, core gases do work against the magnetic field in the expansion phase, and have work done on them in the compression part of the cycle. The core gases play the role of combustion gases and fresh fuel charges in conventional internal combustion engines. If the magnetic field and neutronic control systems are properly phased, net electrical power will appear in or be delivered to the field coils and external circuit. If there were no losses in this lovely concept, and if the oscillation would be stable, we should seek to attain the maximum possible peak gas temperature in order to achieve maximum efficiency in electrical power production. However, one of the principal sources of loss is inherent in the pulsation process itself. This is loss due to thermal radiation from the hot gas in its compressed state, and as it expands outwards into the core void, working against the magnetic field and becoming colder with further expansion. Increased peak gas temperature will result in increased thermal radiation losses, and since these vary roughly as the fourth power of the temperature it is evident that there must be an optimum peak temperature beyond which we must pay more in radiator mass than is gained by increased "pumping" work per cycle. Although the real processes involved are quite complicated, it is a simple matter to find the optimum temperature for any given system geometry if it is assumed that the gas ball radiates always as a gray body, that the core region walls are perfectly absorbing, and that ohmic heating losses due to field penetration into the gas ball and walls are negligible. The optimum gas temperature found under these conditions will always be greater than the true optimum. We do not carry out the analysis here, but leave this as a closing problem of some interest for the reader, who will find that the radiation loss and thus the optimum peak gas temperature depends upon the system frequency.

REFERENCES

1. R. W. Bussard, Nuclear fission rockets: Problems, progress, and promise, paper presented at the Seminar on Astronautical Propulsion, Milano-Varenna, Italy, September, 1960, to be published by Pergamon, London.
2. R. W. Bussard and R. D. DeLauer, "Nuclear Rocket Propulsion," Chapter 2. McGraw-Hill, New York, 1958.
3. R. W. Bussard, Nuclear rocket propulsion possibilities, Chapter 17 *in* "Space Technology" (H. S. Seifert, ed.). Wiley, New York, 1959.
4. J. D. Orndoff and F. P. Durham, Nuclear propulsion, Section IV.E.1 *in* "Astronautics Handbook." McGraw-Hill, New York, 1961.
5. I. G. Henry, Range and accuracy of long-range ballistic missiles, *J. Brit. Interplanet. Soc.* **17**, 88 (1959).
6. K. A. Ehricke, "Space Flight." Van Nostrand, Princeton, New Jersey, 1960.
7. R. M. L. Baker, Jr., Accuracy required for a return from interplanetary voyages, *J. Brit. Interplanet. Soc.* **17**, 93 (1959).
8. R. M. L. Baker, Jr., and M. W. Makemson, "An Introduction to Astrodynamics," Academic Press, New York, 1961.
9. R. M. L. Baker, Jr., Recent advances in astrodynamics, *ARS Journal* **30**, 1127 (1960).
10. C. J. Wang, G. W. Anthony, and H. R. Lawrence, Thrust optimization of a nuclear rocket of variable specific impulse, *ARS Journal* **29**, 341 (1959).
10a. J. H. Irving, Low-thrust flight: Variable exhaust velocity in gravitational fields, Chapter 10 *in* "Space Technology" (H. S. Seifert, ed.). Wiley, New York, 1959.
11. G. Leitmann, Minimum transfer time for a power-limited rocket, *Proc. 11th Intern. Astronaut. Congr., Stockholm,* 1960; also *J. Appl. Mech.* **28**, 171 (1961).
12. H. Preston-Thomas, Interorbital transport techniques, Chapter 10 *in* "Realities of Space Travel" (L. J. Carter, ed.). McGraw-Hill, New York, 1957.
13. H. Preston-Thomas, Some design parameters of a simplified ion rocket, *J. Brit. Interplanet. Soc.* **16**, 575 (1958).
14. R. H. Fox, Optimum velocity programming and propulsion efficiency, Rept. No. UCRL-5135, Lawrence Radiation Laboratory, University of California, Livermore, California (May 26, 1958).
15. C. R. Faulders, Optimum thrust programming of electrically powered rocket vehicles in a gravitational field, *ARS Journal* **30**, 954 (1960).
16. G. M. Schindler, Minimum time flight paths, *ARS Journal* **30**, 352 (1960).
17. H. F. Michielsen, Minimum weight and optimum flight path of low-acceleration space vehicles, Rept. No. LMSD-48381, Lockheed Missiles and Space Division, Sunnyvale, California (January, 1959).
17a. G. Leitmann, Some remarks on the optimum operation of a nuclear rocket, *Proc. 10th Intern. Astronaut. Congr., London, 1959* (1960).
18. R. H. Fox, Powered trajectory studies for low thrust space vehicles, *ARS Journal* **31**, 28 (1961).
19. R. W. Bussard, A nuclear-electric propulsion system, *J. Brit. Interplanet. Soc.* **15**, 297 (1956).
20. D. B. Langmuir, Low-thrust flight: Constant exhaust velocity in field-free space, Chapter 9 *in* "Space Technology" (H. S. Seifert, ed.). Wiley, New York, 1959.
21. G. Leitmann, The nuclear-powered ion rocket, *J. Brit. Interplanet. Soc.* **16**, 587 (1958).
22. H. Preston-Thomas, The nuclear-powered ion rocket, *J. Brit. Interplanet. Soc.* **17**, 101 (1959).

23. L. Spitzer, Jr., Interplanetary travel between satellite orbits, *J. Brit. Interplanet. Soc.* **10**, 249 (1951).
24. R. W. Bussard, Concepts for future nuclear rocket propulsion, *Jet Propulsion* **28**, 223 (1958).
25. E. T. Pitkin, Optimum radiator temperature for space power systems, *ARS Journal* **29**, 596 (1959).
26. J. Kaye and J. A. Welsh, eds. "Direct Conversion of Heat to Electricity," Section B, Chapters 6–11. Wiley, New York, 1960.
27. F. Winterberg, Kernverbrennungsplasmen und magnetische Kernbrennkammern für Strahltriebwerke, *Astronaut. Acta* **4**, 17 (1958).

Author Index

Numbers in parentheses are inserted to assist in locating references when the author's name is not mentioned at the point of reference in the text. Numbers in italic indicate the page on which the full reference is listed.

Adney, J. E., *167*
Aleksandrov, A. D., 256(14), *279*
Anthony, G. W., 407(10), *445*

Baker, G. A., *166*
Baker, R. M. L., Jr., *166*, 406, *445*
Bass, R. W., 256(20), *279*
Beane, B. J., *167*
Behrbohm, H., *166*
Bellman, R., 18(14), *31*, 51, *66*, 127, *165*, *166*, 256, 271, *279*, 282, 283, 284, 285, 289, *290*, 293(1), 298(6, 7), 303, 305, *308*, *309*, 320, *321*
Belza, O., 102(3), *163*
Bergqvist, B., *166*
Berkovitz, L. D., 201(21), 202(21), *204*
Bliss, G. A., 50, 51, *65*, 100(1), 101(1), 102(1), 103(1), *163*, 174(5), 202(5), *203*, 218, *253*, 256, 262(24), 267, 276, *279*, 316(1), *321*
Blum, E. K., *167*, 216, *253*
Boltyanskii, V. G., 177(12), *204*, 256(6, 8, 11), 266, *278*, 302(8), *309*
Bolza, F. D., 43(2), *65*
Box, G. E. P., 206(6), *252*
Breakwell, J. V., 50, *66*, 127, *164*, *166*, 196(19), 202(19), *204*, 267, *279*, *375*
Bromberg, N. S., 251(49), *254*
Brown, H., 242, *254*
Bryson, A. E., 102, 161, *164*, *166*, 206, 224, 251(43), *253*, *254*
Burns, R. E., *166*
Bussard, R. W., 396, 399(2), 401, *408*, 421, 434(1), 435, 436, 437(3, 24), 439(1), *445*, *446*
Butler, T., *167*, 251(45), *254*

Cappellari, J. O., 139(51), *165*, *169*
Carroll, F. J., *166*, 206(15), *253*
Carstens, J. P., 17, 18, *31*
Carstoiu, J., *166*

Cartaino, T. F., 18(13), *31*, *166*
Carter, W. J., *166*
Cauchy, A. L., 206, *252*
Cavoti, C. R., *98*, *169*
Chang, I. D., *166*
Chapman, D. R., 112(13), 120, *164*
Cicala, P., 4, 11(3), *31*, *98*, 101(4), 127, 131, 143, 146(54), *163*, *164*, *165*, *166*, 228, *253*, 256, 267, 271, *279*
Cleaver, A. V., 377(1), *387*
Coddington, E. A., 37, 38, *65*
Cohen, A., 60(24), *66*
Collatz, L., 296, *308*
Corliss, W. R., 377(8), *387*
Cotter, T. P., 233, *254*
Courant, R., 3(1), 12, 15, 24, *31*, 206(5), 211(16), 212, 213, 222, 224, *252*, *253*, 296(2), 300(2), *308*
Curry, H. B., 206(3), *252*

DeLauer, R. D., 399(2), 401, 435, 436, *345*
Denham, W. F., 102, *164*, *166*, 206(15), 251(43), *253*, *254*
Dennis, D. H., 112(11), 113(11), *164*, *166*
Drenick, R., 52, *66*
Dreyfus, S., 251(46, 47), *254*
Dreyfus, S. E., 18(13, 14), *31*, 51, *66*, *166*, *166*, 177(11), *204*, 282, 283, 284, 285, 289, *290*, 297, *308*
Drougge, G., 112(12), 120, 126(12), *164*
Dunn, J. C., 220(28), *253*
Durham, F. P., 401, *445*

Edelbaum, T. N., 17, 18, 23(20), *31*, *32*, 324, *351*
Edwards, R. H., *169*
Edwards, R. N., 242, *254*
Eggers, A. J., 112(11), 113(11), *164*
Ehricke, K. A., 406, *445*
Emerson, R. C., 50, *65*
Eneev, T. M., 50, *65*, *169*, 176(9), *204*

447

Subject Index